S0-BFX-153

Advances in

Clinical Child Psychology

Volume 14

ADVANCES IN CLINICAL CHILD PSYCHOLOGY

A Continuation Order Plan is available for this series. A continuation order will bring delivery of each new volume immediately upon publication. Volumes are billed only upon actual shipment. For further information please contact the publisher.

Advances in Clinical Child Psychology

Volume 14

Edited by
Benjamin B. Lahey
University of Miami
Miami, Florida
and
Alan E. Kazdin
Yale University
New Haven, Connecticut

Plenum Press · New York and London

The Library of Congress cataloged the first volume of this title as follows:

Advances in clinical child psychology. v. 1–

New York, Plenum Press, c1977–

v. ill. 24 cm.
Key title: Advances in clinical child psychology. ISSN 0149-4732

1. Clinical psychology—Collected works. 2. Child psychology—Collected works. 3. Child psychotherapy—Collected works.
RJ503.3.A37 618.9′28′9 77-643411

ISBN 0-306-43957-3

A Division of Plenum Publishing Corporation
233 Spring Street, New York, N.Y. 10013

Printed in the United States of America

This series is dedicated to
the children of the world, especially
MEGAN, EDWARD, ERIN, NICOLE, and MICHELLE

Contributors

Susan Leigh Bauerfeld — *Department of Psychology, Fairleigh Dickinson University, Teaneck, New Jersey 07666*

M. Christopher Borden — *Department of Psychology, Virginia Polytechnic Institute and State University, Blacksburg, Virginia 24061*

Alice S. Carter — *Department of Psychology, Yale University, New Haven, Connecticut 06520-7447*

Donald J. Cohen — *Child Study Center, Yale University School of Medicine, New Haven, Connecticut 06510-8009*

Alice G. Friedman — *Department of Psychology, State University of New York at Binghamton, Binghamton, New York 13902*

G. Davis Gammon — *Child Study Center, Yale University School of Medicine, New Haven, Connecticut 06510-8009*

Robert A. King — *Child Study Center, Yale University School of Medicine, New Haven, Connecticut 06510-8009*

Juliana Rasic Lachenmeyer — *Department of Psychology, Fairleigh Dickinson University, Teaneck, New Jersey 07666*

Susan Dickerson Mayes — *Department of Psychiatry, Pennsylvania State University College of Medicine, Milton S. Hershey Medical Center, Hershey, Pennsylvania 17033*

Keith McBurnett — *Child Development Center, Department of Pediatrics, University of California, Irvine,*

California 92715, and State Developmental Research Institutes, 2501 Harbor Boulevard, Costa Mesa, California 92626

Raymond K. Mulhern — *Division of Psychology, St. Jude Children's Research Hospital, 332 North Lauderdale Street, Memphis, Tennessee 38101*

Daniel Offer — *Department of Psychiatry, Northwestern University, Chicago, Illinois 60611*

Thomas H. Ollendick — *Department of Psychology, Virginia Polytechnic Institute and State University, Blacksburg, Virginia 24061*

Cynthia Pfeffer — *Cornell University Medical College, New York Hospital–Westchester Division, 21 Bloomingdale Road, White Plains, New York 10605*

Kimberly A. Schonert-Reichl — *Department of Educational Psychology and Special Education, University of British Columbia, Vancouver V6T 1Z4, British Columbia, Canada*

Robert L. Sprague — *Institute for Research on Human Development, University of Illinois at Urbana–Champaign, Champaign, Illinois 61820*

Nancy Kaplan Tancer — *New York State Psychiatric Institute, 722 West 168th Street, New York, New York 10032*

Fred R. Volkmar — *Child Study Center, Yale University School of Medicine, New Haven, Connecticut 06510-8009*

David M. White — *Private Practice in Clinical Psychology, 10516 Santa Monica Boulevard, Suite 2, Los Angeles, California 90025*

Preface

Advances in Clinical Child Psychology is an annual series designed to bring summaries of the latest developments in the field to psychologists, psychiatrists, educators, and other professionals who are concerned with troubled children. This volume, like its predecessors, attempts to highlight the important emerging issues and breakthroughs that are likely to guide clinical work and research in our field of inquiry in the near future.

In selecting authors to contribute to this series, we seek out those whose work is innovative, relevant, and likely to influence future work in clinical child psychology and related fields. Each author is chosen either on the basis of potentially important new information or viewpoints in his or her own work, or because the author is especially well qualified to discuss a topic that is not restricted to one program of research.

In this volume, a wide range of particularly important topics is addressed. White and Sprague describe an innovative program of research aimed at identifying the underlying deficit in attention-deficit disorder. Schonert-Reichl and Offer summarize and integrate research on gender differences in psychological symptoms among adolescents. Borden and Ollendick offer a cogent proposal concerning the development and differentiation of subtypes of autism based on social behavior. McBurnett provides a fascinating integrative summary of theories of psychopathology that are applicable to children and that integrate psychological and biological constructs. Friedman and Mulhern describe promising psychological approaches to understanding and helping children with cancer. Bauerfeld and Lachenmeyer provide a most helpful integrative review of the literature on prenatal nutrition and intellectual development, and Mayes provides a statement that advances understanding of the complicated topic of rumination disorder.

In addition, we are fortunate to be able to publish in this volume three of the literature reviews prepared for the DSM-IV Child and Adolescent Psychopathology Work Group. Tancer provides a summary of the literature and issues related to elective mutism; Carter and Volkmar address the controversial topic of sibling rivalry disorder; and King, Pfeffer, Gammon, and Cohen summarize the literature and issues relevant to the proposed diagnostic category of suicidal disorder. These provide a fascinating opportunity to view the efforts of the DSM-IV committees to document and discuss publicly the empirical basis for any changes in the DSM.

This volume marks the last one to be edited by Benjamin B. Lahey and Alan E. Kazdin. After 15 years and 14 volumes, we felt that it was time to turn the editorial control of the series over to persons with new ideas and perspectives. The field is indeed very fortunate that Thomas Ollendick and Ronald Prinz have agreed to assume editorship of the next volume. We wish them and the series the greatest success. We offer our sincere thanks to Plenum Publishing Corporation for the splendid work on the series, to the many consulting editors who helped importantly with the series, and to the over 300 authors and coauthors who have contributed to the series.

Contents

PART I. GENERAL PAPERS

PART II. DSM-IV LITERATURE REVIEWS

I General Papers

1 The "Attention Deficit" in Children with Attention-Deficit Hyperactivity Disorder

DAVID M. WHITE AND ROBERT L. SPRAGUE

1. *Introduction*

Clinical child research has yet to illuminate the nature of the "attention deficit" in children with Attention-Deficit Hyperactivity Disorder (ADHD). Previous research has established clearly that ADHD children perform poorly on many cognitive and intellectual tasks relative to normal (i.e., nonreferred) children. ADHD children have been shown to perform at subnormal levels on the continuous performance test (Klee & Garfinkel, 1983), simple and choice reaction-time tests (Firestone & Douglas, 1975), the Matching Familiar Figures Test (Peters, 1977), the Embedded Figures Test (Campbell, Douglas, & Morgenstern, 1971), the Porteus Mazes (Parry & Douglas, 1983), and tests with multiple-choice formats (e.g., Hoy, Weiss, Minde, & Cohen, 1978). Investigators have suggested that children with ADHD suffer from inattention on the basis of these findings.

Yet such tasks do not address adequately the attentional deficits of ADHD children. Typically, the data produced by these tasks consists of error scores and response-time scores. The nature of the attentional deficits in ADHD children are inferred from the error and response-time

---

DAVID M. WHITE • Private Practice in Clinical Psychology, 10516 Santa Monica Boulevard, Suite 2, Los Angeles, California 90025. ROBERT L. SPRAGUE • Institute for Research on Human Development, University of Illinois at Urbana–Champaign, Champaign, Illinois 61820.

Advances in Clinical Child Psychology, Volume 14, edited by Benjamin B. Lahey and Alan E. Kazdin. Plenum Press, New York, 1992

scores. Speculations are advanced about the construct or process being tapped by the test administered. A number of disadvantages are associated with this analytic approach. Error and response-time scores may bear little relation to the process by which ADHD children achieve their scores. The same error and response-time scores may be achieved by utilization of different attentional strategies. Different scores may be achieved when the same strategies are used. This experimental approach leaves much to be desired in that many questions about the attentional problems of ADHD children are left unanswered.

In the present research an effort was made to study directly the attention allocation processes of children with ADHD. Data have been collected and analyses begun on children with ADHD using a modified version of a task used in behavioral pharmacology with animals (Cumming, 1965; Lanson, Eckerman, & Berryman, 1979). This is the Match-to-Sample (MTS) task. In animal research, MTS typically consists of a center illuminated key containing either a color or a symbol (sample) and two side keys to which the animal can respond. On one of the side keys is the same stimulus as the center (the "match"), and on the other key is a different stimulus.

In the past years the MTS task has been automated (Sprague, Boatz, & Yoos, 1983; White, Sprague, & Chadsey-Rusch, 1987), which allows measurement of attention strategy in an ADHD child as he performs the task.[1] The child is seated on a chair in front of a large panel. On the panel are projected various stimuli; the most recently used is Gibson's letterlike forms (Gibson, 1965). In the center of the panel is a single aperture, which, when the key directly below it is pressed, illuminates showing the "sample" stimulus; the aperture is illuminated only for the time the key is depressed. Aligned in a row above the sample stimulus are six additional apertures, each of which illuminates and displays a stimulus when the button beneath it is pressed. Only one aperture at a time illuminates, even though the child may depress more than one button; only the first button pressed is illuminated. At some location in this row of six apertures is the "match" stimulus that is exactly the same as the sample. In the other five apertures, very similar stimuli, dissimilar stimuli, or blanks as indicated by a dot in the center of the aperture are displayed in counterbalanced fashion.

The child is allowed to examine the sample as long as he wishes, and then examine in any sequence each of the six apertures and try to

[1] In this report male nouns and pronouns are used to refer to ADHD children. These are not instances of "sexist" language; rather, they are accurate reflections of sex ratios. Prevalence studies indicate that there are four or more ADHD boys for every ADHD girl (e.g., Sandoval, Lambert, & Sassone, 1980), and many studies restrict their target samples to male children.

find the match. The child's complete freedom to select apertures in any manner allows him to develop his own strategy. The automated equipment records each time an aperture is inspected and the length of the inspection (recorded in milliseconds). These data allow the investigator to determine the kind of inspection strategy the child is using as well as changes in his strategy over the course of the experiment. The system used to record the data incorporates a microprocessor (the Apple II) to control the sequence of the stimuli, collect the data, and enter the data from floppy disk into the statistical system at the University of Illinois. The equipment produces graphic illustrations of the child's performance in each of the 36 trials of the MTS task. The task lends itself well to individual-subject analysis.

A test button on the panel allows the child to indicate when he wishes to be tested, that is, when he believes he knows where the match is. The test involves pressing the test button first, then pressing a button underneath the aperture where the match is located. A system of reward is incorporated in which the child is awarded 5 points if he is correct on the first test attempt, 4 points if correct on the second attempt, 3 points on the third attempt, and so on. The points were traded in for time playing a computer game following the session.

2. *Hypotheses and Theoretical Model of Attention*

The aim of this study was to contrast the attention allocation processes of ADHD children and normal children. It was anticipated that the children with ADHD would exhibit ineffective attentional strategies in comparison to normal children. These attentional strategies, it was posited, reflect deficiencies in several general attention processes. Specifically, three attention processes were believed to be possibly deficient in children with ADHD, namely (1) impulsive responding, (2) irregularity in exhaustiveness of attention allocation, and (3) underselective attention allocation. Specific measures of each of the deficits were devised, and initial hypotheses concerning differences in attention processes of ADHD and normal children as measured by the MTS task were developed at the outset of the study. These hypotheses follow.

2.1. *Impulsive Responding*

Initially it was anticipated that children with ADHD would be more "impulsive" than normal children in performance of the MTS task. The impulsiveness of children with ADHD has been noted by several researchers. Douglas and Peters (1979), for example, noted that ADHD children, in performing visual match-to-sample tasks, "make their choices more quickly than nonhyperactive controls and give less consideration, in a less organized fashion . . . to alternatives" (p. 296). Their observation is commonly heard also from clinicians, teachers, and other caregivers. Douglas and Peters, however, did not study the attention allocation of the ADHD children directly. In the present study it was anticipated that children with ADHD would spend less time examining the sample and the alternatives than normal children. It was anticipated that the frequency with which the sample and alternatives were inspected would be substantially lower in the ADHD than nonreferred children. Finally, the inspection rate (number of inspections per unit time) of ADHD children was expected to be higher than that of normal children.

2.2. *Attentional Exhaustiveness*

It was predicted that ADHD children would be excessively "narrow" in attention allocation in the MTS task. It was anticipated that children with ADHD would inspect fewer different alternatives than normal children. Many learning-disabled children are overexclusive in attention and are handicapped in situations in which a thorough examination of the environment is required (Lefton, Lahey, & Stagg, 1978; Ross, 1976). This attentional strategy is observed frequently in very young children. Evidence from eye movement research (Vurpillot, 1968) shows that, until the age of 6, children's attention is restricted to a very limited area. In the present study, ADHD children were expected to use a "self-terminating" strategy in searching the various alternatives. That is, they were expected to examine the alternative choices only until they believed they had encountered the match, select the first alternative that appeared to them the same as the sample, and discontinue their search at this point.

2.3. *Underselective Attention*

It was expected that children with ADHD would be underselective in attention allocation in the MTS task. As others have pointed out, children with ADHD often focus upon salient, though irrelevant, aspects of their stimulus environment. This attention strategy has been attributed to a "defective filter mechanism" or an inability to discriminate critical from noncritical stimuli (Cruickshank, 1977). On the other hand, other researchers find that children with ADHD are no more distractible than control children (e.g., Douglas, 1983). In the MTS task the length of time children examine the sample and alternatives was monitored, and the sequence in which they examine the stimuli was likewise electronically recorded. Consequently, it was possible to detect precisely where in the stimulus display children deployed their attention. It was expected that the ADHD children would deploy their attention to stimuli that were presumably uninformative. The nonmatch alternatives were classified as stimuli similar to the sample, stimuli dissimilar to the sample, and blanks. ADHD children were expected, therefore, to attend to alternatives that were unlike the sample (e.g., to dissimilar stimuli and blanks). The normal children were expected to deploy their attention rather to the match and stimuli that were similar to the sample.

3. *Method*

3.1. *Subjects*

Fifteen children with ADHD participated in the study. The children were participants in the Pediatric Psychopharmacology Project at the Institute for Child Behavior and Development at the Urbana–Champaign campus of the University of Illinois. All of the children were diagnosed using a standard procedure. Initially, they were screened for ADHD based upon their scores on ACTeRS (ADHD/H: Comprehensive Teacher's Rating Scale) (Ullmann, Sleator, & Sprague, 1984a). ACTeRS is a rating instrument used by teachers to assess classroom behavior on four subscales: (1) attention, (2) hyperactivity, (3) social skills, and (4) oppositional behavior. Children with ADHD must meet or exceed the cutoff scores for the attention and/or hyperactivity subscales. The cutoff score for boys on the attention subscale is 15; for girls it is 17 (Ullman, Sleator, & Sprague, 1984b; Ullman, Sleator, & Sprague, 1985). ADHD children attain scores at or below these values. The cutoff score for boys on the hyperactivity subscale is 17; for girls it is 15.

If a child passed this initial screening examination, he was given a pediatric examination, a brief neurological examination, and a number of clinical laboratory tests. A social history was obtained from the parent(s) or guardian(s). Considerable weight was given to evidence that the condition was persistent. Sensory defects that may cause attentional deficits (e.g., hearing or vision deficits) were corrected. A child was diagnosed as having ADHD by the pediatician of the project only if hyperactive behaviors persisted despite such correlation. The parent(s) or guardian(s) provided written consent for the child to participate in the study.

The normative, control sample included 38 nonreferred children. The normative sample was selected in the following manner. In the spring of 1981, 66 teachers from a midwestern university town rated 1,365 elementary-school children on ACTeRS (Sprague & Ullmann, 1981). From this sample, 182 children were randomly selected. Because these children had not been referred to the project and because the project was well-known to school administrators, special education staff, and school psychologists as a referral source for children with difficulty, these nonreferred children were classified as "normal." In the following spring (1982), letters explaining the nature of the study were sent to parents of the 182 children. Of the 182 letters sent, 42 parents agreed to permit their children to participate in the study. Due to equipment failure at the outset of the investigation, pilot data on 22 of the children were lost. In the spring of 1984, additional letters were again sent to parents of the 182 nonreferred children. Of the additional letters sent, 19 parents agreed to allow their children's participation in the study. From the second sample, the data from 1 child was lost due to equipment failure. The data from the 20 nonreferred children from the 1982 group and from the 18 children in the 1984 group were aggregated and used, for comparison purposes, as the normative sample. The nonreferred children from the 1982 and 1984 groups did not differ in any of the ACTeRS subscales (Attention, $t = 1.24$, *ns*.; Hyperactivity, $t = 1.41$, *ns*.; Social Skills, $t < 1.00$, Oppositional Behavior, $t = -1.45$, *ns*.).

3.2. *Setting and Equipment*

Microcomputers are much more powerful tools in behavioral science than the electromechanical equipment used in our earliest research. A program with the Apple II microcomputer (with 48 K of RAM, disk drive, color monitor, and interface) not only contrasts the sequence of slides containing the stimuli but records on diskette the following: the exact sequence of responses; the length of each inspection, in milliseconds; interresponse time from the instant a child lifts his finger off a button until the time another button is pressed; all demographic data about the subject including age, sex, grade, ACTeRS scores, and composition of the slide tray used with that child including the sequence of the slides, the six types of stimuli contained in each slide, and the location of each stimulus in reference to the six windows. The interface chassis provides switch-conditioning circuits to the microcomputer for the push button switches on the MTS display panel. The data are transferred by telephone modem to the university mainframe computer, which makes statistical analyses much simpler than the older procedure of having an operator enter data manually with a keyboard while reading printed numbers from a tape produced by a counter as the experiment is being conducted.

Each child participated in the study in either a van or a laboratory room. Both settings contained identical equipment: (1) a programming system and (2) a projection system. The programming system has been discussed. The projection system consisted of one Kodak Carousel Projector with an Ektamar 4- to 6-inch zoom lens. The projector displayed images on a seven-aperture display panel. The display panel was 593 mm × 618 mm with each aperture measuring 76 mm × 83 mm. Rotary solenoid shutters blocked the light from the projector to each aperture until the button beneath that aperture was pressed. Then the rotary solenoid was activated, allowing light to pass to that aperture only for the time the botton was held down.

A remote speaker was located beneath the display panel to project two audio signals generated by the Apple II microcomputer. These signals consisted either of music indicating a correct response or a buzzerlike noise indicating an incorrect response. A counter located prominently in the center top of the panel recorded the cumulative total number of points the child earned for producing correct answers.

3.3. *Match-to-Sample Task*

The task consisted of 39 slides, 3 adaptation slides presented at the beginning of each session and not used in the analysis and 3 sets of 12 (a total of 36) experimental slides presented subsequently. The experimental stimuli came from two sources: (1) 24 of the 36 slides were letterlike forms (Gibson, Gibson, Pick, & Osser, 1962) that were selected from a larger pool of slides utilized in pilot work (Sprague & Ullmann, 1981) and (2) the remaining set of 12 consisted of 3 each of 4 polygon figures—8-sided, 10-sided, 12-sided, and 16-sided. These polygon figures were randomly selected from a pool of figures used in prior studies (Brown & Owen, 1967; Flintoff, Barron, Swanson, Ledlow, & Kinsbourne, 1982). Of the 24 letterlike form slides, half were randomly distributed across the first 12 of 36 trials; the other half were randomly distributed across the last 12 trials. The 12 random polygon figure slides were presented in between (trials 13 through 35) the two sets of letterlike forms.

Each child was randomly assigned to 1 of 4 slide trays of 36 slides. The order of the slides in each of the 4 slide trays was counterbalanced so that the slides in each tray had an equal number of blanks. For example, in the 24 letterlike forms of one set, the match-to-sample display contained slides with one match each along with the following distractors and blanks: (a) 5 slides with 4 distractors and 1 blank; (b) 4 slides with 3 distractors and 2 blanks; (c) 5 slides with 2 distractors and 3 blanks; (d) 5 slides with 1 distractor and 4 blanks; and (e) 5 slides with 0 distractors and 5 blanks.

Polygon figures were counterbalanced in similar fashion. The matches to each of the 8-, 10-, 12-, and 16-sided figures were presented along with the following distractors and blanks: (a) 4 slides with 4 distractors and 1 blank; (b) 4 slides with 2 distractors and 3 blanks; and (c) 4 slides with 0 distractors and 5 blanks.

3.4. *Classification of Alternative Stimuli*

The stimuli presented in the MTS display were classified in four categories, specifically the match, stimuli similar to the sample, stimuli dissimilar to the sample, and blanks. A match was defined simply as an alternative stimulus that was identical to the sample in all features. Blanks were represented by a small solid circle in the center of the aperture. The classification of the stimuli similar to the sample or dissimilar to the sample proved to be more complicated. The basis for the classifications was different for letterlike forms and polygon figures. The classification of the letterlike forms as either similar or dissimilar to the sample was based on normative data from a study on the discrimination of letterlike forms in young children (Gibson, 1965). In the current study the distractors were transformations of the sample stimulus. The distractors included either reversals, line-to-curve transformations, curve-to-line transformations, rotations, or perspective side or perspective back changes of the sample stimulus. These distractors, or transformations of the sample, were classified as similar or dissimilar to the sample depending on the number of discrimination errors with which they were associated in the Gibson *et al.* study.

Gibson found that children of ages 4 through 8 consistently made a greater number of errors for certain kinds of transformations than others. For example, they found that the highest rate of errors occurred for perspective transformations. A moderate rate of errors occurred for rotations and reversals. The lowest rates of error were found for the line-to-curve and curve-to-line transformations. The numbers of errors associated with rotations and reversals and line-to-curve and curve-to-line transformations did not differ significantly.

These normative data served as the basis for classifying distractors as similar or dissimilar to the sample. Theoretically, stimuli similar to the sample should be difficult for children to discriminate from the sample. Consequently, stimuli classified as similar to the sample included those stimuli on which the highest rates of discrimination error occurs: the perspective transformations. Conversely, stimuli classified as dissimilar to the sample include those stimuli that are associated with low rates of discrimination error: line-to-curve and curve-to-line transformations as well as rotations and reversals.

The classification of polygon figures as similar or dissimilar to the sample was based upon objective physical characteristics of these forms. The polygon figures used in the study included 8-sided, 10-sided, 12-sided, and 16-sided forms. The match, obviously, is identical to the sample in all respects. The stimuli similar to the sample possessed the same number of sides as the sample figure but differed from the sample at only one point. The point that would vary was selected at random, with the point moved three units on the grid on which the stimuli were composed in a direction opposite that in the sample. The stimuli dissimilar to the sample differed from the sample in number of sides. Consequently, the stimuli dissimilar to the sample differed from the sample also in their angles, as well as in other factors shown in factor-analytic studies (e.g., Brown & Owen, 1967) to explain parsimoniously the physical dimensionality of polygon forms (e.g., compactness, jaggedness, vertical skewedness, and horizontal skewedness).

3.5. *Testing Procedure*

Each child was given the following verbal instructions:

> You will get to play a matching game where you can earn points to play Space Invaders or Pac-man. Behind each of these windows [the experimenter points to an aperture on the front panel of the MTS device] are pictures that you can only see by pressing the button under each window [points]. You can only press one button at a time, and this yellow light [points] needs to be on before you press a button.
>
> Here's how you play this game. First, you press the button under this window [points] to look at the sample picture. Then you press the buttons in the top row [points] to find the picture that looks *exactly* like or matches the sample picture [points]. You can look at any of the pictures, one at a time, for as long as you want and as many times as you want. When you find the picture that looks just like the sample picture [points], press this green button [points] and then press the button under the window that has the matching picture. If you are right, you will hear this [the experimenter turns on music tape]. If you are wrong, you will hear this [turns on tape with buzzerlike noise]. If you are wrong, keep looking for the matching picture until you find it.
>
> If you are right the first time, you get five points [experimenter holds five fingers]. If you're right the second time, you will get four points [holds up four fingers] and so on down to no points. This counter (points) keeps tract of your points. The more points you earn, the longer you get to play Pac-man or Space Invaders. Do you have any questions? OK, then let's try it together.

The experimenter assists and rewards the child as necessary as he completes the three practice trials.

TABLE 1
Methods of Measurement

Accuracy

The number of points earned in the test phase of a trial. The child receives 5 points for the trial if he is correct on the first test attempt, 4 points if correct on the second attempt, 3 points on the third attempt, and so on. The child receives no points if he requires more than five test attempts to locate the match.

Impulsive responding

Response latency[a]*:* The duration of a trial starting with the viewing phase (at presentation of the "yellow start light") and ending with the test phase (when the child finally selects the match).

Inspection frequency: The overall number of inspections a child devotes to the stimuli in the viewing phase of a trial.

Inspection rate: Inspection frequency divided by the response latency.

Exhaustiveness of attention allocation

Number of different alternative apertures inspected: The number of different alternative apertures inspected during the viewing phase of a trial. The minimum number is 0; the maximum number is 6.

Selectivity of attention allocation[a]

Percentage of response latency devoted to inspection of sample: The sum duration of inspections devoted to the sample in the viewing phase of a trial, divided by the duration of the trial, multiplied by 100.

Percentage of response latency devoted to inspection of match: The sum duration of the inspections devoted to the match in the viewing phase of a trial, divided by the duration of the trial, multiplied by 100.

Percentage of response latency devoted to inspection of stimuli similar to the sample[b]*:* The sum duration of inspections devoted to stimuli similar to the sample in the viewing phase of a trial, divided by the number of such stimuli available for inspection in the MTS display, divided by the duration of the trial, multiplied by 100.

Percentage of response latency devoted to inspection of stimuli dissimilar to the sample: The sum duration of inspections devoted to stimuli dissimilar to the sample in the viewing phase of a trial, divided by the number of such stimuli available for inspection in the MTS display, divided by the duration of the trial, multiplied by 100.

Percentage of response latency devoted to inspection of blanks: The sum duration of inspections devoted to blanks during the viewing phase of a trial, divided by the number of blanks available for inspection in the MTS display, divided by the duration of the trial, multiplied by 100.

Note. The number of stimuli similar to the sample, dissimilar to the sample, and blanks that are available for inspection vary from trial to trial.

[a]Recorded in milliseconds.

[b]The last three percentages weight the number of inspections devoted to stimuli in each classification by the number of such stimuli available for inspection in the MTS display.

3.6. *Measurement*

The theoretical model that inspired this study identified attention strategies that correspond to attention processes that are believed to be possibly deficient in ADHD children: (1) impulsive responding, (2) irregularities in the exhaustiveness of attention allocation, and (3) underselective attention. Methods of measurement were developed for each attention strategy. The measures were generated from the individual responses of each child during the viewing phase and test phase of each of the 36 trials in the MTS task. These measures then could be aggregated across other trials and children. The measures are presented in Table 1.

4. *Results*

4.1. *Single-Subject Analyses*

Most of the analyses to be discussed employ group data; however, reliance on only these might result in the loss of considerable information about the strategies of individual children. Group analyses, obviously, utilize mean or average scores over a number of different children. This procedure can be easily criticized because it is subject to errors of averaging, that is, when the data from a number of different children are added together and divided by the number of children in obtaining a mean for the group, this mean may not reflect very accurately the performance of any subgroup of children or any particular child. This is particularly true when there are one or a few deviant scores on any measure.

For this reason, the inspection strategies of individual children were evaluated both visually and statistically. Examination of the individual data was aided by the analysis of MTS graphics. The Apple II microcomputer produces 36 pages of graphic information for each child, 1 for each of the MTS trials (Sprague *et al.*, 1983). These graphs are very informative. Consider, as an example, the graphs in Figures 1 and 2.

These graphs illustrate the sequence of children's inspections over time as well as the duration of each inspection and between sequential inspections. Numbers on the *y*-axis indicate the position of the apertures the child inspects. Numbers 1 through 6 correspond to positions (1 = lefthand aperature, 2 = next aperature to the right, etc.) in the row of six alternative stimuli. The number 7 refers to the sample stimulus. Inspection time for each aperture is shown in seconds just above each short horizontal line showing which aperture was inspected. Interinspection or interbutton time is shown (in seconds) on the *x*-axis.

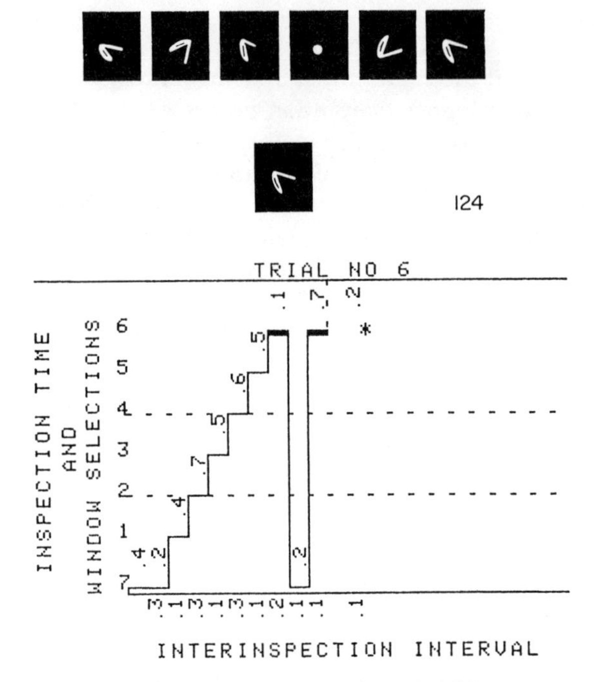

FIGURE 1. Responses of a normal child.

Asterisks indicate the position of the apertures the child inspects after initiation of the test phase of the MTS task. The test phase is indicated by the dashed line from the last aperture the child inspects to the top of the graph. To illustrate, MTS stimuli that were available to the child for inspection when the trial was conducted are shown in the top portion of the figures.

The intent of these figures is to provide an illustration of the differences between ADHD children and normal children in inspection strategies they used in the MTS task. Thus the inspection strategies of a normal child and a child with ADHD are presented as pairs of graphs to an identical MTS display.

Figure 1 presents the inspection strategy of a normal child. The stimulus display contains letterlike forms. In this display, the fourth aperture contains a blank and the sixth aperture contains the match, as indicated by the heavy horizontal line under aperture 6 (A6) as shown in the figure. Perspective back, rotation, perspective side, and reversal changes of the sample are presented in A1, A2, A3, and A5, respectively. After the first inspection of the sample, the child employs an exhaustive search strategy. He or she begins a series of inspections at the

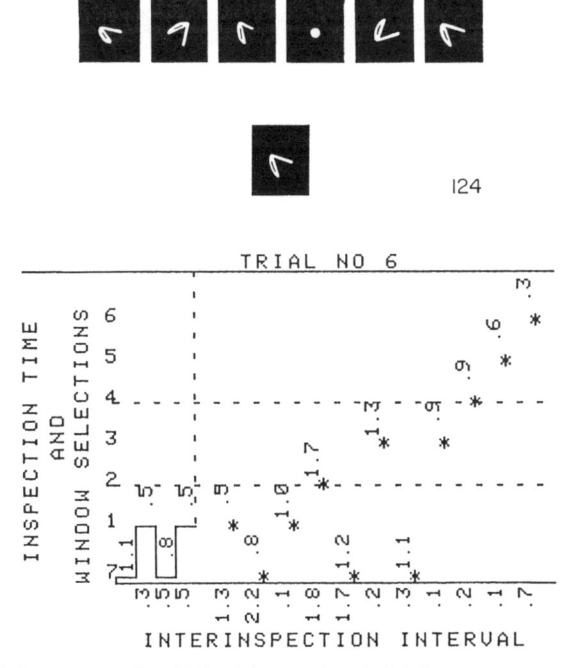

Figure 2. Responses of a child with attention-deficit hyperactivity disorder.

left of the row of six apertures, just as in reading the English language, then systematically searches from left to right for the aperture containing the match. After inspecting the right-most aperture (A6), he reinspects the sample in order to refresh his memory as to its features. Thus having exhaustively inspected the sample and the alternatives in the viewing phase, he correctly identifies the match at A6 in the test phase as indicated by the asterisk after the vertical dashed line.

In Figure 2, the inspection strategy utilized by an ADHD child in response to the same display is depicted. This figure illustrates the limitations inherent in the use of the self-terminating strategy on this task. After inspection of the sample, this child inspects but one alternative aperture. He initially inspects A1, as did the normal child. This aperture contained the perspective back change of the sample stimulus; this transformation resulted in the stimulus defined as "similar to the sample" (see above). This child reinspects the sample (third inspection in the sequence) and the first aperture (fourth inspection). Evidently satisfied that the stimulus located in the first aperture is the correct match, he discontinues his search and inspects none of the other apertures and initiates the test phase of the trial. This child made 10 errors (see 10 asterisks before selecting the correct match (A6) in the test phase that clearly resulted from superficial examination of the alternatives in the viewing phase.

4.2. *Group Statistical Analysis*

A comparison of the attentional strategies of ADHD and normal groups as they performed the MTS task was also made. Differences between ADHD children and normal children were investigated by contrasting the performance of each group over 36 trials of the MTS task. To test the hypotheses discussed previously, a series of multivariate analyses of variance were conducted in which subject group, trial block,[2] and subject grade were incorporated as independent variables and measures of impulsive responding, overexclusive attention allocation, and underselective attention allocation, used as dependent measures. If a significant MANOVA was obtained, then univariate analyses of variance were performed on each of the dependent measures. The ANOVAs will be discussed, in this chapter, only in cases where the MANOVAs initially conducted reached statistical significance.[3]

Prior to the conduct of the statistical analyses, standard normal deviate transformations of all measures were performed to correct for skewedness and kurtosis in the data. Thus all analyses are based on standardized scores.

4.3. *MTS Accuracy*

A summary of differences between ADHD children and normal children in level of matching accuracy is displayed in Figure 3. In Figure 3 "nonreferred" means normal children. As is clearly evident in Figure 3, normal children were more accurate than ADHD children in their ability to select the correct match in the test phase after the viewing phase in which they had a chance to inspect the sample and potential matches ($F = 3.82$; *df* 1, 49; $p < .05$). In Figure 3 and the figures presented subsequently in this report, Tukey's (1977) Box-and-whisker display is shown a method of visual assessment that has the advantage of presenting the entire distribution of scores plus some measures of central tendency. The box encompasses the middle 50% of scores from the 25th to 75th percentiles; the cross in the box displays the mean score; and the

[2] To conduct this analysis, 36 trials of the MTS task were grouped into three trial blocks. The first trial block incorporated trials 1 to 12; the second trial block included trials 13 to 24; and the third trial block included trials 25 to 36.

[3] For the sake of clarity, only the results of the ANOVAs will be discussed. All of the raw data are available upon request.

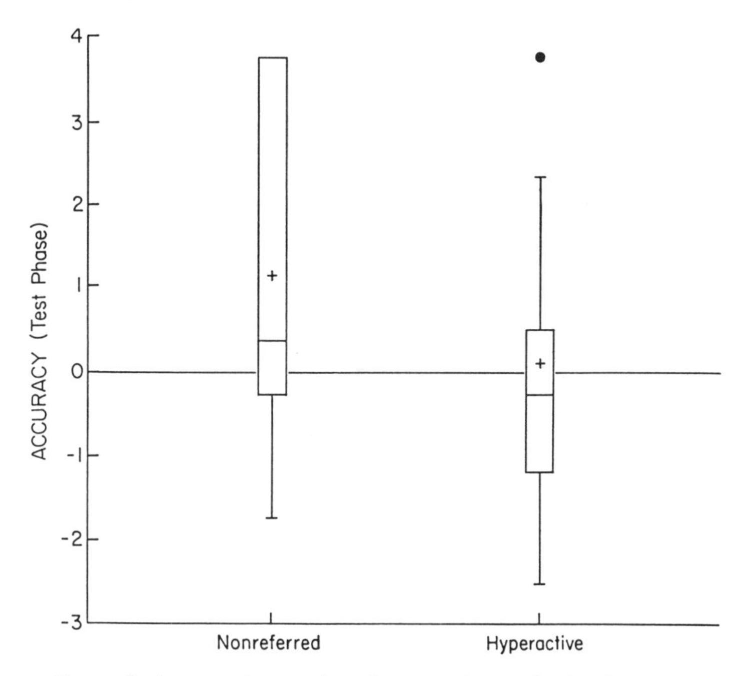

FIGURE 3. Accuracy in test phase by group in standardized scores.

horizontal line in the box shows the median score. The solid lines drawn from the box display the outlying tails of the distribution from the 5th percentile to the lower part of the box and from the 95th percentile to the upper part of the box. The scores lying further out are shown by open circles (95th to 99th percentiles on top and 1st to 5th percentiles on the bottom). The dots represent the most extreme scores (first percentile on the bottom and 99th percentile on top).

4.4. *Impulsive Responding*

4.4.1. *Response Latency*

The differences between ADHD and normal children in response latency, though present, failed to reach statistical significance ($F = 1.45$; *df* 1, 49). The differences were in the theoretically predicted direction, however.

4.4.2. *Inspection Frequency*

The differences between ADHD children and normal children in inspection frequency failed to reach statistical significance ($F = 1.59$; *df* 1,

49). The differences were, however, consistent with theoretical predictions. The inspection frequencies exhibited by ADHD children were lower than those of normal children.

4.4.3. *Inspection Rate*

ADHD and normal children did not differ significantly in inspection rate ($F = 2.00$, *df*; 1, 49). Contrary to predictions, there was a slight tendency for normal children to inspect the individual stimuli more quickly (number of inspections per unit of time) than the ADHD children.

4.5. *Overexclusive Attention Allocation*

4.5.1. *Number of Different Alternative Apertures Inspected*

Differences between ADHD and normal children with respect to the number of different alternatives they inspected are depicted in Figure 4. Of special note, the ADHD children inspected significantly fewer different alternatives than normal children ($F = 11.96$; *df* 1, 49; $p < .001$). This finding provides tentative support for the theory that hyperactive children are overexclusive in their attention allocation. ADHD children de-

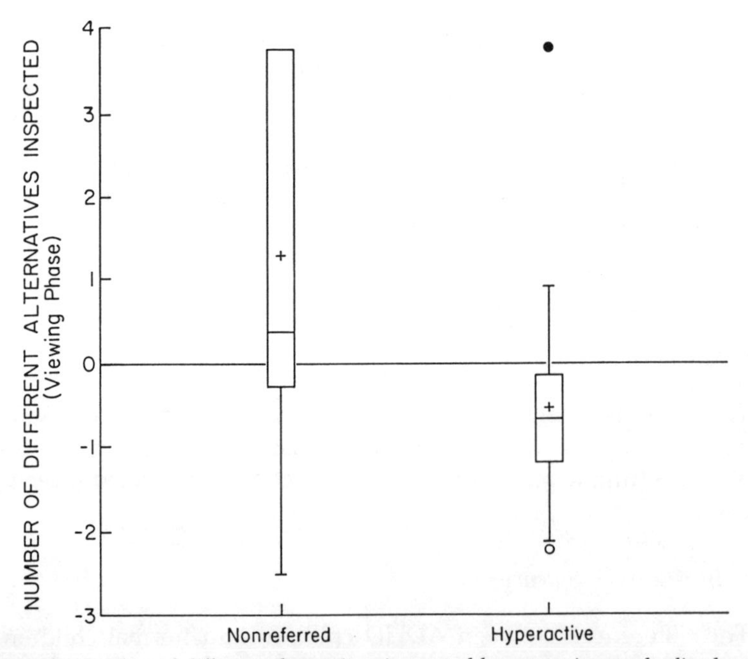

FIGURE 4. Number of different alternatives inspected by group in standardized scores.

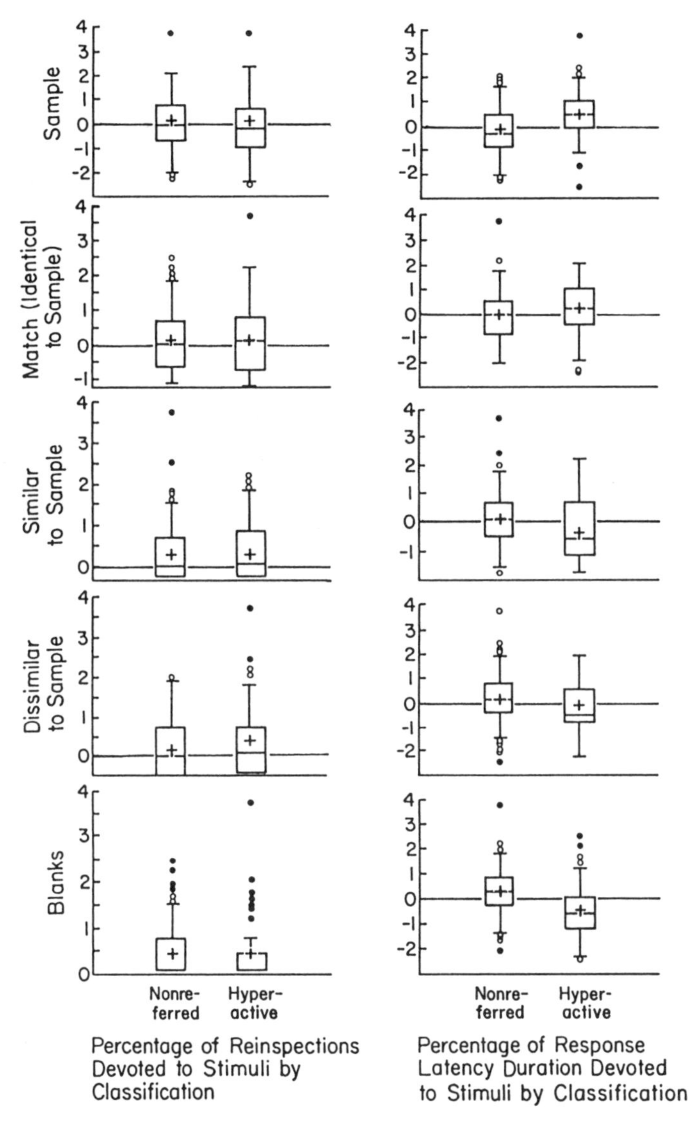

Figure 5. Percentage of response latency duration by group for five kinds of stimuli on standardized scores.

ploy their attention more narrowly than normal children in that they inspect fewer different alternative apertures.

4.6. *Underselective Attention Allocation*

The ADHD and normal children differed in the response latency time they devoted to stimuli of different classifications. A summary of these differences is presented in Figure 5. The findings support only partially the initial theoretical predictions. Nevertheless, they provide valuable information about the attention allocation processes of children with ADHD. The ADHD children generally devoted a higher percentage of their response latency time to the sample than normal children (F = 14.63; *df* 1, 43; $p < .0004$). They also devoted a higher percentage of their response latency duration to the match than normal children (F = 6.24; *df* 1, 43; $p < .01$). On the other hand, normal children devoted a higher percentage of their response latency time to stimuli similar to the sample (F = 4.70; *df* 1, 43; $p < .04$), stimuli dissimilar to the sample (F = 5.71; *df* 1, 43; $p < .02$), and blanks (F = 29.16; *df* 1, 43; $p < .001$) than ADHD children. The latter two findings can be interpreted in the context that normal children have longer overall response latencies, and at the same time they inspect more alternatives, which means that relative to ADHD children, they make more inspections of all alternatives including dissimilar stimuli and blanks, and, consequently, devote more time to viewing these alternatives.

5. *Discussion*

The findings of the present study show that children with ADHD are less proficient than normal children at selecting the correct match to a sample among several alternatives after having a chance to inspect the sample and alternatives. The findings also offer strong support for the position that the matching accuracy of ADHD children is poor, in comparison to normal children, because they tend to use ineffective attentional strategies. Consider the following differences between the children with ADHD and normal children in attentional strategy:

1. The response latencies ("viewing times") of children with ADHD are shorter than those of normal children. This finding suggests that children with ADHD "rush through" the task, whereas normal children have a more reflective approach.
2. The inspection frequencies of children with ADHD are lower than those of normal children. This finding suggests that children with ADHD plan less and are less active than normal children in garnering information about the sample and the alternatives in the viewing phase of the task.
3. The children with ADHD inspect fewer different alternatives than normal children. This finding suggests that children with ADHD are overexclusive in their attention.

   As should be evident from Figure 4, there is little overlap in the distributions of ADHD and normal children on this measure.

The means of the children with ADHD (−.51) and normal children (1.32) differed by nearly as much as two standard deviation units. It should also be noted that the number of different alternatives children inspected was correlated with their matching accuracy ($r = .43$; $p < .001$). Furthermore, consider Figures 3 and 4 presented above; a comparison of these figures suggests they are nearly identical. That is, differences between ADHD and normal children in matching accuracy parallel differences between these groups in the number of different alternatives they inspect.

4. The ADHD and normal children differ in their attentional selectivity. Whereas the children with ADHD devote the majority of their viewing time to the sample and match, the normal children devoted their viewing time largely to alternatives (i.e., to the stimuli similar to the sample, stimuli dissimilar to the sample, and blanks). Children with ADHD thus devote insufficient viewing time to the inspection of nonmatch alternatives (an excellent strategy in this task to help rule out alternatives potentially similar to the sample). Normal children, by contrast, devote their viewing time to a careful comparison and systematic analysis of the alternatives.

It is conceivable that the low matching accuracy of children with ADHD in this task was due to the attention strategies they used. Why might their strategies result in low matching accuracy? One possible reason is that the strategies used placed restrictions on the amount of information these children could obtain about the sample and the alternatives from the MTS display. Information about the sample or alternatives that was never obtained could not be retrieved from short-term memory when these children tried to find the correct match to the sample. Consider the strategies that reflect the processes of impulsive responding, attentional exhaustiveness, and attentional selectivity.

5.1. *Impulsive Responding*

The viewing times of the children with ADHD are shorter than those of normal children. The short viewing times of children with ADHD place upper bounds upon the amount of information they can gather from the MTS display. The inspection frequencies of the children with ADHD are lower than the normal children, as well. The children with ADHD are less active than normal children in scanning the display and lack information about stimuli they never inspect or inspect only superficially (e.g., only once). Their strategy places restrictions on the information about the stimuli that is accessible to recall from their short-term memory when faced with the task of selecting the correct aperture in the test phase. It should be emphasized that inspection frequencies and response latencies correlate positively with matching accuracy (r = .65 and .54; $p < .001$).

5.2. *Attention Allocation Exhaustiveness*

The children with ADHD inspect fewer alternative variants of the sample than the normal children. The children with ADHD use a self-terminating strategy in inspection of the stimuli, whereas normal children use a more exhaustive search approach. The self-terminating strategy used by children with ADHD places restrictions upon the information they have access to for processing. The children with ADHD lack information about those alternative stimuli they never view.

5.3. *Attentional Selectivity*

The children with ADHD differ from normal children in their selective attention. The children with ADHD devote their viewing time primarily to the sample and the match. Normal children, by contrast, devote their viewing time to alternatives, particularly to the stimuli similar to the sample, stimuli dissimilar to the sample, and blanks. The children with ADHD generally do not devote their viewing time to the inspection of alternatives because they devote the majority of their viewing time to the sample. The children with ADHD, therefore, can obtain little information about the nonmatch alternatives they view for only short periods of time. Further, the analysis of alternatives is critical to successful performance of this task because it allows the exclusion of nonmatch alternatives. Indeed, the exclusion of nonmatch alternatives (or the oddity in a 2-alternative MTS task) has been shown (Schroeder, 1976) to be an excellent strategy to use to train matching accuracy in children with mental retardation. In contrast to the ADHD children, the normal children emphasize the careful and systematic examination of alternatives so that exclusion of alternatives deceptively similar to the sample is, for them, not a serious problem.

It is asserted occasionally that children with ADHD search stimuli "more quickly" than normal children in complex cognitive tasks. However, the present findings clearly show this conclusion to be incorrect. To the contrary, inspection rates are found to be slightly higher in normal than ADHD children. It appears that the children with ADHD inspect fewer different alternatives than the normal children, which results in higher error rates and shorter response latencies. The inspection of relatively few different alternatives results in high error rates due to the loss of information about alternatives that occurs. The inspection of few alternatives results also in short latencies because it takes less time to inspect one or a few different alternatives than to inspect most or all of them.

Douglas (1983) has suggested that children with ADHD can be taught to use effective cognitive strategies in the performance of problem-solving tasks. In her training program children are taught specific problem-solving strategies that aim toward helping them become more effective in deployment of their attention. The strategies might focus on teaching these children to develop more organized and exhaustive scanning techniques (e.g., working methodologically from left to right when information is organized in rows, or from top to bottom of a page); focusing (e.g., teaching these children to check in an organized manner for critical attributes, or perhaps crossing out examples that do not fit the criteria); and organizing their time and activities more effectively (e.g., writing down assignments in a special pocketbook). The teaching of cognitive strategies to remediate problems of attention has been used with other populations observed in children, as well, including children with learning disabilities (Torgesen, 1982) and mental retardation (Borkowski & Cavanaugh, 1979; Brown, 1974).

The cognitive and behavioral problems observed in children with ADHD are often attributed to impulsivity. The impulsivity of children with ADHD is evidenced presumably by the short response times they obtain in cognitive tasks. This impulsivity is sometimes the target of behavior training programs for children with ADHD. However, in the authors' view, it is only when such children are taught cognitive strategies required for success in solving problems that they will encounter sufficient success to make it attractive for them to spend enough time on structured problems to arrive at the right answers. By contrast, simply teaching children with ADHD to "slow down" (i.e., not to be impulsive) will do little to improve their task performance. Such instructions have little effect on their performance if they persist in using ineffective strategies; they simply use these inappropriate strategies more slowly. On the other hand, if the intervention is aimed at teaching these children to attend selectively (i.e., to attend to essential, distinctive aspects of the stimuli presented), then the performance deficits that often are attributed to impulsivity can possibly be overcome.

Acknowledgments

Preparation of this chapter was supported in part by National Institute of Mental Health Grant MH18909 to Robert L. Sprague.

We gratefully acknowledge Gerald L. Clore, Donelson E. Dulany,

Bruce Rapkin, Frank R. Rusch, Janice Rusch, and Esther K. Sleator, who also served as the pediatrician on the project, for their comments on an earlier draft of this chapter.

6. *References*

Borkowski, J. G., & Cavanaugh, J. C. (1979). Maintenance and generalization of skills and strategies by the retarded. In N. R. Ellis (Ed.), *Handbook of mental deficiency: Psychological theory and research* (2nd ed.; pp. 569–617). Hillsdale, NJ: Lawrence Erlbaum Associates.

Brown, A. L. (1974). The role of strategic behavior in retardate memory. In N. R. Ellis (Ed.), *International review of research in mental retardation, Vol. 7* (pp. 55–111). New York: Academic Press.

Brown, D. R., & Owen, D. H. (1967). The metrics of visual form: Methodological dyspepsia. *Psychological Bulletin, 68,* 243–259.

Campbell, S. B., Douglas, V. I., & Morgenstern, G. (1971). Cognitive styles in hyperactive children and the effect of methylphenidate. *Journal of Child Psychology and Psychiatry, 12,* 55–67.

Cruickshank, W. M. (1977). *Learning disabilities in home, school and community.* Syracuse: Syracuse University Press.

Cumming, W. W. (1965). The complex discriminated operant: Studies of matching-to-sample and related problems. In D. J. Mostofsky (Ed.), *Stimulus generalization* (pp. 284–330). Stanford: Stanford University Press.

Douglas, V. I. (1972). Stop, look and listen: The problem of sustained attention and impulse control in hyperactive and normal children. *Canadian Journal of Behavioral Science, 4,* 259–282.

Douglas, V. I. (1983). Attention and cognitive problems. In M. Rutter (Ed.) *Developmental neuropsychiatry* (pp. 280–329). New York: Guilford Press.

Douglas, V. I., & Peters, K. G. (1979). Toward a clearer definition of the attentional deficit of hyperactive children. In G. A. Hale & M. Lewis (Eds.), *Attention and cognitive development* (pp. 173–247). New York: Plenum Press.

Firestone, P., & Douglas, V. I. (1975). The effects of reward and punishment on reaction times and autonomic activity in hyperactive and normal children. *Journal of Abnormal Child Psychology, 3,* 201–215.

Flintoff, M. M., Barron, R. W., Swanson, J. M., Ledlow, A., & Kinsbourne, M. (1982). Methylphenidate increases selectivity of visual scanning in children referred for hyperactivity. *Journal of Abnormal Child Psychology, 10,* 145–161.

Gibson, E. J. (1965). Learning to read. *Science, 148,* 1066–1072.

Gibson, E. J., Gibson, J. J., Pick, A. P., & Osser, H. (1962). A developmental study of the discrimination of letter-like forms. *Journal of Comparative and Physiological Psychology, 55,* 897–906.

Hoy, E., Weiss, G., Minde, K., & Cohen, N. (1978). The hyperactive child at adolescence: Cognitive, emotional, and social functioning. *Journal of Abnormal Child Psychology, 6,* 311–324.

Gibson, E. J., Gibson, J. J., Pick, A. P., & Osser, H. (1962). A developmental study of the discrimination of letter-like forms. *Journal of Comparative and Physiological Psychology, 55,* 897–906.

Klee, S. H., & Garfinkel, B. D. (1983). The computerized continuous performance task: A new measure of inattention. *Journal of Abnormal Child Psychology, 11,* 487–496.

Lanson, R. N., Echerman, D. A., & Berryman, R. (1979). Effects of sodium pentobarbital on matching behavior in the pigeon. *Pharmacology Biochemistry & Behavior, 11,* 159–164.

Lefton, L. A., Lahey, B. B., & Stagg, D. I. (1978). Eye movement in reading disabled and normal children: A study of systems and strategies. *Journal of Learning Disabilities, 11,* 549–558.

Parry, P. A., & Douglas, V. I. (1983). Effects of reinforcement on concept identification in hyperactive children. *Journal of Abnormal Child Psychology, 11,* 327–340.

Peters, K. G. (1977). *Selective attention and distractibility in hyperactive and normal children.* Unpublished doctoral dissertation, McGill University.

Ross, A. O. (1976). *Psychological aspects of learning disabilities and reading disorders.* New York: McGraw-Hill.

Sandoval, J., Lambert, N., & Sassone, D. (1980). The identification and labeling of hyperactivity in children: An interactive model. In C. K. Whalen and B. Henker (Eds.), *Hyperactive children: The social ecology of identification and treatment* (pp. 145–171). New York: Academic Press.

Schroeder, S. (1976). Visual motor performance and receptive language in a visually impaired profoundly retarded boy. *Research in the Retarded, 3,* 3–13.

Sprague, R. L., Boatz, H., & Yoos, S. (1983, May). Apple microcomputer operates MTS (Match-to-Sample Device): A saga of 18 years with tangled wires and frayed nerves. In R. L. Sprague (Chair), *Portable Laboratory Operated by Apple II Microcomputer.* Poster session at the meeting of the Association for Behavior Analysis, Milwaukee.

Sprague, R. L., & Ullmann, R. K. (1981, August). Attention in hyperactive attention deficit children: Cognitive and classroom behavior correlates. In D. K. Routh (Chair), *Hyperactive children: Issues in diagnosis and treatment.* Symposium at annual meeting of the American Psychological Association, Los Angeles.

Torgesen, J. K. (1982). The study of short-term memory in learning disabled children: Goals, methods, and conclusions. In K. D. Gadow & I. Bialer (Eds.), *Advances in learning and behavioral disabilities* (Vol. 1; pp. 117–149). Greenwich, CT: JAI Press.

Tukey, J. W. (1977). *Exploratory data analysis.* Reading, MA: Addison-Wesley.

Ullmann, R. K., Sleator, E. K., & Sprague, R. L. (1984a). A new rating scale for diagnosis and monitoring of ADD children. *Psychopharmacology Bulletin, 20,* 160–164.

Ullman, R. K., Sleator, E. K., & Sprague, R. L. (1984b). ADD children: Who is referred from the schools? *Psychopharmacology Bulletin, 20,* 308–312.

Ullman, R. K., Sleator, E. K., & Sprague, R. L. (1985). Introduction to the use of ACTeRS. *Psychopharmacology Bulletin, 21,* 915–920.

Vurpillot, E. (1968). The development of scanning strategies and their relation to visual differentiation. *Journal of Experimental Child Psychology, 6,* 632–650.

White, D. M., Sprague, R. L., & Chadsey-Rusch, J. (1987). *The use of the match-to-sample paradigm to study psychoactive medication effects on cognitive strategies in children.* Unpublished manuscript.

2 Gender Differences in Adolescent Symptoms

KIMBERLY A. SCHONERT-REICHL
AND DANIEL OFFER

1. Introduction

The belief that *all* adolescents experience difficulty and manifest behaviors comparable to psychiatric symptoms may have led mental health professionals and researchers to minimize the importance of the psychiatric symptoms that *some* adolescents do manifest. Indeed, if all teenagers experience turmoil, then there remains the assumption that the symptoms are temporary and will dissipate after adolescence. Support for this hypothesis is given by Offer, Ostrov, and Howard (1981), who found that mental health professionals often possessed distorted perceptions of disturbed adolescents and characterized the pathological symptoms they observed as normal rather than recognizing the seriousness of them.

Until very recently, assumptions about "normative" adolescent development have been based on the clinical experiences of psychiatrists working with emotionally disturbed adolescents. From the early part of the century, clinicians have described adolescence as a time when the personality is severely strained leading to intense inner turmoil. Blos (1970) states

> The more-or-less orderly course of development during latency is thrown into disarray with the child's entry into adolescence. . . . Adolescence cannot take its normal course without regression. (p. 11)

Despite the prevailing belief that adolescence is marked by disturbance, however, few investigations of adolescent disturbance exist.

KIMBERLY A. SCHONERT-REICHL • Department of Educational Psychology and Special Education, University of British Columbia, Vancouver V6T 1Z4, British Columbia, Canada. DANIEL OFFER • Department of Psychiatry, Northwestern University, Chicago, Illinois 60611.

Advances in Clinical Child Psychology, Volume 14, edited by Benjamin B. Lahey and Alan E. Kazdin. Plenum Press, New York, 1992

Moreover, although gender differences in child and adult disturbance and symptomatology have been extensively examined (Chesler, 1972; Dohrenwend & Dohrenwend, 1969, 1976a,b; Eme, 1980; Garai, 1970), the examination of gender differences in adolescent disturbance and symptomatology has been virtually ignored. Researchers may have overlooked examining gender differences in adolescent symptoms, in part, because they believed that these differences were the same as those exhibited in adulthood (Eme, 1980) and therefore did not merit further examination. Nevertheless, we do not know to what extent the multitude of findings that have emerged from the adult literature are generalizable to adolescents. The meager literature that does exist indicates that significant changes in symptomatology of boys and girls occur during adolescence. Rutter and Garmezy (1983) indicate that the incidence of behavioral and psychological difficulties increases during adolescence, and significant sex differences become apparent. For example, although in childhood boys generally outnumber girls in frequency of psychological disorders and behavior problems (Achenbach, 1982), this pattern becomes reversed in adulthood (Dohrenwend & Dohrenwend, 1976a,b). That is, prior to the onset of adolescence, girls are mentally healthier than boys, whereas, after adolescence, this state of affairs is reversed. Furthermore, adolescent males and females differ in the types of symptoms they exhibit, with girls exhibiting more internalizing symptoms (e.g., anxiety, depression) and boys exhibiting more externalizing symptoms (e.g., conduct disorders, delinquency).

The examination of gender differences in adolescent symptomatology is just beginning. Studies of differences among adolescent boys and girls may greatly expand our understanding of this stage of life. If we do not more fully understand the gender differences that exist among adolescents, intervention strategies and programs designed to facilitate healthy adolescent development will be unsuccessful if they treat adolescent boys and girls as a homogeneous group.

As with any emerging area of study, it is important to begin by first presenting the definitional and conceptual background. In this chapter, we have assumed that the approach to learning about adolescent development must be broad-based in order to gain further insight into this time of life; therefore, we define the word *symptom* broadly and do not limit our review to only those studies investigating psychiatric symptomatology. Instead, we review research related to the symptoms manifested by both nonclinic and clinic-referred male and female adolescents as well as include research on the psychological problems and concerns of adolescents. This approach is designed to give the reader a more comprehensive picture of the differences that exist between adolescent boys and girls on a broad spectrum of difficulties and problems. In addition to gender differences, several other demographic variables have a significant impact on symptomatology. Race and class combine with gender. Our focus here, however, is on gender differences. We do not examine the possible interactive effects of gender with race and class due to both the lack of research in the area as well as the lack of space.

The purpose of this chapter is to provide a review of research on gender differences in adolescent disturbance and symptomatology. First, historical perspectives of adolescence will be presented as background. Second, we will put forth a thorough review of the existing literature on prevalence rates of disturbance among adolescents and gender differences in adolescent diagnoses and symptomatology, both normative and psychiatric. Also in this section we include a review of the existing research on gender differences in adolescents' self-reported problems. Third, we will address several of the various measurement issues it is necessary to be cognizant of when assessing adolescent symptoms. Fourth, themes and issues relevant to the treatment and help-seeking behavior of disturbed adolescent boys and girls will be delineated. Finally, we discuss several of the existing hypotheses regarding the mechanisms that underlie gender differences, the limitations of existing studies, and implications for future research.

2. *Background: Historical Perspectives on Adolescence*

In order to provide a context with which to view adolescent disturbance, we provide the historical perspectives of the adolescent age-period that may have led researchers to overlook more fully examining adolescent disturbance and symptomatology. As will be seen, adolescence has typically been characterized as a time of physical and emotional upheaval, with various authors indicating that mental disorders and deviant behaviors appear more frequently during this time period than in any other period in the life span. Increases in drug and alcohol abuse (Bergeret, 1981; Jessor, 1982), accident and suicide rate (Garfinkel, Froese, & Hood, 1982), and the onset of delinquent behavior (Farrington, Ohlin, & Wilson, 1986) are often cited as evidence in designating adolescence as a tumultuous and difficult period of life.

Historians generally credit G. Stanley Hall as the father of the scientific study of adolescence, although earlier writers acknowledged this age-period. For example, Aries (1962) notes that in a thirteenth-century translation from Latin, ancient Byzantine writers made reference to the adolescent age-period. Jean Jacques Rousseau, in 1762, also made reference to the time of adolescence as we know it today (Rousseau, 1911 translation). Nevertheless, G. Stanley Hall's *Adolescence,* published in

1904, really signified the beginning of the scientific study of adolescent development.

Hall subscribed to a four-stage approach to development: infancy, childhood, youth, and adolescence. Adolescence is the period of time from about 12 to about 23 years of age, or when adulthood is achieved. According to Hall (1904), adolescence is a period of "*Sturm und Drang*" (i.e., storm and stress), full of contradictions and wide swings in mood and emotion. Hall, influenced by Charles Darwin, emphasized the biological basis of adolescence. This focus is illustrated in the following statement:

> Nature arms youth for conflict with all the resources at her command-speed, power of shoulder, biceps, back, leg, jaw-strengthened and enlarged skull, thorax, hips, makes man aggressive and prepares woman's frame for maternity. (Hall, 1904, p. xi)

Hall (1904) points out the differences that emerge between the sexes during adolescence, emphasizing aggression in men and preparation for childbearing in women. Further, Hall (1904) described the adolescent age-period as beginning at puberty and ending when full adult status has been attained.

As can be seen, Hall defines the beginning of adolescence by physiological change and the end by psychosocial change. Currently, many definitions of adolescence exist, most emphasizing the physical, psychological, social, and cognitive changes that occur during this age period. For example, Inhelder and Piaget (1958) point out that adolescence is characterized as a time when formal operations emerge, a time when the individual is able to generate hypotheses and consider possibilities and alternatives.

Erikson (1963) notes that "adolescence is a period of rapid change–physical, physiological, psychological, and social; a time when all sameness and continuities relied on earlier are more or less questioned again" (p. 261). Erikson (1963) characterized adolescence as a time that one's own identity is established. In describing his theory concerning adolescent identity formation, Erikson (1963) states:

> The danger of this stage is role confusion. Where this is based on a strong previous doubt as to one's sexual identity, delinquent and outright psychotic episodes are not uncommon. If diagnosed and treated correctly, these incidents do not have the same fatal significance which they have at other ages. (p. 262)

Erikson (1963) also believed that conflict with parents inevitably arises as a result of the adolescent's search and conquest of an adult identity.

Anna Freud's (1958) statement, in her classic paper on adolescence, published in the *Psychoanalytic Study of the Child*, clearly conveys the way many individuals think about adolescent boys and girls:

> Adolescence constitutes by definition an interruption of peaceful growth which resembles in appearance a variety of other emotional upsets and structural upheavals. The adolescent manifestations come close to symptom formation of the neurotic, psychotic or dissocial order and merge almost imperceptibly into borderline states, initial, frustrated or fully fledged forms of all the mental illnesses. (p. 267)

As is illustrated in Anna Freud's description, adolescence is a period of turmoil. In her view, adolescent aggressive impulses are characteristically magnified, sometimes to the point of criminal behavior. Further, Anna Freud believed that equilibrium during adolescence was itself abnormal and if adolescents would not experience turmoil, they eventually become very disturbed. In her own words, Anna Freud (1958) stated: "to be normal during the adolescent period is by itself abnormal" (p. 275).

Psychological difficulties arising during adolescence have often been attributed to the difficulties associated with puberty and other psychosocial changes that occur along with it and because all adolescents go through puberty, then all must experience psychological problems. Undoubtedly, the physiological, psychological, and social changes that take place during adolescence are intense; however, they are now not thought to be as devastating as previously believed. Indeed, the empirical evidence does not support such claims and instead indicates that the mean frequency of disorders in general remains constant through the periods studied, although the nature of the symptoms appear to be age-related (Achenbach, 1982; Rutter, Graham, Chadwick, & Yule, 1976).

The storm and stress theory of adolescence spurred a number of researchers to more closely examine the physical, social, and psychological changes that take place during adolescence. Believing that adolescence is necessarily and characteristically a time of emotional disturbance, several researchers began to more closely investigate the adolescent age-period for evidence of psychological difficulties (Bandura, 1964; Csikzentmihalyi & Larson, 1984; Douvan & Adelson, 1966; Offer, 1969; Offer & Offer, 1975).

The view that the period of adolescence is tumultuous went relatively unchallenged until the investigations of Offer and Vaillant in the 1970s. Vaillant (1974, 1975) and Offer (1969) presented data indicating that the majority of individuals experience adolescence as relatively pleasant and successful. Currently, considerable evidence in the literature has accumulated suggesting that the vast majority of adolescents enjoy life, are happy with themselves, and have positive feelings toward their parents (Douvan & Adelson, 1966; Mitchell, 1980; Offer, 1969; Offer & Offer, 1975; Offer, Ostrov, & Howard, 1981, 1984). These empirical investigations are generally in accord in suggesting that approximately

80% of teenagers do not experience marked or persistent stress and turmoil. As can be surmised, much of this research conducted over the past two decades indicates that, for the majority of teenagers, adolescence is *not* a time of severe turmoil and distress.

3. *Epidemiological Studies*

3.1. *Prevalence Rates of Disturbance*

One implication of an 80% prevalence rate of normality among adolescents is that about 20% of adolescents are disturbed. Indeed, the majority of existing investigations examining prevalence of psychiatric disturbance among children and adolescents are in agreement in finding that approximately 20% are disturbed (Bernstein, Cohen, Schwab-Stone, Valex, & Siever, 1990; Bird *et al.*, 1988; Bjornesson, 1974; Esser, Schmidt, & Woerner, 1990; Graham & Rutter, 1973; Kashani *et al.*, 1987; Krupinski *et al.*, 1967; McGee *et al.*, 1990; Offord *et al.*, 1987; Rutter *et al.*, 1976; Weyerer, Castell, Biener, Artner, & Dilling, 1988; Whitaker *et al.*, 1990).

One frequently cited investigation that examined rates of psychiatric disturbance among adolescents was conducted by Rutter and his colleagues (1976) on the Isle of Wight, an island off the coast of England. They concluded, that among the 14- and 15-year-olds they investigated, the prevalence rate of psychiatric disturbance was 21%.

The findings from other epidemiological investigations examining rates of disturbance among children and adolescents living in countries other than the United States are in agreement with Rutter *et al.*'s (1976) findings. Krupinski *et al.*, (1967) reported a prevalence rate of 17.5% of adolescent disturbance in a small Australian town, and Bjornesson (1974) found the same rate in an industrial town in Scandinavia. In New Zealand, McGee *et al.* (1990) reported a prevalence rate of 22% for a community sample of 15-year-olds. The results of other investigations are in line with these findings (Bird *et al.*, 1988; Esser *et al.*, 1990; Weyerer *et al.*, 1988).

Although in the United States relatively few studies have attempted to ascertain the prevalence of emotional disturbance among adolescents, the findings from investigations that have been conducted are in agreement with the findings of studies conducted outside of the United States. For example, Kashani *et al.* (1987) examined the prevalence of psychiatric disorders in a community sample of adolescents in Columbia, Missouri, and found a prevalence rate of disturbance to be 18.7%. Whitaker *et al.* (1990) found an overall prevalence rate of 17.9% in New

York, and Bernstein *et al.* (1990), also in New York, found that 17.0% of the adolescents in their sample received an AXIS II diagnosis.

With regard to findings specifically on gender differences in epidemiological studies, results are mixed. For instance, Rutter *et al.*'s (1976) findings indicated that a larger percentage of 14-year-old boys than girls were considered to be disturbed. This finding suggesting a higher rate of disturbance among young adolescent boys is in agreement with Leslie (1974) who found a prevalence rate of 21% for 13- and 14-year-old boys and a prevalence rate of only 14% for 13- and 14-year-old girls. Kashani *et al.* (1987), on the other hand, found no significant sex differences.

It appears that, in the majority of more recent studies, adolescent females outnumber adolescent males in terms of rate of psychiatric disturbance. McGee *et al.* (1990), for example, found that more adolescent girls than boys received a psychiatric diagnosis (25.9% vs. 18.2%).

Offord (1986) recently conducted a large-scale survey investigation examining the psychiatric health of children aged 4 to 16. The target population was all children living in Ontario, Canada, who were born between January 1, 1966, and January 1, 1979. A stratified random sample was compiled from the 1981 census file to insure that the children and adolescents selected were representative of both urban and rural areas. Of those selected for participation, 91% agreed to be in the study, yielding a total sample of 3,294 children. A number of measures were included in the study; most relevant for purposes here are the checklists that were used to measure several disorders (i.e., neurosis, somatization, conduct disorder, hyperactivity). Separate forms were completed by teachers and parents for the children aged 4 to 12 and by parents and their children, aged 12 to 16. The results of this study indicated a 19.6% prevalence rate of psychiatric disturbance among these age groups for urban populations. This rate was somewhat lower for rural and small urban populations (14.9%). With regard to gender differences in disturbance, Offord's (1986) data indicated that adolescent girls had higher rates of disturbance than did adolescent boys (21.7% vs. 18.6%).

In summary, although the majority investigations are in agreement in suggesting that approximately 20% of adolescents are disturbed, there are mixed results regarding gender differences in rate of disturbance. Although a few studies have found that boys outnumber girls, others have found the reverse to be true, whereas still others have found that gender differences do not exist in rate of disturbance among adolescents. It should be noted that not all of the existing epidemiological investigations specifically examined gender differences in prevalence rate of disturbance. In addition, many studies did not separate children from adolescents when determining prevalence rates.

3.2. *Comparisons with Child and Adult Populations*

Previous research suggests that the many changes that occur during adolescence are accompanied by changes in the distribution of disturbance between the sexes. Prior to adolescence, girls are mentally healthier, whereas after adolescence, an opposite pattern emerges. These changes in the prevalence of mental illness between the sexes may be linked to the increase in the prevalence of depression that occurs from childhood to adolescence (e.g., Rutter, 1989). Although it appears that in childhood there is an equal distribution of depression between the sexes (Fleming, Offord, & Boyle, 1989; Kashasni *et al.*, 1983; Velez, Johnson, & Cohen, 1989), in adolescence there is a preponderance of adolescent females diagnosed with depression (e.g., Garrison, Jackson, Marsteller, McKeown, & Addy, 1990; Kandel & Davies, 1982; Reinherz *et al.*, 1989; Rutter, 1986). The research findings indicating a higher incidence of depression among adolescent girls are in accord with the research findings on adult depression indicating that depression is more prevalent in adult women then men (Weissman & Klerman, 1979).

Offord *et al.*'s (1987) findings suggest an increase in rate of disturbance from childhood to adolescence and consequently underline the importance of signifying the adolescent age-period as a separate and unique group with which to conduct psychiatric investigations. Examining prevalence of disturbance in children and adolescents aged 4 to 16 years, Offord *et al.* found a rate of 15.8% in the 4- to 11-year-old group and a rate of disturbance of 20.2% in the 12- to 16-year-old group. In addition, the rate of disturbance was related to both age and sex. For children ranging in age from 4 to 11 years, the rate of disorders was higher for boys than for girls (19.5% vs. 13.5%). This pattern reversed for the 12- to 16-year-olds and indicated a greater preponderance of disturbance among the girls in comparison to the boys (21.8% vs. 18.8%). It is important to note that this change in rate of disorder for the sexes would have been obscured if Offord *et al.* (1987) had not separated the younger age-group from the adolescent age-group. Indeed, Offord (1986) found a prevalence rate of one or more disorders in children and adolescents combined to be 18.4% for boys and 16.7% for girls, thereby indicating that overall more boys are disturbed.

3.3. *Gender Differences in Diagnostic Categories*

In addition to the research findings that indicate a higher rate of disturbance among adolescent girls, researchers have also found that the sexes differ with regard to the type of disturbances they manifest in adolescence. For example, Whitaker *et al.* (1990) examined lifetime prevalence of selected DSM-III-defined psychiatric disorders in a large sample of adolescents enrolled in grades 9 through 12. Overall, the most common disorders among the adolescents were dysthymic disorder, depression, and generalized anxiety disorders. These were followed closely by bulimia, obsessive–compulsive disorder, panic disorder, and anorexia nervosa. Adolescent girls were significantly more likely to be diagnosed with eating disorders (anorexia nervosa and bulimia), major depression, and generalized anxiety disorder. These authors also noted a trend toward higher rates of dysthymic disorder in girls. Kashani *et al.* (1987) found similar findings among a community sample of adolescents. Nevertheless, others have argued that there are inconsistent findings with regard to the higher incidence of depression in adolescent girls (Fleming & Offord, 1990) and that these gender differences are perhaps due to the marked inconsistency in the measurement of depressive disorders.

In accord with Whitaker *et al.* (1990), other researchers have found that adolescent girls are more likely than adolescent boys to be diagnosed with disorders such as depression and anxiety (e.g., Bernstein, Garfinkel, & Hoberman, 1989). Kashani *et al.* (1987), investigating a sample of 150 adolescents, found that girls were more likely than boys to be diagnosed with anxiety disorders and depression (both major depression and dysthymic disorder). This is in accordance with findings from other investigations examining adolescent depression (Kandel & Davies, 1982). In contrast, Kashani *et al.* (1987) found that adolescent boys were more likely than adolescent girls to receive diagnoses of conduct disorder and alcohol and drug dependence. These differences between adolescent boys and girls are in the expected direction of males demonstrating more externalizing disorders and females demonstrating more internalizing disorders that has been found in the literature among adult populations (e.g., Weissman & Klerman, 1979).

Nevertheless, not every study has found that adolescent girls predominate on internalizing disorders. In an investigation specifically examining obsessive–compulsive disorders in children and adolescents, Swedo, Rapoport, Leonard, Lenane, and Cheslow (1989) noted that boys outnumbered girls. In addition, Honjo *et al.* (1989) found that adolescent boys were more likely than adolescent girls to have obsessive–compulsive symptoms.

In the Canadian study conducted by Offord *et al.* (1987), a higher incidence of behavior problems among adolescent boys was found. Specifically, Offord *et al.* (1987) found that prevalence of hyperactivity was higher for adolescent boys than for adolescent girls (7.3% versus 3.4%), whereas girls outnumbered boys with regard to emotional disorders (13.6% vs. 4.9%). Somatization disorder was significantly higher for girls than for boys (10.7% vs. 4.5%). In addition, Offord *et al.*'s (1987) findings revealed that conduct disorders were more frequent in adolescent boys than in adolescent girls (10.4% vs. 4.1%). Interestingly, however, there was an increase in conduct disorders among girls from childhood to adolescence. Indeed, whereas only 1.8% of the 4- to 11-year-old girls were given a diagnosis of conduct disorder, 4.1% of the girls in the 12- to 16-year-old group received such a diagnosis. This increase was relatively less dramatic for boys (6.5% for the 4- to 11-year-olds compared to 10.4% for the 12- to 16-year-olds). Other researchers, however, have suggested that externalizing disorders decrease with age for boys (Verhulst *et al.*, 1990).

Paget, Noam, and Borst (1990) investigated a sample of severely disturbed adolescents between the ages of 11 and 17 years who were psychiatrically hospitalized. These researchers hypothesized that adolescent girls in a clinical sample would be more prone to affective disorders than conduct disorders. Using the Diagnostic Interview Schedule for Children (DISC-C; Costello *et al.*, 1984), subjects were classified into either conduct, affective, or mixed diagnoses based on items that inquire about behaviors and emotions both past and current. Results indicated that psychiatric diagnosis and gender were related, with girls more likely to have an affective disorder diagnosis. Boys and girls did not, however, differ with regard to diagnosis of conduct disorder or mixed disorder.

Recently, McGee *et al.* (1990) found that the disorders where adolescent boys predominated were attention-deficit disorder, aggressive conduct disorder, and school phobia. For all the other disorders these researchers investigated, girls outnumbered boys approximately 2:1. These disorders included overanxious disorder, separation anxiety, simple phobia, social phobia, major depressive episode (both past and current), conduct disorder (nonaggressive), and oppositional disorder. Although McGee *et al.*'s (1990) overall findings indicated that adolescent girls were more likely to be diagnosed with internalizing disorders, it should be noted that these researchers also found that a large proportion of the adolescent girls in their study received diagnoses of conduct disorder and oppositional disorder.

Kashani and Orvashel (1988), in an investigation examining anxiety disorders in adolescence, found that a preponderance of females received a diagnosis of an anxiety disorder and were sufficiently impaired by their symptoms to be identified as cases.

Finally, with regard to gender differences in the diagnosis of schizophrenia, it has been suggested that equal percentages of males and females become schizophrenic, although age of onset for schizophrenia occurs earlier in men than women (Westermeyer & Harrow, in press).

4. *Gender Differences in Specific Adolescent Symptoms: Internalizing and Externalizing Symptoms*

As with gender-based differences on prevalence of disturbance and diagnoses, there has been a rising interest in differences in the symptoms manifested by adolescent boys and girls. The assessment of adolescent symptomatology is a complex endeavor. Previous researchers in this field have shown that assessment of a "single symptom" is generally an inappropriate strategy for identifying emotional disturbance and its correlates (Rutter & Garmezy, 1983). Instead, one needs to examine both the number of symptoms that the individual possesses as well as their level of severity. Nevertheless, identifying gender differences in adolescent symptoms will be able to provide one with more information about how disturbance is manifested differentially by the sexes.

Perhaps because so many professionals have believed that adolescence is fraught with turmoil, many have overlooked examining gender differences in symptomatology among this age group. The information that does exist suggests that more inwardly turned symptomatology is characteristic of adolescent girls, whereas a greater proclivity toward acting out is characteristic of adolescent boys. For instance, research has shown that adolescent girls report significantly more psychosomatic symptoms and depressive symptoms, whereas adolescent boys report a significantly higher frequency of aggression and acting-out symptoms (Kandel & Davies, 1982). These two types of symptoms, that is internalizing and externalizing, must be considered in discussing adolescent symptomatology.

Achenbach and Edelbrock (1981) conducted a study of 1,300 children and adolescents who had been referred to a clinic for problem behavior and 1,300 randomly selected nonreferred children and adolescents. All participants ranged in age from 4 to 16 years. Although no significant gender difference in total problem behavior or social competence was found, there were numerous gender differences on specific parent-reported symptoms. Specifically, boys tended to be higher on the externalizing symptoms, and girls were higher on the internalizing symptoms. For example, boys were reported to act too young for their age, be cruel to animals, destroy their own things as well as others' things, be disobedient at school, fight, hang around with other children who get in trouble, be impulsive, attack people, set fires, steal, swear, threaten people, and vandalize. In contrast, girls were reported as being too dependent, to cry a lot, bite fingernails, have aches and pains, and be unhappy, sad, or depressed.

When do these differences between the sexes begin to emerge? It appears that gender differences in psychiatric symptomatology exist even among young adolescents. For example, Kurdek (1987), investigating a sample of seventh and ninth graders using the Symptom Checklist-90-R (SCL-90-R; Derogatis, 1983), found that the nature of symptomatology differed for adolescent boys and girls. In a factor analysis, the factor accounting for the largest amount of variance for boys included items that related to alienation (e.g., people unfriendly, lonely with people, lonely, never feeling close). For girls the factors that accounted for the largest amount of variance included items relating to somatization (e.g., pains in chest, nausea, heart pounding, trembling, tense, weak in parts of body, faintness, nervousness, fearful) and depression (e.g., trouble concentrating, hopeless, lonely, worthless, restless). For boys, the most frequently reported symptom was "feeling uneasy when people are watching or talking about you" and for girls, the most frequently reported symptom was "worrying too much about things." Interestingly, 6 symptoms appeared among the 10 most frequent symptoms for both girls and boys. These were "feeling uneasy when people are watching or talking about you"; "feeling that you are watched or talked about by others"; "repeated unpleasant thoughts that won't leave your mind"; "feeling easily annoyed or irritated"; "trouble concentrating"; and "soreness of your muscles."

Esser, Schmidt, and Woerner (1990), in a longitudinal study of 356 German children and adolescents found that although at age 8, boys' symptom ratings were higher than those of girls, this was no longer the case at age 13. The severe symptoms that more frequently occurred in male adolescents included disciplinary trouble at school, hyperactive behavior, tics, alcohol and medical drug abuse, poor peer relations, lying, and destruction to property. In contrast, adolescent girls were more likely to have symptoms that included nail biting, enuresis, hypochondriac anxiety, and drug abuse. For both boys and girls, respiratory symptoms and poor peer relations increased during adolescence, whereas phobias, hyperactive behavior, food refusal or food faddishness, and sleep disturbances decreased from childhood to adolescence.

Almqvist (1986), in Finland, also has found gender differences in psychopathology during adolescence. Investigating a community sample of 6,482 adolescents born in the year 1955 in Helsinki, Finland (excluding those who died during childhood), Almqvist (1986) found several salient differences between adolescent boys and girls with regard to self-reported psychopathology. For example, psychiatric hospital treatment with a severe diagnosis, such as psychosis, was commoner among boys. Alcoholism and drug addiction were also found to be more common among the adolescent boys. Girls, on the other hand, were more likely to have symptoms related to neuroses and somatic disorders. Severe disorders, overall, were found to be equally common in both sexes, although girls were more likely to obtain a diagnosis of borderline and seek treatment for depression and suicidal ideation than were boys. There was a higher frequency of physical injuries, accidents, smoking, coffee drinking, and alcohol consumption among boys. Overall, when gender differences were evidenced in relation to psychological symptoms, girls were most likely to be higher. As Almqvist (1986) states:

> According to this evaluation, based on subjectively reported problems, forms of behaviors and symptoms, psychological disturbances were more frequent among girls than boys, girls had a higher frequency of mild disturbances than boys, the frequency of severe disorders was higher among girls than among boys, and girls had a higher frequency of subjectively experienced disturbances. (p. 300)

Ostrov, Offer, and Howard (1989) investigated self-image, delinquency, and symptoms in a large sample of adolescents from three Chicago-area schools. With regard to self-image, results indicated that adolescent girls reported significantly poorer functioning than did adolescents boys on scales relating to depression and anxiety, body image, and psychopathology. This concern with body image by adolescent girls has been found by others (e.g., Hodgson, Feldman, Corber, & Quinn, 1986; Marks *et al.*, 1983). In addition, the girls expressed more conservative sexual attitudes than did the boys. With regard to delinquency, adolescent boys reported a greater amount of delinquent behavior over the previous year than did girls. Finally, with respect to the psychiatric symptomatology, significantly more girls than boys attested to a greater degree of symptomatology both during the previous 2 weeks and during the previous year.

Ostrov *et al.*'s (1989) results indicated greater psychological disturbance among adolescent girls. Boys, on the other hand, were more likely to report behavior disorders and to have poorer educational and vocational goals in comparison to adolescent girls.

These differences in symptomatology are evidenced in the kinds of diagnoses that adolescents are given by their therapists. That is, with regard to gender differences in diagnoses given by therapists, adolescent males are more likely to receive a diagnosis such as delinquency, antisocial behavior, or learning disorders and adolescent females are more likely to receive a diagnosis of depression or anxiety (Seiffge-Krenke, 1989).

One special note regarding adolescent depression and depressive symptomatology needs to be made. Researchers have recently shown that the types of symptoms that are manifested by depressed adolescent boys and girls differ. For example, Gjerde, Block, and Block (1988) found that depressed adolescent males exhibited more externalizing symptoms, whereas depressed adolescent females exhibited more internalizing symptoms.

In summary, it appears that gender differences in symptomatology do exist during the adolescent age-period. Teenage girls more frequently manifest symptoms that are turned inwardly, such as depression and anxiety, whereas teenage boys manifest more externalizing symptoms, such as aggression and acting out (Achenbach & Edelbrock, 1981; Almqvist, 1986; Ostrov *et al.*, 1989). Nevertheless, these differences are not as clear-cut as one might initially assume.

5. *Gender Differences in the Self-Reported Problems of Adolescents*

Several studies have been conducted to obtain much needed information about the health concerns and problems of adolescents in order to design and implement specific interventions to meet the needs of adolescents. Many of these studies also collected information about the concerns and psychological problems of adolescent boys and girls. Following, we review the investigations that examined gender differences with regard to the perceived problems of adolescents.

Sternlieb and Munan (1972) conducted a study assessing 1,408 adolescents' (ages 15–21) perceptions of their own health and personal problems. Findings revealed that females indicated greater concerns for problems than males in the areas of nervousness, headaches, and sexual relationships. Males, on the other hand, expressed more concerns than females on issues relating to acne, adaptation to work, and drug and alcohol problems. As might be expected from these findings, when these same adolescents were queried about their interests in obtaining information regarding a number of health-related topics, girls more frequently indicated an interest in obtaining information about birth control, whereas boys indicated a greater interest in obtaining information about dealing with drugs, venereal disease, and alcohol.

With regard to perceived vulnerability to illness, more females than males perceive themselves as vulnerable to illness and express concerns about their health and about becoming sick (Radius *et al.*, 1980). However, adolescent boys, particularly those 16 years of age and older, describe themselves as doing things that are not good for their health.

Adolescent girls more frequently report physical problems than adolescent boys. For example, Dubow *et al.* (1990) reported that girls were significantly more likely to report headaches, frequent colds and coughs, fatigue, stomach aches, muscle and bone aches, nail biting, visual problems, chest pains, dizziness, sleeping problems, and vomiting than were adolescent boys. In addition, these researchers found that adolescent girls predominated with regard to psychological problems such as moodiness, anxiety, irritability, depression, loss of appetite, and suicidal ideation.

Research has suggested that adolescent girls are more likely than adolescent boys to associate emotional problems with poor health. Alexander (1989), in a study examining gender differences in adolescent health concerns, found that whereas emotional and social concerns were associated with poorer perceived health among 13-year-old girls, physical concerns were associated with poor health for same-aged boys. Further, Alexander (1989) found that girls' health concerns related to body image and social relationships.

Garrick, Ostrov, and Offer (1988) found that adolescent girls with many physical complaints displayed specific disturbance in their psychological functioning. On the other hand, for adolescent boys, somatic symptomatology was related to a poor self-image.

House, Durfee, and Bryan (1979) carried out a study designed to obtain information regarding adolescents' perceptions of their own psychological problems. A survey instrument was administered to 1,349 adolescents enrolled in two senior high schools and one junior high school. The findings revealed that adolescent girls expressed more frequent concerns than boys on areas relating to personal appearance (e.g., weight), relationship with parents, emotional stress, and sex-related problems. In contrast, adolescent boys expressed more frequent concerns than girls on problems relating to substance abuse. Feldman *et al.*'s (1986) and Marks *et al.*'s (1983) findings are in agreement with these findings indicating that adolescent girls are concerned about being overweight, feeling depressed, and having nervous and emotional problems and adolescent boys are more concerned about drug and alcohol abuse.

Body image and weight appear to be frequent concerns of adolescent girls. For example, Dubow *et al.* (1990) found that adolescent girls report more distress on issues relating to weight. Specifically, these researchers found that, whereas only 16% of the adolescent boys indicated that they were concerned about feeling overweight, over half (53%) of the adolescent girls reported such. Casper and Offer (1990) have found similar results indicating that female adolescents are preoccupied with weight and dieting as opposed to male adolescents and go on to suggest that the fairly common thoughts and concerns about weight and dieting among adolescent girls are reflective of society's greater emphasis on thinness for women. However, they note that adolescent girls, or boys for that matter, who possess substantial weight and/or dieting concerns are most likely to have other psychological problems as well.

In addition to concerns about weight, other researchers have found that adolescent girls are more likely than boys to report concerns relating to grades and future schooling (Eme, Maisiak, & Goodale, 1979).

6. *Assessment Issues*

Three major assessment methods have been used to assess symptomatology and disturbance in adolescents. These include the clinical interview, teacher and parent reports, and self-reports. Currently it appears that an adolescent's self-report is necessary to obtain a "complete picture" of symptomatology. Although problems with recall and accuracy may arise when relying on the report of the adolescent, relying on the adolescent's self-report has a number of advantages. First, the report is from the adolescent's perspective. Second, there is lower cost because of not having to collect data from multiple sources. Finally, researchers have found the self-report of the adolescent to be reliable and valid (Achenbach & Edelbrock, 1987; Shain, Naylor, & Allessi, 1990). Indeed, unlike children, for whom the validity of self-report may be suspect, clinical researchers have suggested that the self-report of the adolescent is critical for the study of emotional disturbance (Edelbrock, 1987; Langner *et al.*, 1976; Lavik, 1977; Weissman, Orvaschel, & Padian, 1980). This point is particularly well illustrated in a recent study conducted by Shaffer *et al.* (1990) investigating adolescent suicide. These researchers found that adolescents' self-reports of suicide attempts are higher than those obtained through traditional interview techniques.

It appears that adolescents themselves have the most complete knowledge of their feelings and behaviors across situations. Adolescents may typically have strong inhibitions about sharing personal information with adults that, in turn, makes diagnosis more difficult. Indeed, at around 15, it appears that a change in whom the adolescent chooses to confide occurs (Rivenbark, 1971: Seiffge-Krenke, 1987). Rather than seeing his or her parents as a confidant, the adolescent prefers to share personal information with his or her peers.

Changes in cognitive abilities also allow the adolescent the capacity to hide his or her true feelings by allowing him or her to put on an external "facade" (Broughton, 1981). Adults may have more difficulty in estimating the real degree of stress the adolescent is experiencing and may easily overlook the adolescent's inner suffering. Indeed, it appears that adolescents' symptoms which are reported by parents, teachers, and mental health professionals are often different from those reported by adolescents themselves. This point is illustrated in a study conducted by Pierce and Klein (1982). These researchers found that parents and adolescents only agreed on 7 of 52 items on a behavior rating scale. The agreement was only on those items that reflected overt behavioral manifestations, such as enuresis, eating disorders, and stealing. The differences were reflected in those in which adolescents reported symptoms relating to depression and anxiety.

Researchers have also shown that prevalence of disturbance increases when the self-report of the adolescent is taken into account. The research conducted by Rutter and colleagues (1976) illustrates this point. These researchers found that prevalence of psychiatric disorder among 14- to 15-year-olds was 13% when only parent interviews were taken into account, whereas this rate increased to 21% based on interviews with the adolescents themselves (Graham & Rutter, 1973; Rutter, Graham, Chadwick, & Yule, 1976). Rutter *et al.* (1976) noted that many adolescents who appeared "normal" to parents and teachers were diagnosed as having a disorder based on the adolescent interview. In addition, there was a large discrepancy in the proportion of adolescents who were rated as looking sad during the psychiatric interview and those who reported feelings of sadness. These authors go on to state that nearly all of the disorders that were not "observable" involved some type of emotional disorder, frequently depression. Rutter *et al.*'s (1976) findings lend support to the importance of obtaining the self-report of the adolescent, especially with regard to internalizing symptoms that may not be readily apparent to an observer. Other researchers concur with Rutter, suggesting that parents identify less depression for their adolescents than adolescents identify for themselves (Fleming & Offord, 1990).

One begins to doubt whether or not parents (or others) are reliable sources for evaluating adolescent problems. Nevertheless, the question must also be raised if whether or not the adolescent is a reliable source of information, specifically with regard to more externalizing symptoms that the adolescent may be reluctant and unwilling to acknowledge. It is without doubt that therapists are somewhat insecure of adolescents' perceptions of their emotional difficulties and motivation for treatment. Self-reports of psychopathology or symptoms alone may often be insufficient to determine whether or not an underlying disorder exists. Following the self-report, independent comprehensive and systematic evaluations are needed to establish whether the symptoms reflect a psychiatric disorder. Nonetheless, previous research suggests that the psychological sensitivity of adolescents does allow us to use the adolescent's own self-observation for finding out how an adolescent really feels about him- or herself, and for learning about the adolescent's concerns and problems (Casper & Offer, 1990).

7. *Clinical Implications*

Related to the issue of how to adequately identify disturbance and symptoms in adolescent boys and girls is the issue of treatment. Undoubtedly, those concerned with designing and implementing successful programs for disturbed adolescents should first become cognizant of the differences that do exist in the help-seeking behaviors of adolescent boys and girls. Indeed, because adolescence represents a time when certain psychological disturbances may become exacerbated or begin to emerge, it appears to be an opportune time to intervene.

7.1. *Gender Differences in Help-Seeking Behaviors*

What do people do when they experience emotional pain? Some individuals attempt to alleviate their distress by approaching some type of helping agent, either formal (e.g., mental health professional, clergy, teacher) or informal (e.g., family, friends). We call these attempts to cope with emotional pain "help-seeking" behaviors. In recent years, interest in the help-seeking behavior of both disturbed and nondisturbed adolescents has increased (Dubow, Lovko, & Kausch, 1990; Feldman, Hodgson, Corber, & Quinn, 1986; Marks *et al.*, 1983; Offer, Ostrov, & Howard, 1987; Seiffge-Krenke, 1989; Whitaker *et al.*, 1990). This interest has been spurred partly because the adolescent age-period appears to be a crucial time for mental health intervention due to the several behavioral and emotional difficulties that are said to increase during adolescence (e.g., suicide, delinquency, drug and alcohol abuse) as well as because of the belief that some adult disturbances are first seen during adolescence, such as schizophrenia. As Seiffge-Krenke (1989) states:

> Diagnostically speaking, adolescence is a period when we may be able to detect early signs of potentially serious trouble that could arise later, offering us a unique opportunity to intervene in a way that may preclude pathological solutions to the age-related developmental tasks confronting every adolescent. (p. 473)

Despite the increased efforts to more fully understand the help-seeking behavior of adolescents, little is yet known. Nevertheless, researchers have now begun to identify salient issues related to the help-seeking behaviors of adolescents. For example, Kellam, Branch, Brown, and Russell (1981) examined adolescents' willingness to seek free psychological help when it was offered to them. Results of their study indicated that more girls (25%) than boys (20%) came for treatment. Other investigators concur with these findings, which suggest that adolescent girls are more likely than adolescent boys to seek help. For example, McGee *et al.* (1990) found that more girls than boys seek help (15% versus 9%).

Several investigations addressing adolescent help-seeking have been primarily concerned with obtaining data necessary for designing specific intervention programs and have been conducted by medical professionals (Feldman, Hodgson, Corber, & Quinn, 1986; Hodgson, Feldman, Corber, & Quinn, 1986; House, Durfee, & Bryan, 1979; Riggs & Cheng, 1988). One such study was conducted to determine students' willingness to utilize a school-based clinic (Riggs & Cheng, 1988). Findings of this investigation indicated that, although the majority of adolescents experiencing emotional distress expressed a willingness to go to a school-based clinic for help with their problems and concerns, many would only do so if confidentiality was guaranteed. Results from other research are in accord with Riggs and Cheng's (1988) findings suggesting the importance adolescents place on the issue of confidentiality (Marks, Malizio, Hock, Bordy, & Fisher, 1983). One shortcoming of this investigation, however, was that the authors did not examine differences between the sexes or who adolescents actually go to for help with emotional problems and concerns.

House, Durfee, and Bryan (1979) conducted a study aimed at gathering information regarding the problems and social concerns of low-income southern rural adolescents. These authors also examined the professional and nonprofessional resources that adolescents would go to for help with their concerns. Although these researchers did not examine gender differences, their investigation provides useful information about adolescents' help-seeking behaviors. Subjects were given a list of eight helping professionals (i.e., doctor, nurse, teacher, druggist, social worker, psychologist, guidance counselor, preacher) and were then asked to indicate both a first and second choice of whom they would seek help from for those problems that they had experienced during the previous 6 months. Results revealed that although guidance counselors were more frequently nominated by the adolescents as helping agents for problems relating to family and getting along with others, the majority of the adolescents' responses indicated a preference for seeking help from doctors for both emotional and health-related problems. In response to the open-ended question "If you had a problem with your health or your emotions you would want to talk with what adults?" adolescents replied that family and friends would most frequently be sought followed by school personnel, physicians, and ministers. Other research findings are in agreement with these findings, which suggest that teenagers prefer to seek help from friends or parents for emotional problems (Feldman, Hodgson, Corber, & Quinn, 1986).

Another investigation examining the help-seeking behaviors of adolescents was carried out by Hodgson, Feldman, Corber, and Quinn (1986) in Ontario, Canada. Although the adolescents in this study were queried about their utilization of helping agents for emotional problems, the primary purpose of this survey was to obtain information regarding health care utilization by adolescents for physical problems. Results indicated that girls more frequently nominated friends and boys more frequently nominated parents when asked who they can go to for help with personal problems. In addition, adolescent girls more frequently consulted physicians than did adolescent boys. Overall, few adolescents reported that they had no one with whom to discuss personal problems. These findings are in agreement with the findings of an earlier study conducted by Sternlieb and Munan (1972) who found that adolescents prefer to discuss problems deemed "personal" with parents and friends.

An investigation that specifically examined adolescents' mental health service utilization was carried out by Whitaker *et al.* (1990). These researchers found that the majority of disturbed adolescents had not come into contact with a mental health professional, with the exception of teens with eating disorders. Because of the higher preponderance of eating disorders among adolescent girls, these findings would suggest that adolescent girls are more likely to come into contact with mental health professionals.

Most recently, Dubow, Lovko, and Kausch (1990) examined demographic differences with regard to adolescents' health problems and perceptions of helping agents. These authors addressed several of the deficits of previous investigations by including in their survey items related to adolescents' ratings of the degree of severity of their problems as well as by distinguishing between formal and informal sources of help. Results of this comprehensive questionnaire indicated that when adolescents sought help, females most frequently did so from friends, and boys most frequently did so from parents. With regard to ratings of helpfulness, over 90% of the adolescents in their survey indicated that friends and family were "somewhat" or "a great deal" helpful. These were followed by doctors (75%), nurses and other health professionals (69%), teachers (63%), guidance counselors (59%), clergy (58%), and principals (40%). Girls were more likely than boys to perceive friends, nurses, and other adults as helpful. Both girls and boys were unaware of the majority of the professional helping agencies available in the community. Although Dubow *et al.*'s (1990) investigation addressed many of the deficits in previous investigations, no differentiation was made between the help-seeking behaviors of those adolescents who would be considered emotionally disturbed and those who would not be considered as such. In addition, these authors did not specifically assess adolescents' utilization of mental health care professionals.

7.2. *Gender Differences in Social–Cognitive Ability*

What developmental changes occur during adolescence that would lead us to believe that adolescents are more capable of seeking help and benefiting from treatment? Adolescence is characterized by the emergence of new mental capabilities that allow the adolescent to consider possibilities and alternatives, a time when the individual is able to generate hypotheses and possible solutions (Inhelder & Piaget, 1958). Besides influencing adolescents' perceptions in the cognitive realm, these changes in mental capabilities have repercussions for adolescents' perceptions in the social realm. That is, adolescents' ability to think more abstractly, consider possibilities, and hypothesize in matters of scientific problems or physical objects also allows them to use more sophisticated thinking about their social world. This merging of both cognitive and social developmental theory has been designated as the theory of "social cognition."

Previous research has found that as children become older, they gain increasing sophistication in their ability to understand both the internal and external factors that have an influence on mental illness (Coie & Pennington, 1976; Dollinger, Thelen, & Walsh, 1980; Kalter & Marsden, 1977; Kazdin, Griest, & Esveldt-Dawson, 1984; Marsden & Kalter, 1976; Whiteman, 1967). These earlier investigations indicate that the ability to think in more complex and abstract ways about aspects of mental illness increases with advancing age in late childhood and early adolescence.

Undoubtedly, this growing complexity in their conceptions about mental illness would have an influence on adolescents' willingness to participate in treatment. That is, Piaget's theory of cognitive development would also suggest that adolescents might be more capable of the kind of hypothetical–deductive reasoning necessary for reflecting about possible courses of action for seeking help. In addition, these more sophisticated cognitive abilities would allow the adolescent the opportunity to benefit from psychotherapeutic interventions.

These growing cognitive abilities, however, have been hypothesized to contribute to depression and social withdrawal among adolescents with disabilities (Elkind, 1985).

Gender differences with regard to social–cognitive ability exist in adolescence. Specifically, it appears that disturbed adolescent girls score higher on measures assessing different aspects of social–cognitive ability, such as moral reasoning (Schonert, 1992) and ego development (Paget, Noam, & Borst, 1990). Other research has indicated that females, in general, score higher in domains theoretically related to social cognitive ability, such as empathy (Hoffman, 1977), altruism (Krebs, 1975), and the decoding of visual and auditory cues (Hall, 1978). Thus, adolescent girls might be more able to benefit from the traditional insight-oriented treatment approaches than would adolescent boys.

Researchers have also found that the manner in which symptoms are manifested is related to social–cognitive ability. For example, Noam, Didisheim, and Recklitis (1985) found that externalizing symptoms were related to lower levels of moral development, whereas internalizing symptoms were associated with higher levels of moral development. This research suggests that the manner in which psychopathology is manifested would have an impact on the development of social–cognitive ability, which, in turn, would have an impact on help seeking and treatment.

7.3. *Therapeutic Interventions*

Despite the hypothesis that adolescents (particularly females) possess the cognitive capabilities to benefit from psychotherapeutic intervention, it appears that accepting help from therapists is chosen relatively rarely by adolescents (Offer, Howard, Schonert, & Ostrov, 1991). For example, in a study examining coping strategies among teenagers, Seiffge-Krenke (1989) found that only 9% of adolescents perceived seeking therapeutic help as a possible option. Severity of problems was not found to be directly linked to whether or not an adolescent chose therapy; many other factors were involved. In fact, these researchers found that as problems increased, the propensity to enter therapy decreased. The adolescents in this study with high problem intensity tended to use different types of problem-avoiding behavior, such as withdrawal.

The need for privacy appears to be great for adolescents. This brings us to the question of what leads adolescents accept therapeutic help? Seiffge-Krenke (1989) examined 266 nonclinical and 108 clinical adolescents and found that high psychotherapy motivation, high scores in school-related problems, and a positive attitude toward the helpfulness of therapy were most related to the willingness to accept therapeutic assistance. Also predictive of whether or not adolescents would accept psychotherapy were the quality of relations with parents, neurotic symptoms as well as actual experiences with the mentally ill or other related institutions. As Seiffge-Krenke (1989) concludes:

> From these results we can conclude that it is not so much the pressure of special problems that drives an adolescent to seek therapeutic help but rather a combination of his or her basic willingness to take advice at all, confidence in and familiarity with therapeutic procedures, and especially good relationship with parents. (p. 471)

Although Seiffge-Krenke (1989) did not specifically examine if males or females were more likely to seek help, other researchers have found that females are more likely than males to seek therapeutic assistance (McGee *et al.*, 1990). As has been found, it is not only that gender differences exist in the disturbances themselves but also who seeks treatment. Researchers have found that far more boys than girls are referred for counseling as children, whereas the reverse is found around the age of 15. It appears that adolescent girls are more likely to use informal sources of help and demonstrate a greater openness in expressing feelings and disclosing problems (Seiffge-Krenke, 1989).

The ability of adolescent girls to more openly express their feelings and problems is perhaps related to their psychological defense mechanisms. Recently, Noam and Recklitis (1990) examined the relationship between defenses and symptoms among psychiatrically hospitalized adolescents. Their results indicated that externalizing symptoms were associated with defense mechanisms that locate the problem outside of the self (e.g., displacement, regression), and internalizing symptoms were associated with defense mechanisms that locate the problem within the self (e.g., masochism). These findings suggest that adolescents who manifest internalizing symptoms (who are most likely to be female) might be more able to recognize their problems and seek treatment, whereas those adolescents with externalizing symptoms (who are most likely to be male) might be less likely to seek treatment because they place their problems outside of themselves. Nevertheless, although adolescents may be more likely to seek treatment, research has also found that adolescents with defenses that involve turning against the self are significantly more likely to be suicidal (Recklitis, Noam, & Borst, 1990).

In summary, research findings suggest that, for the most part, adolescents do not obtain the help they need. Unfortunately, it is not entirely clear why some adolescents seek help from mental health professionals and others do not. It may be that those adolescents seeking help from mental health professionals are those who do so through their parents' initiative rather than their own. This is especially noteworthy when one considers that during adolescence individuals gain an increasing ability to conceal distress and put on an external facade (Broughton, 1981). Thus, parents may be unaware of their son's or daughter's internal states and therefore be unable to take action toward intervention. One could also speculate that those adolescents whose disturbance is outwardly manifested would be more likely to encounter parental intervention than those adolescents whose disturbance is turned inwardly, such as depressed feelings. In contrast, it may be that those individuals who display more externalizing symptomatology, such as delinquency and aggression, are more likely to come into contact with the juvenile justice system and not obtain the psychiatric help they may need. Future efforts should attempt to determine what differences exist between those adolescents who obtain help from a mental health professional through their own volition and those who do so under parental coercion as well as the relationships among social–cognitive ability, symptomatology, and help-seeking behavior. Further understanding of these variables may greatly enhance our ability to reach adolescents in order to intervene and prevent problems that would lead to poor adult adjustment.

8. Discussion

8.1. Why Do Gender Differences Exist?

In this review we have demonstrated that gender differences in adolescent symptoms do exist, with adolescent girls manifesting more internalizing symptomatology and adolescent boys manifesting more externalizing symptomatology. Undoubtedly, the reasons as to why gender differences exist in the expression of psychiatric symptomatology among adolescents are complex. Although the mechanisms that underlie these differences remain unclear, researchers have spent much time investigating why these differences exist, exploring both biological and psychosocial processes.

One hypothesis as to why differences in prevalence rates and number of symptoms reported is higher for adolescent girls than for adolescent boys concerns the possibility that females overreport in general. For example, researchers have suggested that women are more able to freely express their concerns and problems as a consequence of the social role they occupy (Gove & Tudor, 1973). That is, expressing one's feelings may be more acceptable for females than it is for males. However, studies investigating this hypothesis (Amenson & Lewinsohn, 1981; Bryson & Pilon, 1984; King & Buchwald, 1982) have found no evidence of a sex bias in reporting or that females are more open in acknowledging their psychological difficulties (e.g., Nolen-Hoeksema, 1987; Weissman & Klerman, 1977). Thus we should accept that these differences exist and that adolescent girls are truly reporting their concerns.

The gender intensification hypothesis suggested by Hill and Lynch (1983) posits that the changes that occur during puberty stimulate adolescent boys and girls to focus on stereotypic gender roles. That is, as both boys and girls become pubertal, they begin to more strongly identify with either the masculine or feminine stereotype. Research has demonstrated that androgyny and masculinity is linked with higher self-esteem (Lau, 1989) and effective coping mechanisms (Peterson, Sarigiani, & Kennedy, 1991). In addition, recent research suggests that body image is a salient component of adolescent girls' self-esteem and that body image is an important correlate of depression in adolescence (Allgood-Merton, Lewinsohn, & Hops, 1990).

A number of recent investigations suggest that adolescence is a more stressful developmental period for girls than for boys (Allgood-Merten, Lewinsohn, & Hops, 1990; Hops, Sherman, & Biglan, 1989; Rutter, 1986) and that the developmental changes that occur during puberty differentially affect boys and girls. Gove and Herb (1974), in their review of gender differences in mental illness, give an explanation that relies predominantly on sex-role theory. They suggest that in adolescence, the female is restricted from participating in activities that are deemed as too "masculine" and experiences a sudden limit of opportunities that are confined to her sex role. This sudden limiting of previously enjoyed activities is said to produce anxiety and conflict. One example frequently cited (Eme, 1980) is related to academic achievement. Whereby academic achievement in the elementary-school years is rewarded for girls, in adolescence girls are socialized to believe that they should not outdo adolescent boys. Furthermore, other researchers argue that the greater incidence of mental illness and psychiatric symptomatology among women compared to men is due to women having more responsibility for the psychological well-being of others (Veroff, Douvan, & Kulka, 1981).

Probably one of the most unequivocal gender differences in the literature is that of the male preponderance of antisocial behaviors and related externalizing symptoms (Feshbach, 1970; Hoffman, 1977; Maccoby & Jacklin, 1974). This finding is especially noteworthy when one considers that Kohlberg *et al.* (1972) in a review of the predictors of adult psychopathology from childhood psychopathology stated that antisocial behavior is the single most powerful predictor of adult maladjustment. Researchers have also stated that this gender difference is real and cannot be explained away by suggesting that males and females have different ways of expressing aggression (Feshbach, 1970). Indeed, the aggressive and antisocial behavior of adolescent males is expressed in delinquent behaviors (Eme, 1980) and all externalizing symptoms in general (Anthony, 1970).

Factors related to the biological changes of adolescence include the cyclic release of gonadotrophin, which results in, among other things, menstruation. Symptoms characteristic of premenstrual syndrome include irritability, tension, anxiety, and depression (Bardwick, 1971; Conger, 1977), and these symptoms have been correlated with a number of psychiatric problems.

In addition, females are also more negatively affected by the physical changes that accompany puberty, which in turn leads to stress. Research has reported that females experience more shame and anxiety over a change such as menstruation (Conger, 1977). Further, adolescent females have to worry about the possibility of an unwanted pregnancy. This fear is undoubtedly communicated to daughters by parents of females who indicate that it is their number 1 worry (Hoffman, 1977).

To summarize, the number of hypotheses offered suggest that females, as they make the transition into adolescence, are more likely to experience stress than are adolescent males. Moreover, this stress appears to be expressed via internalizing symptoms rather than externalizing symptoms, resulting in a greater incidence of neurotic symptomatology.

8.2. Limitations

8.2.1. Limitations of Existing Epidemiological Investigations

This review of research has been undertaken in an attempt to distinguish the types of symptoms and related behaviors that are differently distributed among the sexes in adolescence. One problem, however, is that limited information is available on adolescence disturbance. Two reasons for the scarcity of research in this area are put forth. First, researchers may have overlooked examining the prevalence rates and types of disturbance among adolescents, in part, because the 20% prevalence rate is virtually identical to that found in epidemiological studies of adults (Uhlenhuth, Balter, Mellinger, Cisin, & Clinthorne, 1983) and therefore does not merit further examination. Second, perhaps because of the widespread belief that disturbance in this age group is so expectable, researchers may have believed that studying it is not worth the effort. That is, perhaps as a result of the belief that normal (i.e., nonpatient) adolescents experience turmoil, professionals working with teenagers may have minimized the importance of the emotional disturbances that some adolescents do manifest (Offer, Ostrov, & Howard, 1981).

A few existing problems that are evident in the existing epidemiological investigations need to be delineated. Indeed, the majority of these previous studies suffer from several problems that limit their generalizability to a wide sample of adolescents. First, a paucity of research is available on prevalence of disturbance among adolescents using currently accepted diagnostic criteria (McGee *et al.*, 1990). Relatedly, there is a lack of agreement in how disturbance (i.e., caseness) and prevalence are defined (Brandenburg, Friedman, & Silver, 1990). Second, the majority of epidemiological studies on adolescent disturbance have utilized school-based samples and therefore are not generalizable to those adolescents not in school as well as institutionalized adolescents. This most likely results in an underestimate in rates of disturbance and would also appear to exclude a larger number of males because of their greater likelihood of being categorized as delinquent and being incarcerated. Third, few studies exist that have included community-based samples that reflect the socioeconomic, cultural, and ethnic diversity of adolescents living in the United States. Finally, not all studies have categorized children separately from adolescents and boys from girls.

8.2.2. *Limitations of Studies on Adolescent Help-Seeking*

Although several studies have been carried out examining adolescent help-seeking behavior, these investigations also possess several limitations. First, the majority of investigations have examined adolescents' help-seeking behaviors with regard to the medical professions (e.g., doctors, nurses, etc.), and little attention has been given to adolescents' help-seeking behaviors with regard to the utilization of mental health professionals. Second, many of the studies have not differentiated between the use of formal (e.g., physicians, psychiatrists) and informal (e.g., parents, peers) helping agents (e.g., Parcel, Nader, & Meyer, 1977). Third, few investigations have made a distinction between the help-seeking behaviors of those youth who are psychiatrically diagnosible and those who are not. Fourth, few studies exist that have assessed adolescents' perceptions of the helpfulness of the helping agents with whom they do seek for assistance. Finally, gender differences have not always been explicitly examined.

8.3. *Conclusion and Implications for Future Research*

In conclusion, gender differences clearly exist in both the type of symptoms that are manifested as well as the type of help-seeking that is employed. Nevertheless, the picture is far from clear. Future research should more closely examine gender-based differences in adolescent symptomatology. One focus could be gender-based differences in willingness and ability to obtain help for emotional disturbance. Of particular interest would be to examine the relationship between internalizing or externalizing symptomatology and the likelihood of seeking help. In addition, future research should more closely examine the link between social cognitive ability and help-seeking. Clinicians and researchers should become aware of the gender differences that do exist so that adolescent boys and girls are not treated as a homeogeneous group, and, as a consequence, appropriate intervention strategies can be devised.

9. *References*

Achenbach, T. M. (1982). *Developmental psychopathology.* New York: Wiley.

Achenbach, T. M., & Edelbrock, C. S. (1981). Behavioral problems and competencies reported by parents of normal and disturbed children aged four through sixteen. *Monographs of the Society for Research in Child Development, 46,* No. 1.

Achenbach, T. M., & Edelbrock, C. (1987). *Manual for the Youth Self-Report and Profile.* Burlington: University of Vermont Department of Psychiatry.

Alexander, C. S. (1989). Gender differences in adolescent health concerns and self-assessed health. *Journal of Early Adolescence, 9,* 467–479.

Allgood-Merton, B., Lewinsohn, P. M., & Hops, H. (1990). Sex differences and adolescent depression. *Journal of Abnormal Psychology, 99,* 55–63.

Almqvist, F. (1986). Sex differences in adolescent psychopathology. *Acta Psychiatrica Scandinavica, 73,* 295–306.

Amenson, C., & Lewinsohn, P. M. (1981). An investigation into the observed sex differences in the prevalence of unipolar depression. *Journal of Abnormal Psychology, 90,* 1–13.

Anthony, J. (1970). Behavior disorders. In P. Mussen (Ed.), *Carmichael's manual of child psychology* (pp. 667–764). New York: Wiley.

Aries, P. (1962). *Centuries of childhood.* New York: Vintage Books.

Bandura, A. (1964). The stormy decade: Fact or fiction? *Psychology in the Schools, 1,* 224–231.

Bardwick, J. M. (1971). *Psychology of women: A study of bio-cultural conflict.* New York: Harper & Row.

Bergeret, J. (1981). Young people, drugs . . . and others. *Bulletin on Narcotics, 33,* 1–14.

Bernstein, D. P., Cohen, P., Schwab-Stone, M., Valex, C. N., & Siever, L. J. (1990). *The epidemiology of Axis II disorders.* Unpublished manuscript, New York State Psychiatric Institute.

Bernstein, G. A., Garfinkel, B. D., & Hoberman, H. M. (1989). Self-reported anxiety in adolescents. *American Journal of Psychiatry, 146,* 384–386.

Bird, H. R., Canino, G., Rubio-Stipec, M., & Gould, M. S. (1988). Estimates of the prevalences of childhood maladjustment in community sample in Puerto Rico. *Archives of General Psychiatry, 45,* 1120–1126.

Blos, P. (1970). *The young adolescent: Clinical studies.* London: Collier–MacMillan.

Bjornesson, S. (1974). Epidemiological investigations of mental disorders of children in Reykjavik, Iceland. *Scandinavian Journal of Psychology, 15,* 244–254.

Brandenburg, N. A., Friedman, R. M., & Silver, S. E. (1990). The epidemiology of childhood psychiatric disorders: Prevalence findings from recent studies. *Journal of the American Academy of Child and Adolescent Psychiatry, 29,* 76–83.

Broughton, J. M. (1981). The divided self in adolescence. *Human Development, 24,* 13–32.

Bryson, S. E., & Pilon, D. J. (1984). Sex differences in depression and the method of administering the Beck Depression Inventory. *Journal of Clinical Psychology, 40,* 529–534.

Casper, R. C., & Offer, D. (1990). Weight and dieting concerns in normal adolescents: Fashion or symptom? *Pediatrics, 86,* 384–390.

Chesler, P. (1972). *Women and madness.* New York: Avon.

Cleary, P., Mechanic, D., & Greenly, J. (1982). Sex differences in medical care utilization: An empirical investigation. *Journal of Health and Social Behavior, 23,* 106–118.

Coie, J. D., & Pennington, B. F. (1976). Children's perceptions of deviance and disorder. *Child Development, 47,* 407–413.

Costello, A. J., Edelbrock, C., Dulcan, M. K., Kalas, R., & Klavic, S. H. (1984). *Development and testing of the NIMH Diagnostic Interview Schedule for Children in a clinical population: Final report.* (Contract #RFP-DB-0027). Rockville, MD: Center for Epidemiological Studies, National Institute of Mental Health.

Csikszentmihalyi, M., & Larson, R. (1984). *Being adolescent: Conflict and turmoil in the teenage years.* New York: Basic Books.

Conger, J. (1977). *Adolescence and youth.* New York: Harper & Row.

Derogatis, L. R. (1983). *SCL-90-R: Administration, scoring and procedures Manual II.* Towson, MD: Clinical Psychometric Research.

Dohrenwend, B., & Dohrenwend, B. (1969). *Social status and psychological disorder.* New York: Wiley.

Dohrenwend, B., & Dohrenwend, B. (1976a). Sex differences and psychiatric disorders. *American Journal of Sociology, 81,* 1447–1454.

Dohrenwend, B., & Dohrenwend, B. (1976b). Social status and attitude toward psychological disorder. *American Sociological Review, 32,* 417–433.

Dollinger, S. J., Thelen, M. H., & Walsh, M. L. (1980). Children's conceptions of psychological problems. *Journal of Clinical Child Psychology, 9,* 191–194.

Douvan, E., & Adelson, J. (1966). *The adolescent experience.* New York: Wiley.

Dubow, E. F., Lovko, K. R., Jr., & Kausch, D. F. (1990). Demographic differences in adolescents' health concerns and perceptions of helping agents. *Journal of Clinical Child Psychology, 19,* 44–54.

Edelbrock, C. (1987). Psychometric research on children and adolescents. In C. G. Last & M. Hersen (Eds.), *Issues in diagnostic research* (pp. 219–240). New York: Plenum Press.

Elkind, D. (1985). Cognitive development and adolescent disabilities. *Journal of Adolescent Health Care, 6,* 84–89.

Eme, R. F. (1980). Sex differences in childhood psychopathology: A review. *Psychological Bulletin, 83,* 574–595.

Eme, R., Maisiak, R., & Goodale, W. (1979). Seriousness of adolescent problems. *Adolescence, 14,* 93–99.

Erikson, E. (1963). *Childhood and society.* New York: Norton.

Erikson, E. (1968). *Identity: Youth and crisis.* New York: Norton.

Esser, G., Schmidt, M. H., & Woerner, W. (1990). Epidemiology and course of psychiatric disorders in school-age children—Results of a longitudinal study. *Journal of Child Psychology and Psychiatry, 31,* 243–263.

Farrington, D. P., Ohlin, L. E., & Wilson, J. K. (1986). *Understanding and controlling crime.* New York: Springer.

Feldman, W., Hodgson, C., Corber, S., & Quinn, A. (1986). Health concerns and health-related behaviors of adolescents. *Canadian Medical Association Journal, 134,* 489–493.

Feshbach, S. (1970). Aggression. In P. Mussen (Ed.), *Carmichael's manual of child psychology* (Vol. 2; pp. 159–259). New York: Wiley.

Fleming, J. E., & Offord, D. R. (1990). Epidemiology of childhood depressive disorders: A critical review. *Journal of the American Academy of Child and Adolescent Psychiatry, 29,* 571–580.

Fleming, J. E., Offord, D. R., & Boyle, M. H. (1989). The Ontario child health study: Prevalence of childhood and adolescent depression in the community. *British Journal of Psychiatry, 155,* 647–654.

Freud, A. (1958). Adolescence. *Psychoanalytic Study of the Child, 13,* 255–278.

Garai, J. (1970). Sex differences in mental health. *Genetic Psychology Monographs, 81,* 123–142.

Garfinkel, B. D., Froese, A., & Hood, J. (1982). Suicide attempts in children and adolescents. *American Journal of Psychiatry, 139,* 1257–1261.

Garrick, T., Ostrov, E., & Offer, D. (1988). Physical symptoms and self-image in a group of normal adolescents. *Journal of the American Medical Association, 29,* 73–80.

Garrison, C. Z., Jackson, K. L., Marsteller, F., McKeown, R., & Addy, C. (1990). A longitudinal study of depressive symptomatology in young adolescents. *Journal of the American Academy of Child and Adolescent Psychiatry, 29,* 581–585.

Gjerde, P. F., Block, J., & Block, J. H. (1988). Depressive symptoms and personality during late adolescence: Gender differences in the externalization-internalization of symptom expression. *Journal of Abnormal Psychology, 97,* 475–486.

Gove, W. R., & Herb, T. R. (1974). Stress and mental illness among the young: A comparison of the sexes. *Social Forces, 53,* 256–265.

Gove, W. R., & Tudor, J. F. (1973). Adult sex roles and mental illness. *American Journal of Sociology, 78,* 812–835.

Graham, P., & Rutter, M. (1973). Psychiatric disorders in the young adolescent. *Proceedings of the Royal Society of Medicine, 66,* 58–61.

Hall, G. S. (1904). *Adolescence: Its psychology and its relation to physiology, anthropology, sociology, sex, crime, religion, and education.* New York: D. Appleton.

Hall, J. A. (1978). Gender effects in decoding nonverbal cues. *Psychological Bulletin, 85,* 845–858.

Hill, J. P., & Lynch, M. E. (1983). The intensification of gender-related role expectations during early adolescence. In J. Brooks-Gunn & A. Petersen (Eds.), *Girls at puberty: Biological and psychosocial perspective* (pp. 201–208). New York: Plenum Press.

Hodgson, C., Feldman, W., Corber, S., & Quinn, A. (1986). Adolescent health needs II. Utilization of health care by adolescents. *Adolescence, 21,* 383–390.

Hoffman, L. W. (1977). Changes in family roles, socialization, and sex differences. *American Psychologist, 32,* 644–657.

Hoffman, M. L. (1977). Sex differences in empathy and related behaviors. *Psychological Bulletin, 84,* 712–722.

Honjo, S., Hirano, C., Murase, S., Kaneko, T., Sugiyama, K., Ohtaka, T., Aoyama, Y., Takei, K., Inoko, D., & Wakabayashi, S. (1989). Obsessive-compulsive symptoms in childhood and adolescence. *Acta Psychiatrica Scandinavica, 80,* 83–91.

Hops, H., Sherman, L., & Biglan, A. (1989). Maternal depression, marital discord, and children's behavior: A developmental perspective. In G. R. Patterson (Ed.), *Depression and aggression in family interactions* (pp. 185–208). Hillsdale, NJ: Erlbaum.

House, E. A., Durfee, M. F., & Bryan, C. K. (1979). A survey of psychological and social concerns of rural adolescents. *Adolescence, 14,* 361–376.

Inhelder, B., & Piaget, J. (1958). *The growth of logical thinking.* New York: Basic Books.

Jessor, R. (1982). Problem behavior and developmental transition in adolescence. *Journal of School Health, 52,* 295–300.

Kalter, N. M., & Marsden, G. (1977). Children's understanding of their emotionally disturbed peers. II. Etiological factors. *Psychiatry, 40,* 48–54.
Kandel, D. B., & Davies, M. (1982). Epidemiology of depressive moods in adolescents. *Archives of General Psychiatry, 39,* 1205–1212.
Kashani, J. H., & Orvaschel, H. (1988). Anxiety disorders in mid-adolescence: A community sample. *American Journal of Psychiatry, 145,* 960–964.
Kashani, J. H., Beck, N. C., Hoeper, E. W., Fallahi, C., Corcoran, C. M., McAllister, J. A., Rosenberg, T. K., & Reid, J. C. (1987). Psychiatric disorders in a community sample of adolescents. *American Journal of Psychiatry, 144,* 584–589.
Kazdin, A. E., Griest, D. L., & Esveldt-Dawson, K. (1984). Perceptions of psychopathology among psychiatric inpatient children. *Journal of Clinical Child Psychology, 13,* 147–156.
Kellam, S. G., Branch, J. D., Brown, C. H., & Russell, G. (1981). Why teenagers come for treatment. *Journal of the American Academy of Child Psychiatry, 20,* 477–495.
King, D. A., & Buchwald, A. M. (1982). Sex differences in subclinical depression: Administration of the Beck Depression Inventory in public and private disclosure situations. *Journal of Personality and Social Psychology, 42,* 963–969.
Kohlberg, L., LaCrosse, J., & Ricks, D. (1972). The predictability of adult mental health from childhood behavior. In B. Wolman (Ed.), *Manual of child psychopathology* (pp. 1217–1284). New York: McGraw-Hill.
Krebs, D. (1975). Empathy and altruism. *Journal of Personality and Social Psychology, 32,* 1124–1146.
Krupinski, J., Baikie, A. G., Stoller, A., Graves, J., O'Day, D. M., & Polke, P. (1967). A community health survey of Heyfield, Victoria. *Medical Journal of Australia, 54,* 1204–1211.
Kurdek, L. A. (1987). Gender differences in the psychological symptomatology and coping strategies of young adolescents. *Journal of Early Adolescence, 7,* 395–410.
Langer, T. S., Gersten, J. C., McCarthy, E. D., Eisenberg, J. G., Greene, E. L., Herson, J. H., & Jameson, J. D. (1976). A screening inventory for assessing psychiatric impairment in children 6 to 18. *Journal of Consulting and Clinical Psychology, 44,* 286–296.
Lau, S. (1989). Sex role orientation and domains of self-esteem. *Sex Roles, 21,* 415–422.
Lavik, N. J. (1977). Urban-rural differences in rates of disorder: A comparative psychiatric population study of Norwegian adolescents. In P. J. Graham (Ed.), *Epidemiological approaches in child psychiatry* (pp. 223–251). Orlando, FL: Academic Press.
Leslie, S. A. (1974). Psychiatric disorders in young adolescents of an industrial town. *British Journal of Psychiatry, 125,* 113–124.
Maccoby, E., & Jacklin, C. (1974). *The psychology of sex differences.* Stanford: Stanford University Press.
Marks, A. M., Malizio, J., Hoch, J., Brody, R., & Fisher, M. (1983). Assessment of health needs and willingness to utilize health care resources of adolescents in a suburban populations. *The Journal of Pediatrics, 102,* 456–460.
Marsden, G., & Kalter, N. M. (1976). Children's understanding of their emotionally disturbed peers. I. The concept of emotional disturbance. *Psychiatry, 39,* 277–238.
Messenger, C. B., & McGuire, J. (1981). The child's conception of confidentiality in the therapeutic relationship. *Psychotherapy: Theory, Research, and Practice, 18,* 123–130.
McGee, R., Feehan, M., Williams, S., Partridge, F., Silva, P., & Kelly, J. (1990). DSM-III disorders in a large sample of adolescents. *Journal of the American Academy of Child and Adolescent Psychiatry, 29,* 611–619.
Mitchell, J. R. (1980). Normality in adolescence. *Adolescent Psychiatry, 8,* 201–213.
Noam, G. G., & Recklitis, C. J. (1990). The relationship between defenses and symptoms in adolescent psychopathology. *Journal of Personality Assessment, 54,* 311–327.
Noam, G. G., Didisheim, D., & Recklitis, C. J. (1985, July). *Cognitive and moral development*

in relationship to symptoms in a group of adolescent patients. Paper presented at the 8th Biennial Meeting of the International Society for the Study of Behavioral Development, Tours, France.

Nolen-Hoeksema, S. (1987). Sex differences in unipolar depression: Evidence and theory. *Psychological Bulletin, 101,* 259–282.

Offer, D. (1969). *The psychological world of the teenager.* New York: Basic Books.

Offer, D., & Offer, J. B. (1975). *From teenage to young manhood: A psychological study.* New York: Basic.

Offer, D., Ostrov, E., & Howard, K. I. (1981). The mental health professional's concept of the normal adolescent. *Archives of General Psychiatry, 38,* 149–152.

Offer, D., Ostrov, E., & Howard, K. I. (1984). *Patterns of adolescent self-image.* San Francisco: Jossey-Bass.

Offer, D., Ostrov, E., & Howard, K. I. (1987). Epidemiology of mental health and mental illness among adolescents. In J. D. Noshpitz (Ed.), *Basic handbook of child psychiatry* (pp. 82–88). New York: Basic.

Offer, D., Howard, K. I., Schonert, K. A., & Ostrov, E. (1991). To whom do adolescents turn for help? Differences between disturbed and nondisturbed adolescents. *Journal of the American Academy of Child and Adolescent Psychiatry, 30,* 623–630.

Offord, D. R. (1986). *Ontario child health study: Summary of initial findings.* Ontario, Canada: Queen's Printer for Ontario.

Offord, D. R., Boyle, M. H., Szatmari, P., Rae-Grant, N. I., Links, P. S., Cadman, D. T., Byles, J. A., Crawford, J. W., Blum, H. M., Byrne, C., Thomas, H., & Woodward, C. A. (1987). Ontario Child Health Study II: Six-month prevalence of disorder and rates of service utilization. *Archives of General Psychiatry, 44,* 832–836.

Ostrov, E., Offer, D., & Howard, K. I. (1989). Gender differences in adolescent symptomatology: A normative study. *Journal of the American Academy of Child and Adolescent Psychiatry, 28,* 394–398.

Paget, K. F., Noam, G. G., & Borst, S. (1990, June). *Ego development, psychiatric diagnoses and gender in adolescence: A developmental psychopathology study.* Paper presented at the annual meeting of the American Psychological Society, Dallas, TX.

Parcel, G. S., Nader, P. R., & Meyer, M. P. (1977). Adolescent health concerns, problems, and patterns of utilization in a triethnic urban population. *Pediatrics, 60,* 157–164.

Petersen, A. C., Sarigiani, P. A., & Kennedy, R. E. (1991). Adolescent depression: Why more girls? *Journal of Youth and Adolescence, 20,* 247–271.

Pierce, L., & Klein, H. (1982). A comparison of parent and child perception of the child's behavior. *Behavioral Disorders, 7,* 69–74.

Radius, S. M., Dillman, T. E., Becker, M. H., Rosenstock, I. M., & Horvath, W. J. (1980). Adolescent perspectives on health and illness. *Adolescence, 15,* 375–384.

Recklitis, C. J., Noam, G. G., & Borst, S. R. (1990, March). *Adolescent suicide and defense mechanisms: Differentiating attemptors from ideators and non-attemptors in a sample of adolescent psychiatric patients.* Paper presented at the Biennial Meeting of the Society for Research in Adolescence, Atlanta, GA.

Reinherz, H. Z., Stewart-Berghauer, G., Pakiz, B., Frost, A. K., Moeykens, B. A., & Holmes, W. M. (1989). The relationship of early risk and current mediators to depressive symptomatology in adolescence. *Journal of the American Academy of Child and Adolescent Psychiatry, 28,* 942–947.

Riggs, S., & Cheng, T. (1988). Adolescents' willingness to use a school-based clinic in view of expressed health concerns. *Journal of Adolescent Health Care, 9,* 208–213.

Rivenbark, W. (1971). Self-disclosure among adolescents. *Psychological Reports, 28,* 35–42.

Rousseau, J. J. (1911). *Emile.* London: Dent-Everyman's.

Rutter, M. (1986). The developmental psychopathology of depression: Issues and perspectives. In M. Rutter, C. E. Izard, & P. B. Read (Eds.), *Depression in young people* (pp. 3–32). New York: Guilford Press.

Rutter, M. (1989). Isle of Wight revisited: Twenty-five years of child psychiatric epidemiology. *Journal of the American Academy of Child and Adolescent Psychiatry, 28,* 633–653.

Rutter, M., Graham, P., Chadwick, D. F. D., & Yule, W. (1976). Adolescent turmoil: Fact or fiction. *Journal of Child Psychology and Psychiatry, 17,* 35–56.

Rutter, M., & Garmezy, N. (1983). Developmental Psychopathology. In *Mussen's Handbook of Child Psychology,* E. M. Hetherington (Sec. Ed.), *Socialization, personality and social development,* Vol. 4 (pp. 775–911). New York: John Wiley & Sons.

Schain, B. N., Naylor, M., & Alessi, N. (1990). Comparison of self-rated and clinician-rated measures of depression in adolescents. *American Journal of Psychiatry, 147,* 793–795.

Schonert, K. A. (1992). Sex differences in moral reasoning among emotionally disturbed adolescents. In S. Feinstein (Ed.), *Adolescent psychiatry: Developmental and clinical studies.* Chicago: University of Chicago Press.

Seiffge-Krenke, I. (1989). Problem intensity and the disposition of adolescents to take therapeutic advice. In M. Brambring, F. Losel, & H. Skowronek (Eds.), *Children at risk: Assessment, longitudinal research and intervention* (pp. 457–477). New York: Walter de Gruyter.

Shaffer, D., Vieland, V., Garland, A., Rojas, M., Underwood, M., & Busner, J. (1990). Adolescent suicide attempters: Response to suicide-prevention programs. *Journal of the American Medical Association, 264,* 3151–3155.

Sternlieb, J. J., & Munan, L. (1972). A survey of health problems, practices, and needs of youth. *Pediatrics, 49,* 177–186.

Swedo, S. E., Rapoport, J. L., Leonard, H., Lenane, M., & Cheslow, D. (1989). Obsessive-compulsive disorder in children and adolescents. *Archives of General Psychiatry, 46,* 335–341.

Uhlenhuth, E. H., Balter, M. B., Mellinger, G. D., Cisin, I. H., & Clinthorne, J. (1983). Symptom checklist syndromes in the general population: Correlations with psychotherapeutic drug use. *Archives of General Psychiatry, 40,* 1167–1173.

Vaillant, G. E. (1974). The natural history of male psychological health, II: Some antecedents of healthy adult adjustment. *Archives of General Psychiatry, 31,* 15–22.

Vaillant, G. E. (1975). The natural history of male psychological health, III: Empirical dimensions of mental health. *Archives of General Psychiatry, 32,* 420–426.

Velez, C. N., Johnson, J., & Cohen, P. (1989). A longitudinal analysis of selected risk factors for childhood psychopathology. *Journal of the American Academy of Child and Adolescent Psychiatry, 28,* 861–864.

Verhulst, F. C., Koot, H. M., & Berden, G. F. M. G. (1990). Four-year follow-up of an epidemiological sample. *Journal of the American Academy of Child and Adolescent Psychiatry, 29,* 440–448.

Veroff, J., Douvan, R., & Kulka, R. A. (1981). *The inner American.* New York: Basic Books.

Weissman, M. M., & Klerman, G. L. (1977). Sex differences in epidemiology of depression. *Archives of General Psychiatry, 34,* 98–111.

Weissman, M. M., & Klerman, G. L. (1979). Sex differences and the etiology of depression. In E. S. Gomberg & V. Franks (Eds.), *Gender and disordered behavior* (pp. 381–425). New York: Brunner/Mazel.

Weissman, M. M., Orvaschel, H., & Padian, N. (1980). Children's symptoms and social functioning self-report scales: Comparison of mothers' and children's reports. *Journal of Nervous and Mental Disorder, 168,* 736–740.

Westermeyer, J. F., & Harrow, M. (in press). Schizophrenia and adolescence: A developmental life-span perspective. In P. Tolan & B. Cohler (Eds.), *The handbook of clinical research and practice with adolescents.*

Weyerer, S., Meller, I., & Thaler, J. (1982). The importance of artifactual factors in the relationship between sex and mental disorders. *International Journal of Social Psychology, 83,* 73–80.

Weyerer, S., Castell, R., Biener, A., Artner, K., & Dilling, H. (1988). Prevalence and treatment of psychiatric disorders in 3 to 14-year-old children: Results of a representative field study in the small town rural region of Traunstein, Upper Bavaria. *Acta Psychiatrica Scandinavica, 77,* 290–296.

Whitaker, A., Johnson, J., Shaffer, D., Rapoport, J. L, Kalikow, K., Walsh, B. T., Davies, M., Braiman, S., & Dolinsky, A. (1990). Uncommon troubles in young people. *Archives of General psychiatry, 47,* 487–496.

Whiteman, M. (1967). Children's conceptions of psychological casuality. *Child Development, 38,* 143–156.

3 The Development and Differentiation of Social Subtypes in Autism

M. Christopher Borden
and Thomas H. Ollendick

1. Introduction

Over 40 years of research on the behavioral syndrome of autism have yielded significant advances in our understanding of this perplexing disorder. As with most disciplines, the conceptualization of autism has been characterized by a series of reorganizations with adaptation (accommodation) to changes as new developments occur. For example, Kanner's (1943) assertion of good cognitive potential in autistic persons was refuted by studies suggesting that as many as 70% to 80% were mentally retarded, with most of these individuals scoring in the moderate to severe ranges of intelligence (e.g., DeMyer *et al.*, 1974; Wing & Gould, 1978). Accordingly, the American Psychiatric Association now includes Mental Retardation among its associated diagnostic features (DSM-III, 1980). In fact, cognitive deficiency is now viewed by some as central to the pathogenesis of autistic disturbance (Rutter, 1983).

Other significant developments include the validation of autism as distinct from other psychiatric conditions (e.g., schizophrenia). Rutter and Garmezy (1983) summarize the current position succinctly:

> Autism differs from schizophrenia in family history, evidence of cerebral dysfunction, symptom patterns, course of disorder, and level of intelligence. Moreover, the age of onset of severe psychiatric disorders of a kind usually termed psychoses follows a markedly bipolar distribution with one peak in infancy (autism) and another (schizophrenia) in adolescence. (p. 786)

M. Christopher Borden and Thomas H. Ollendick • Department of Psychology, Virginia Polytechnic Institute and State University, Blacksburg, Virginia 24061.

Advances in Clinical Child Psychology, Volume 14, edited by Benjamin B. Lahey and Alan E. Kazdin. Plenum Press, New York, 1992

(See Rutter and Schopler, 1988, for a review of the differences between autism and mental retardation as well.)

Similarly, considerable reorganization has occurred in the conceptualization of what causes autism. Specifically, early models posited a direct relationship between the presumably cold and rejecting tendencies of parents and autistic outcomes. However, as Schreibman (1988) points out, the deviant interactions that were considered necessary for the development of autism have never been observed systematically. Moreover, failure to empirically validate psychopathology in parents (e.g., Cantwell, Baker, & Rutter, 1978) and the ongoing discovery of biological correlates have shifted the focus of etiological research from interpersonal (interactive) processes to examination of factors within individual autistic persons.

Other advances in recent research have called into question the specificity of autism and its status as a unitary syndrome. Whereas historical accounts emphasized the homogeneity of clinical presentation and etiology, much attention has recently been drawn to the fact that there is undoubtedly etiologic heterogeneity as well as widely varying clinical presentation (Rutter & Schopler, 1988). Moreover, individual variations in cognitive and social impairments have led to the identification of cognitive (Fein, Waterhouse, Lucci, & Snyder, 1985) and social (Wing & Gould, 1979; Wing & Attwood, 1987) subtypes. Siegel, Anders, Ciaranello, Bienenstock, and Kraemer (1986) have empirically subdivided the autistic syndrome based on observations of co-occurring behaviors. Clearly, these studies carry the implication that identification of more clinically homogeneous subgroups will improve research and treatment practices.

Rutter and Schopler (1988) assert, however, that there may be a single basic *deficit* in autism and that research should continue to be directed toward its possible elucidation. Current trends in autism research suggest that many are doing just that. For example, Rutter (1983) and Dawson (1983) have concluded that a basic cognitive deficit involving impaired language, sequencing, abstraction, and coding functions exists in most autistic persons. Others (e.g., Fein, Pennington, Markowitz, Braverman, & Waterhouse, 1986) have argued that social symptoms might more fruitfully be viewed as primary. In this vein, reciprocity of social interchange is regarded as the central deficiency (e.g., Rutter, 1983; Rutter & Garmezy, 1983). Consistent with many theories of early development (e.g., Sroufe, 1979), we suggest that social, cognitive, and affective functions are all important and that they are highly interdependent on each other (see Dawson & Galpert, 1986). Thus the affective and social deficits of autistic children are likely to significantly influence cognitive development just as cognitive processes impact social and affective development (Dawson & Galpert, 1986). In this light, it is interesting to note, as Fein *et al.* (1986) have, that Rutter's (1983) argument for the primacy of cognitive impairment attributes autistic children's difficulty to managing meaningful or affectively charged material. Perhaps the issue of primacy might best be replaced by one of emphasis. Accordingly, researchers may investigate the impact of social processes on cognitive functioning and vice versa. Rutter and Garmezy (1983) illustrate this notion when they emphasize the absence of reciprocal interchange in autism and state: "This observation is important if only because it forces any explanatory mechanism to an operation in the very early stages of development" (p. 789). Consistent with the view of social and cognitive functions as interdependent, the interfacing area of social cognition has received considerable attention in recent conceptualizations of autism (see Baron-Cohen, 1988, for a comprehensive review).

The current effort will focus on the early development and differentiation of social behaviors in autistic children. Specifically, social *outcomes* as defined by Wing's (Wing & Gould, 1979; Wing & Attwood, 1987) social subtypes will serve as the behavioral phenotypes toward which some of the early processes of autistic social and cognitive development may be examined. Consistent with Valsiner's (1987) conception of the developmental approach to psychology, an emphasis will be placed on the variable expressions of outcome or phenotype that may arise from different developmental processes. The first section of this review will consider the evolution of autism as a diagnostic entity with particular attention to the taxonomies forwarded by the American Psychiatric Association. The second section will address the historical changes in conceptualization of autistic etiology. Next, a developmental perspective will be presented as the conceptual basis for the analysis of social subtypes and their differentiation. The fourth section will provide a description of Wing's social subtypes and a review of relevant research. Finally, postnatal processes leading to the early differentiation of social–behavioral outcomes (i.e., Wing's social subtypes) will be examined. Whereas many researchers have acknowledged the importance of adopting a developmental perspective with regard to autism, few have attempted to examine the processes that may account for the differentiation of specific behavioral outcomes. The present effort, although speculative and based on scant empirical evidence, will advance previous conceptualizations by attempting to do so.

2. *Diagnostic Issues*

2.1. *Kanner's Syndrome, 1943*

An historical review of the autism literature highlights the lack of consensus among professionals as to which features of the condition are diagnostic and the degree to which there is overlap with other early-onset disorders. In fact, autism has undergone numerous conceptual and diagnostic permutations since Kanner (1943) first published an account of 11 case histories. Kanner (1943) described "Autistic Disturbances of Affective Contact," characterized by an inability to relate to people and situations from the beginning of life (autistic aloneness), an anxiously obsessive desire to maintain sameness, presence of repetitive or ritualistic behaviors, peculiarity in language usage (including mutism), essentially normal physical development, and good cognitive potential.

In subsequent years, researchers and clinicians highlighted the autistic aloneness and maintenance of sameness features above other diagnostic criteria (Eisenberg & Kanner, 1956). As several authors (e.g., Newsom, Hovanitz, & Rincover, 1988; Newsom & Rincover, 1981; Rutter, 1978a,b) have observed, the emphasis on these two features had a paradoxical effect, leading to the *broadening* of the diagnosis of autism that has plagued the field ever since. Despite support for a unique childhood disorder from academic and clinical circles, Infantile Autism was not *formally* recognized as distinct from Schizophrenia, Childhood Type until 1980 (American Psychiatric Association, 1968).

2.2. *Infantile Autism, 1980*

The third edition of the *Diagnostic and Statistical Manual of Mental Disorders* (DSM-III; American Psychiatric Association, 1980) included the following criteria in its definition of Infantile Autism: early onset (< 30 months), pervasive lack of responsiveness to others (autism), deficits in language development and peculiarities in language use, and bizarre responses to various aspects of the environment (e.g., resistance to change, peculiar interest in or attachments to animate or inanimate objects). Further, it provided differential criteria for diagnosing Schizophrenia and recognized Mental Retardation as an associated feature in 70% of all cases.

The essential behavioral features of Kanner's (1943) original conceptualization of autistic disturbances appear to be retained in DSM-III's depiction of Infantile Autism. The early-onset criterion, which at first seems to represent a dramatic change in definition, actually has had no pronounced effect on the identification of autistic individuals. Specifically, an epidemiological study by Wing and Gould (1979) found that only 6% of autistic children have an age of onset later than 3 years. However, the recognition of Mental Retardation as a frequently observed associated feature represents a significant conceptual point of departure from "Kanner Syndrome" (1943). Moreover, this change increased the breadth of autism from an assessment standpoint and introduced further heterogeneity within the group of individuals labeled autistic.

2.3. *Autistic Disorder, 1987*

The recent revision of the American Psychiatric Association's taxonomy (DSM-III-R, 1987) includes Autistic Disorder as a severe form of the more common Pervasive Developmental Disorder. Criteria are arranged in three major clusters: (a) qualitative impairment in reciprocal social interaction; (b) qualitative impairment in verbal and nonverbal communication, and in imaginative activity; and (c) markedly restricted repertoire of activities and interests. Onset during infancy or childhood is also included among the descriptive characteristics of Autistic Disorder, though this criterion is not necessary for diagnosis. In addition, criteria are considered to be met only if the behavior is abnormal for the person's developmental level. Finally, comorbidity with Mental Retardation is recognized, and the previously held belief that Autistic Disorder was more common in upper socioeconomic strata has been dismissed.

The provision of descriptive items in DSM-III-R would appear to be a positive step in reducing diagnostic ambiguity; however, the requirement that the behavioral items be judged abnormal for the person's developmental level may compromise simultaneously the interrater and cross-temporal reliabilities of the Autistic Disorder diagnosis. Due to subjective judgments and changes with development, what at first glance would appear to be a significant advance in the valid and reliable identification of persons with autism may be contributing to new sources of diagnostic ambiguity. Simply stated, little if any progress has been made in identifying persons who represent a *unitary* syndrome. The implication, as the remainder of this chapter will maintain, is that Autistic Disorder describes a number of disturbances that await empirical differentiation and validation.

2.4. *Alternative Taxonomies*

Of course, alternative frameworks for classifying individuals with autism have also been proposed. Most notably, the *International Classification of Diseases–9th edition* (ICD-9) (World Health Organization, 1978) includes the following groupings of psychoses with origin specific to childhood: Infantile autism, disintegrative psychosis, and other. However, as Wing and Attwood (1987) pointed out, the major problem with ICD-9 is the similarity between clinical descriptions and resultant overlap among these three categories. For example, disintegrative psychosis differs from infantile autism only in that onset occurs after a period of normal development (>30 months) (Wing & Attwood, 1987).

Rutter and Schopler (1987) observed that ICD-9 (World Health Organization, 1978) and DSM-III (American Psychiatric Association, 1980) have concentrated on the same four sets of diagnostic criteria. Rutter (1978b) summarizes these dimensions: (1) onset before 30 months, (2) impaired social development that has a number of special characteristics and is not consistent with the child's level of intellectual functioning, (3) delayed and deviant language development that also has certain defining features and is out of keeping with the child's intellectual level, and (4) insistence on sameness, as shown by stereotyped play patterns, abnormal preoccupations, and resistance to change. As described earlier, DSM-III-R (American Psychiatric Association, 1987) also retains these criteria, with less emphasis on the age of onset as a distinguishing feature. Moreover, Wing's (e.g., 1981; Wing & Gould, 1979) research on socially impaired autistic and nonautistic mentally retarded persons indicates that abnormalities of social interaction, verbal and nonverbal communication, and imaginative activities occur together so frequently that they may be referred to as "the triad of social and language impairment." Consistent with the more formal diagnostic criteria, children with the triad were shown to spend much of their time engaged in stereotyped activities (Wing, 1981). Thus there appear to be commonalities among socially impaired mentally retarded and autistic children with "the triad" and those diagnosed under either American Psychiatric Association or World Health Organization schemes. However, the issue of heterogeneity among those diagnosed autistic, regardless of the classification system endorsed, remains to be resolved.

A critical first step toward understanding the number of disturbances that are proposed to fall under the diagnostic label of autism and their conceptual distinctions would seem to be an analysis of the developmental processes that may account for individual differences in their expression. Accordingly, the early development of individual variation in social behavior among autistic individuals will be examined. As suggested earlier, social behavior, independent of the issue of primacy, may be systematically observed at an early age; thus, a stage approach with regard to conceptual emphasis is most appropriate. An understanding of past and current thought regarding the etiology of autistic disturbances will provide a conceptual basis on which the examination of differential development of social "style" may proceed.

3. *Etiological Perspectives*

Theories of the etiology of autism have ranged from the initial emphasis on parent characteristics and behavior to the more recent attention to organic factors. As Schreibman (1988) suggests, the progression from psychogenic to biological models of autism reflects the broader historical movement of the field of psychology. Consequently, the realization of shortcomings to psychodynamic thinking has led to the proliferation of more empirically and experimentally based biological and learning theories. The following sections will address highlights in this theoretical progression. An integrative perspective consonant with recent trends in developmental theory will be outlined.

3.1. Psychogenic Theories

Early conceptualizations of autism focused on the personality characteristics of parents. Kanner's (1943) original work made reference to the great degree of obsessiveness in the families of the 11 index children and stated that, "in the whole group, there are very few really warmhearted fathers and mothers" (p. 250). Nonetheless, Kanner (1943) attributed the children's extreme autistic aloneness mainly to organic factors:

> The children's aloneness from the beginning of life makes it difficult to attribute the whole picture exclusively to the type of the early parental relations with our patients. We must then, assume that these children have come into the world with the innate inability to form the usual, biologically provided affective contact with people, just as other children come into the world with innate physical and intellectual handicaps. (p. 250)

Subsequent writings (e.g., Eisenberg & Kanner, 1956; Kanner, 1949) corroborated the observation that the parents of autistic children appeared detached, cold, and obsessive.

Taken to their extreme, these suggestions of parent pathology were solidified into propositions of "emotional refrigeration" as the primary cause of the disorder. For example, Bettleheim (1967) forwarded a psychoanalytic model in which such activities as toilet training set the stage for reciprocal withdrawal between the parents and their child and ultimately led to parental hostility and rejection. As Schopler and Mesibov (1986) note, the emphasis on psychoanalytic theories in the 1950s and 1960s resulted in numerous open-minded therapies in which children were removed from their families and that served to decrease rather than to increase appropriate behavior (Schopler, Brehm, Kinsbourne, & Reichler, 1971).

The growing popularity of learning theory was reflected in Ferster's (1961) attempt to reconcile the behavior of autistic individuals with an analysis of their reinforcement histories. However, as Schreibman (1988) indicates, Ferster's ideas failed to receive empirical support or to account for some aspects of autism (e.g., cognitive deficits) and had greater impact on the evolution of treatment for autistic children than on the conceptualization of the disorder's etiology.

Numerous theoretical variations on the theme of psychogenic etiology have been proposed (see Cantwell, Baker, & Rutter, 1978, for a comprehensive review.) The general approaches have been grouped under three headings: (1) the occurrence of severe stress early in the child's life, (2) deviant personality characteristics in parents, and (3) deviant parent–child interaction patterns (Cantwell & Baker, 1984; Schopler, 1983). These examples reflect the prevailing emphasis on parents as primary etiologic agents and highlight the frequent lack of attention to the impact a handicapped child may have on his or her parents. The effects of children on their caregivers have been well documented (Bell, 1968, 1971). It stands to reason, as Rimland (1964) and Rutter (1968) suggest, that any lack of social responsiveness on the part of parents might be directly related to social and behavioral deficits exhibited by their autistic children. Nonetheless, descriptive, naturalistic studies of the interactions between autistic children and their caregivers are rare (Dawson & Galpert, 1986). Increased attention to and more systematic analysis of proximate child–parent effects is clearly warranted in future studies of development in autism.

3.2. *Genetic Models*

Attempts to elucidate a biological marker in the genesis of autism have led some researchers to examine the familiality of the syndrome. In fact, genetic factors have weighed significantly in the minds of many researchers since Kanner's (1943) suggestion of the syndrome's "innateness." However, as several authors (Folstein & Rutter, 1977, 1988; Pauls, 1987) have indicated, studies of autism in twins and families have been plagued by methodological weaknesses, precluding confident interpretation of their results. Specifically, families with several versus just one affected member and monozygotic as opposed to dizygotic twins have been overrepresented in these samples, presumably because they are more "interesting" (Folstein & Rutter, 1988). The reports of 32 twin pairs prior to 1977 support this claim. Nearly twice as many MZ twins as DZ twins were studied, whereas the proportion of "fraternal" twins is approximately twice that of "identical" twins in the general population (Folstein & Rutter, 1977). Further, many opposite-sexed twin pairs appeared in these studies despite the fact that autism has been shown to exist much more frequently in males (Folstein & Rutter, 1977). The American Psychiatric Association (DSM-III-R) (1987) indicates that research supports a 3-4:1 male to female ratio in autism. Other methodological problems in twin and family research pertain to the diagnostic criteria and procedures used, the determination of zygosity, and the often-made assumption that autism represents an etiologically homogeneous population (see Folstein & Rutter, 1988, for a more thorough review of these and other methodological concerns in genetic research with regard to autism).

Folstein and Rutter (1977) avoided some of the noted pitfalls in a study of 21 same-sexed twin pairs in which one member of each dyad had been diagnosed autistic. Specifically, an English sample of 11 MZ and 10 DZ twin pairs was ascertained through multiple sources, emphasizing equal interest in DZ as MZ and discordant as well as concordant cases (Folstein & Rutter, 1988). As Mittler (1971, cited in Folstein & Rutter, 1988) suggests, the proportion of MZ to DZ twins in the general population is approximately equal when only same-sexed pairs are considered. Thus Folstein and Rutter's (1977) sample was less biased than many of those utilized in previous research. Of the total population of 21 twin pairs, 4 MZ twins were concordant for autism as compared to no DZ pairs (Folstein & Rutter, 1977). The authors thus calculated the concordance rate to be 36% in monozygotic and 0% in dizygotic twins (Folstein & Rutter, 1977).

More recently, Ritvo, Freeman, Mason-Brothers, Mo, and Ritvo (1985) reported concordance rates of 95.7% in MZ pairs and 23.5% in DZ pairs from their study of 40 sets of twins. However, Folstein and Rutter (1988) caution that (1) the method of sample ascertainment in that study (e.g., largely voluntary replies) led to disproportionate emphasis on monozygotic pairs and (2) their inclusion of opposite-sexed pairs should be reflected in twice as many DZ as MZ pairs for the sample to be representative where zygosity is concerned. In short, twin studies of autism provide some evidence for the involvement of genetic factors. Nonetheless, caution must be exercised in interpreting twin findings given the methodological limitations noted. Further, it should be understood that such research does not provide information regarding the nature (or number) of genetic defects that may be involved (Folstein & Rutter, 1988).

Studies of related disorders in the families of autistic probands are based on the assumption that autism may be the most severe expression of a more basic genetically transmitted cognitive disorder (e.g., Pauls, 1987). Again, Folstein and Rutter (1977) may be credited with early advances in this research area. Specifically, 6 of the discordant twins in their sample (5 MZ and 1DZ) showed some cognitive disorder characterized as either severe speech delay, learning disability, or mental retardation (Folstein & Rutter, 1977). Summing these and the data reported, the authors concluded that 9 of 11 MZ twins (82%) were concordant for cognitive or language disorder versus 1 out of 10 (10%) of the DZ twins.

August, Stewart, and Tsai (1981) attempted a further test of the notion that cognitive disturbance may be inherited rather than autism *per se*. Briefly, these investigators collected data with regard to the IQ, reading ability, and mathematical performance of all siblings of 41 autistic cases and those of 15 Down syndrome control subjects (August *et al.*, 1981). Consistent with the findings of Folstein and Rutter (1977), a higher rate of cognitive dysfunction was observed for the siblings of autistic probands than for those of control individuals. Specifically, 15% of the sibs of autistic as compared to 3% of the sibs of Down syndrome individuals were impaired cognitively. Moreover, all 8 of those cognitively impaired siblings in the study were mentally retarded, raising the possibility that mental retardation is familially aggregated rather than autism (Folstein & Rutter, 1988). Still, the rate of autism in the siblings of autistic subjects, as supported by twin (e.g., Folstein & Rutter, 1977) and nontwin sibling (e.g., August *et al.*, 1981; Rutter, 1968) research is approximately 2%. As Rutter and Garmezy (1983) point out, this represents a 50-fold increase over the prevalence in the general population. Clearly, further investigation into the familiality of autism is warranted, though the evidence to date does not support any particular mechanism of genetic transmission. In fact, Folstein and Rutter (1988) suggest that etiological and genetic heterogeneity is likely, even in biased samples such as those reported earlier (e.g., ones chosen for having more than one autistic case).

An additional avenue through which researchers have implicated genetic factors in the etiology of autism is the association of the syndrome with disturbances of known genetic origin. For example, Down syndrome, phenylketonuria, tuberous sclerosis, and fragile X have been found to co-occur with some autistic cases (see Folstein & Rutter, 1988, for a review). The present discussion will be limited to fragile X as it has received the most attention in the recent literature. As Bregman, Leckman, and Ort (1988) summarize, "fragile X syndrome is a recently described X-linked disorder which is surpassed only by Down syndrome as the most prevalent form of mental retardation of genetic origin" (p. 343). Eighty percent of males with the fragile X are mentally retarded as are approximately one-third of heterozygous females (Payton, Steele, Wenger, & Minshew, 1989). The predominance of fragile X in males and its association with autism, recalling that autistic disturbances occur 3 to 4 times more frequently in males, present a tempting, though unsupported argument for simple X-linked Mendelian inheritance (e.g., Payton *et al.*, 1989). However, the association of fragile X with autism is apparently neither simple nor universal. Specifically, reports on the incidence of fragile X in persons with autism range from 0 to 53% (Payton *et al.*, 1989). A modal study within this range reported fragile X in 20% to 25% of 40 autistic males, 85% of whom were mentally retarded, and concluded that the fragile X marker was more highly correlated with autism than with mental retardation (Gillberg & Wahlstrom, 1985). In contrast, Bregman *et al.* (1988) found autism in only one of their 14 male subjects with fragile X and charged that the previously reported high incidences may be a function of differing diagnostic interpretations of observed behavior (e.g., gaze aversion and social avoidance). Further, Payton *et al.* (1989), stressing careful diagnosis, performed chromosome analyses on 85 autistic males and found a 2.4% incidence of fragile X abnormality. These authors concluded that the incidence of fragile X in autistic males is no greater than that found in the mentally retarded population in general. In summary, evidence for a high frequency of association between autism and fragile X is conflicting. Moreover, methodological weaknesses including small sample size, the diagnostic procedures employed, and sample ascertainment bias limit the conclusions that can be drawn from these findings.

3.3. *Pre-, Peri-, and Neonatal Complications*

The third area of etiologic research with regard to autism is the investigation of factors occurring during pregnancy, delivery, or shortly after birth. The general strategy has been to identify a number of autistic persons and to retrospectively compare available medical records from pregnancy, delivery, and the neonatal period with those of normal, sibling, or matched mental-age control groups. Torrey, Hersh, and McCabe (1975) provided one of the early reports from a sample of 14 autistic subjects identified by the National Institute of Neurological Disease and Stroke Collaborative Prenatal Study ($N = 30{,}000$ pregnancies). These investigators found a significantly greater incidence of maternal bleeding after the first trimester in the pregnancies that produced autistic (64%) children compared to those that yielded low IQ controls (29%). However, as Bryson, Smith, and Eastwood (1988) point out, their control group was inappropriate in that it was unmatched for intellectual level. Subsequent studies employing larger autistic and normal sibling control samples (e.g., Deykin & MacMahon, 1980; Finegan & Quarrington, 1979) found high rates of several presumed pathologic factors in the pregnancies and deliveries of autistic children but failed to link any specific factor with the observed outcome. For example, Deykin and MacMahon (1980) reviewed the obstetrical records of 145 autistic individuals and their 330 unaffected siblings. With regard to perinatal complications, eight possible events were studied: Caesarian section, forceps delivery, fetal malposition, hemorrhage during delivery, prolonged (labor > 12 hours) and precipitous (labor < 1 hour) delivery, cord problems, and excess maternal weight gain. All events were found to occur more frequently in autistic children, but their low incidence precluded statically significant findings unless data were collapsed across all eight variables (Deykin & McMahon, 1980). However, the prenatal information from that study supported earlier work with regard to incidence of midtrimester bleeding (e.g., Torrey *et al.*, 1975). Further, birth order (firstborn) was shown to carry an elevated risk of autism, independent of the possibly higher frequency of reproductive problems among firstborns, and a higher incidence of maternal use of prescribed drugs was found in the autistic group (Deykin & McMahon, 1980). Other prenatal events that have been proposed to relate to autistic outcome include gestational hormonal exposure (Funderburk, Carter, Tanguay, Freeman, & Westlake, 1983) and presence of various maternal viral infections (see Konstantareas, 1986, for a review).

More recently, optimality scales have been employed in the analysis of obstetrical records (e.g., Bryson *et al.*, 1988; Gillberg & Gillberg, 1983), largely in response to the observation that the optimum is more readily and precisely definable than is the average or subnormal (Prechtl, 1968, 1980, cited in Bryson *et al.*, 1988). Accordingly, pre-, peri-, and neonatal complications are expressed as percentages relative to the optimal or best possible obstetrical condition (defined as a score of 100) (Bryson *et al.*, 1988). Using this strategy with a 61-item optimality scale and sample of 21 autistic cases (derived from a population of 20,800 between the ages of 6 and 14), Bryson *et al.* (1988) found that suboptimal prenatal scores significantly differentiated autistic children from siblings, normal children, and IQ matched controls. Moreover, suboptimal neonatal scores distinguished autistic subjects from their siblings and normal control children but not from IQ matched individuals. Gillberg and Gillberg (1983) provided similar evidence for reduced pre- and neonatal optimality in autism. However, the most striking of these findings is that *prenatal suboptimality* is specific to autism and not accounted for by mental retardation (Bryson *et al.*, 1988). Further, obstetrical conditions were shown to be unrelated to functional level (i.e., IQ) in the autistic group but positively related to nonverbal intelligence in the IQ-matched control group (Bryson *et al.*, 1988). As the authors concluded, this finding provides evidence for the independence of autism and mental retardation with regard to the role of obstetrical factors in their respective etiologies (Bryson *et al.*, 1988). Finally, Bryson *et al.* (1988) emphasize that the findings in their study were accounted for by approximately one-fourth of their autistic subjects. Thus, three-fourths of their autistic sample were not characterized by this pattern of results; this is consistent with the view that autistic disturbance may arise from multiple etiologies.

As noted, numerous investigations of obstetrical factors have been reported in the autism literature, each implicating some combination of pre-, peri-, or neonatal events in the etiology of the syndrome (see Konstantareas, 1986, for a review and discussion of methodological limitations). As with the genetic research reviewed, many weaknesses in method may be detailed that temper confidence in drawing firm conclusions, however. For example, small sample sizes, ascertainment biases, inadequate control groups, retrospective data collection, and inconsistent diagnostic procedures limit comparisons between studies and generalization to autism as a diagnostic group. Moreover, the implicit assumption of a direct relationship between obstetrical suboptimality and autistic outcome, present in many of these retrospective studies, parallels that in more general studies of deviant infant and child development. Specifically, Pasamanick and Knobloch (1961) coined the term *reproductive casualty* to describe the sequelae of harmful pre- and neonatal events that result in damage to the fetus or newborn and are generally localized to the central nervous system. Sameroff and Chandler (1975) reviewed many studies in which particular infant or parent characteristics were presumed to allow for long-range prediction of outcome in a linear, main effect fashion (see Sameroff, 1975). In response, these authors point out that "studies that have followed the developmental course of supposedly vulnerable infants have typically found that the initial difficulties were attenuated with the passage of time and that the earlier expectations of negative outcomes were not realized" (Sameroff & Chandler, 1975, p. 189). Accordingly, an organismic or transactional model, consistent with the perspective taken in this review, was outlined in which "early factors that have enduring consequences are assumed to do so because of persistent influences acting throughout the life span, rather than at discrete points in development" (Sameroff & Chandler, 1975, p. 189). Subsequent research (e.g., Zeskind & Ramey, 1978, 1981) has demonstrated that the early effects of fetal malnutrition on mental and intellectual development may be ameliorated or exacerbated depending upon the respective supportive or unsupportive nature of the caretaking environment to which the infant and child is exposed over time.

The important point, with particular relevance to this and the earlier etiologic discussion, is that cold and rejecting parents, genetic factors (e.g., fragile X), obstetrical suboptimality, or neurological insult *alone* do not produce the outcome of autism. Moreover, these factors do not interact in a simple linear or additive fashion (i.e., obstetrical complication or genetic factor → neurological deficiency → autism). For example, Folstein and Rutter (1977) hypothesized that autism may result from the interaction of deleterious obstetrical events with a familial predisposition to cognitive deficiency. Rather, it is proposed that a complex of mutual influences (e.g., parent–child transactions) operate over time to amplify or dissipate the effects of early developmental insults or constitutional characteristics in the majority of cases (cf. Sameroff & Chandler, 1975). It is not disputed that *severe* physical or developmental insult may have a significant impact on observed outcome; however, it is suggested that such occurrences do not lead to autistic disturbance independent of other, more enduring (i.e., environmental) influences. Whereas the present effort does not purport to answer the question of etiology, the organismic or transactional perspective applies equally to the developmental processes that produce differences in phenotypic expression (social subtypes).

3.4. *Neurological Models*

The final area of etiologic research that has received considerable attention in recent formulations concerns the neurological functioning of autistic individuals. Again, the evidence for involvement has been obtained from a variety of sources.

Some studies of neurological functioning in autistic persons have attempted to identify gross structural abnormalities that correlate with outcome. Thus computerized axial tomography (CAT scans), positron emission tomography (PET scans), postmortem neuropathological examination, and examination of histological preparations have been employed. Rutter and Schopler (1988) assert, however, that the balance of available evidence does not support aberration of brain structure in the majority of persons with autism. "That is to say, unlike the case with severe mental retardation or cerebral palsy, autism in *not* usually associated with gross abnormalities of brain structure or histology. Moreover, it is *unusual* for generalized brain damage to give rise to autism" (Rutter & Schopler, 1987, p. 416; emphasis in original). Nonetheless, much research effort continues to be directed toward identification of specific neurostructural foci. For example, recent reports, employing magnetic resonance imaging (MRI), have implicated subtle abnormalities in forebrain (e.g., Gaffney, Kuperman, Tsai, & Minchin, 1989) and cerebellar (e.g., Courchesne, Yeung-Courchesne, Press, Hesselink, & Jernigan, 1988) structure. The conflicting results of these studies exemplify the diversity of brain systems that have been implicated in autistic etiology. Detailed description of these and the numerous other studies of brain structure is not within the scope of this chapter. However, Gaffney *et al.* (1989) provide a brief review of relevant brain-structural research that illustrates nicely the lack of consensus in this area. It may well be that the disparate structural findings reflect, once again, the etiologic heterogeneity of autistic disturbances. Consistent with this view and the individual-difference perspective taken here, Fein *et al.* (1986) propose that "the most fruitful kind of neuropsychological theorizing will probably be that which tries to relate clinical diversity to the diversity of implicated brain systems, and predicts specific associations among behavioral symptoms and between brain dysfunction and behavioral outcome" (p. 209).

Other research concerning the neurological etiology of autism has focused on indices of abnormal neurological functioning and associated conditions. In the interest of brevity, only two of these will be considered here, though such accounts are abundant in the autism literature. Golden (1987) indicates that there is uniform agreement that autistic children have abnormal electroencephalograms (EEGs) and carry an elevated risk for having a seizure disorder relative to normal children of the same age. For example, DeMyer *et al.* (1973) found irregular EEGs, including focal spikes, spike and wave discharges, and severe slowing, in 60% of their subjects ($N = 126$). Employing a smaller sample of autistic individuals ($N = 17$), DeLong (1978) similarly found a high rate of abnormal EEGs (47%). Further, Ornitz's (1987) recent review of the literature indicates that several researchers have reported abnormal EEGs in as high as 50% to 80% of their autistic subject populations; he notes, however, that other studies have found lower incidences. Interestingly, Ornitz (1987) suggests that the occurrence of abnormal EEGs in autistic persons reflects the extent to which the disturbance(s) occurs in association with various organic syndromes. Accordingly, the pre-, peri-, and neonatal insults, discussed in the previous section, would be proposed to directly impact neurological functioning in infants and children with autism.

With regard to the development of seizures, the findings appear to be equally clear-cut and suggest an increased incidence during adolescence (e.g., Lotter, 1974; Gillberg & Steffenburg, 1987). Rutter and Bartak (1971) found that 29% of the nonepileptic children in their study ($N = 64$) developed seizures during adolescence. Further, Deykin and MacMahon (1979) compared 132 autistic to 51 partially autistic children with regard to the age-specific incidence of seizures. By 19 years of age, the cumulative risk for seizure development was 23% in the autistic group and 12.5% in the partially autistic group. In addition, risk for the development of seizures appears to be significantly higher in those autistic individuals who also have mental retardation (Bartak & Rutter, 1976; Rutter & Garmezy, 1983). Finally, summarizing the research findings prior to 1988, Gillberg (1988) indicates that there is unequivocal support for the association between infantile spasms and autistic outcome and that about one-third of all cases of autism have been affected by epileptic fits by early adulthood.

Numerous other neurological correlates have received attention in the past and recent autism literature, including examination of handedness and kinesiologic analysis of gait (see Golden, 1987). Further, much research has been reported with regard to neurochemical and neurophysiologic models of autism. However, the majority of these studies involve specific and extremely complex mechanisms and hypotheses that preclude delineation here. (See Ornitz [1983, 1987] and Anderson and Hoshino [1987] for reviews of neurophysiologic and neurochemical research, respectively.)

In short, considerable evidence has been garnered for the involvement of neurological factors in the etiology of autism. However, the definition of subject populations and use of inadequate control groups (cf. Deykin & MacMahon, 1979, who used a "partially autistic" control group) render many of the findings difficult to interpret. To date, no single neurological finding or mechanism has received unanimous endorsement. Nonetheless, recent conceptualizations afford a primary etiologic role to nonspecific physical damage to the central nervous system (DeMyer, 1987; Schopler & Mesibov, 1987, both cited in Bryson *et al.*, 1988). As Rapin (1987) correctly asserts, the building of strong theories regarding the pathogenesis of autism must account for *all* of the core symptoms and apply to *all* autistic cases. Accordingly, there is a great need to empirically define the core manifestations of the disturbance(s) and, thereby, to ensure that homogeneous populations are being studied (Rapin, 1987).

The preceding review of etiologic models and hypotheses provides support for a number of factors that relate to autistic outcome. However, as Rutter and Schopler (1988) suggest, the preponderance of available information does not support any single mechanism but indicates etiologic as well as phenotypic heterogeneity. Consistent with this view, no specific etiology or behavioral outcome is wholly endorsed by the present perspective. Rather, each of the described models is proposed to exert influence in at least some subset of individuals diagnosable as autistic. Moreover, it seems likely, given the mutuality of influences impinging on development, that the etiologies of autism are not mutually exclusive. Nevertheless, considerable evidence points to impairment in neurological functioning, independent of its origin, which may have a significant impact on behavior (attention and responsiveness to stimulation). This position will be more fully elaborated and supported by research findings in subsequent sections of the chapter.

4. *A Developmental Perspective*

In his text on social development, Cairns (1979) argues cogently for a psychobiological orientation to development; he states that "behavior, whether social or nonsocial, is appropriately viewed in terms of an organized system and its explanation requires a holistic analysis." Indeed, dynamical systems theory (e.g., Bertalanffy, 1933, 1962, cited in Cairns, 1986) serves as the conceptual foundation for the present perspective on variable social expressions of autistic disturbance. Within this view, developmental "information" exists not simply in the biological states of the organism or in its experience (i.e., the context or social environment, loosely speaking) but in the dynamic coaction between the two (Oyama, 1985). The overriding tendency for laymen and scientists to view behavioral development in dichotomous terms such as learned/innate, genetic/environmental, nature/nurture (see Johnston, 1987) serves to obscure an understanding of the processes that may account for individual differences in behavioral expression.

As an example, some of the etiologic research cited earlier supports a neurological basis to autism; however, as Cairns (1986) points out, only modest information exists as to how such a biological correlate actually mediates autistic outcome. From a developmental perspective, the important question is *how* neurological deficiency, as one of many characteristics of a particular individual, interacts over time with various experiential factors to construct an autistic behavioral phenotype. This point was raised earlier with regard to the research on perinatal complications and other medical correlates. Of critical import to this and the foregoing is the distinction between process and outcome that, as Valsiner (1987) points out, can serve as a useful basis for separating developmental and nondevelopmental types of analyses.

4.1. *Explanation/Process vs. Description/Outcome*

In illustrating the process/outcome distinction, Valsiner (1987) notes that Piaget's stage description of children's cognitive development is often referred to as "Piaget's developmental theory." However, the actual theory of Piaget *explains* the equilibration of structures through continuous assimilation and accommodation processes; in contrast, the stage account *describes* the outcome or products of development with no attention to the mechanism(s) by which transition occurs from one stage to the next (Valsiner, 1987). It is interesting to note at this juncture that the DSM-III-R's (American Psychiatric Association, 1987) requirement for diagnostic items to be judged abnormal for the person's developmental level reflects a nondevelopmental notion of discrete maturational stages. Whereas the application of such stage conceptualizations may be appropriate as a heuristic tool, the present perspective maintains that information regarding development is conspicuously absent.

4.2. *Developmental and Nondevelopmental Analyses*

Valsiner (1987) clearly distinguishes developmental from nondevelopmental approaches to psychology by examining categorically whether or not outcomes and the processes that produced them are variable and changing or immutable and stable. Of four possible combinations, those in which stable process produces stable outcome and in which stable process produces variable outcome represent nondevelopmental thinking (Valsiner, 1987). In both cases, there is no allowance for feedback from the outcome of a process to modify the mechanism of change itself. *In contrast, developmental approaches involve dynamic reorganization of the process that produced a particular outcome, be it stable or variable.* The first developmental case is that in which variable processes lead to a stable outcome. For example, homicide, suicidal behavior, and accidental injury all may result in death. However, as Valsiner (1987) notes, the development of the process itself may not be inferred from the outcome observed. The second developmental case, and the one on which the remainder of this chapter will focus, is that in which variable processes produce variable outcomes. Valsiner (1987) provides the following example:

> A child learns to speak. This involves the acquisition of the acoustic form and semantic function of the first words. Once these signs have become parts of the child's lexicon, the child's action is qualitatively transformed by the use of signs. The use of signs, was previously an outcome of the child's learning process, now it becomes a means that is used by the child to reorganize his cognitive processes (Luria, 1979). What previously has been an outcome of a process has now fed into that process and changed it qualitatively, affording the production of novel outcomes. (p. 5)

4.3. *Relevance to Autism*

In the present context, *reliably different* patterns of deviant social behavior (i.e., social subtypes) in autistic persons (Volkmar, Cohen, Bregman, Hooks, & Stevenson, 1989) are proposed to develop as a function of continuous malfunction in organism–environment transactions across time that prevent these children from normally or adaptively organizing their world (cf. Sameroff, 1975). The three social subtypes constitute *variable outcomes*, and the series of transactions over time that might lead to each social "style" may be taken as *variable processes*. Moreover, within each of the three processes so defined, there are reorganizations in which the behavioral outcome may feedback and influence the process that produced it. Specifically, an autistic infant's autonomic nervous system and internal function may influence his/her responsiveness to caretaker stimulation. Further, the infant's behavioral manifestation of impaired autonomic functioning (e.g., extreme irritability) may alter the caregiver's sensitivity or tendency to respond to the infant's signals in the future (Lamb & Easterbrooks, 1981). The resulting parent–child transactions over time may serve to feedback and alter the organization and function of the child's autonomic nervous system and, consequently, his/her reactivity and responsivity to future stimulation. Thus behavior patterns may function to organize internal states just as internal functioning may influence overt behavior (Cairns, 1986). This latter point is of particular importance because, as Cairns (1986) points out, "behavior is seen as the leading edge of adaptation, an organismic function that is highly flexible and responsive to changing internal and external conditions" (p. 19).

4.4. *Key Developmental Concepts*

Embedded in the foregoing discussion are several key concepts that will be given brief mention here. (See Cairns [1986] and Dawson and Galpert [1986] for insightful reviews of social developmental concepts with relevance to autism and their integration into a treatment model, respectively.)

The first concept, *structure–function bidirectionality,* emphasizes the reciprocal determination of biological structure and behavioral function. As Rapin (1987) states in her presentation of a neurologic perspective to autism, "although I doubt that environmental influences alone can cause autism, I am equally convinced that environment influences brain development and function in everyone, normal or handicapped" (p. 710). The implication, consistent with the present perspective, is that neurological development or structure may impact behavioral expression or function and vice versa.

As Cairns (1979) suggests, the second concept, *ontogenetic functionalism,* asserts that the first priority with regard to social behavior is the accommodation of persons to their immediate circumstances and relationships. It follows that particular behaviors that may have served an adaptive purpose in early development may have little relevance for subsequent adaptation and development (Cairns, 1986). For example, behavioral stereotypes and insistence on sameness may serve the function of maintaining a manageable level of stimulation (cf. Wing, 1978). Specifically, the limited capacities of autistic individuals to process sensory information may require that they restrict their behavioral repertoire (Wing, 1978). Whereas the performance of rigid behavioral sequences and resisting environmental change may be an acceptable and adaptive means of preventing sensory overload in early development, these behaviors become more unacceptable and dysfunctional with regard to social development and integration as the child grows older. The importance and relevance of ontogenetic functionalism to the present discussion of autism pertains to an appreciation of the adaptive significance or function behaviors may serve for the individual at particular times and in specific contexts (cf. Cairns, 1986). This, of course, has significant implications for treatment.

The current use of *plasticity,* our third concept, is perhaps best captured in the two previous concepts. Specifically, social development, much more than cognitive and physical development, requires the elimination of old patterns as well as the addition of new ones (Cairns, 1986). Accordingly, reorganization must occur in relationships over time, and social behavior must serve to adapt the individual to the situation at hand (Cairns, 1986). With regard to autism, an individual's restricted repertoire of activities and interests may preclude adaptive realignment of relationships or generalization of learned social skills from one context to another. Thus, as Cairns (1986) points out, "continued and patient support should be expected in each concrete relationship and setting in order for the changes to become consolidated in new relationships" (p. 21).

As noted earlier, lack of reciprocity in social relationships has been forwarded as the basic social deficit of autistic persons (e.g., Rutter, 1983; Rutter & Garmezy, 1983). Consistent with the proposed mechanism of the early differentiation of social subtypes, Cairns (1986) suggests that sensory–attentional deficits should be reflected in anomalies in social responding and its by-products (e.g., social reciprocity, social synchrony, imitation, and social attachment patterns). Accordingly, deficits in *social synchrony and reciprocity,* our last concept, are proposed to form the basis of autistic social impairments. The discussion will now turn to the social subtypes that will serve as a measure of developmental outcome in the analysis to follow.

5. *Wing's Social Subtypes*

In an epidemiological study of children with autism and autisticlike conditions, Wing and Gould (1979) identified three distinct subtypes based on the quality of impairments in social interaction: (1) social aloofness, (2) passive interaction, and (3) active but odd interaction. A fourth group, subsuming the normally sociable mentally retarded, will not be considered in the present discussion. The authors concluded that subclassification of individuals based on the severity of social impairment yielded closer correspondence to behavioral, psychological, and medical variables than did a system based on the diagnosis of autism or lack thereof (Wing & Gould, 1979). Individuals with and without a history of autism were found in each of the subtypes of social impairment. The aloof group contained the largest number of autistic subjects, though the difference between the number of individuals in this group and those in either the passive or active-but-odd groups was not statistically significant (Wing & Gould, 1979).

Several authors (Wing & Attwood, 1987; Prizant & Schuler, 1987) have attempted to detail the characteristics of individuals who typify each of these impaired social interaction "styles." Further, Volkmar and his colleagues (Volkmar *et al.*, 1989) have examined the reliability of the subtyping scheme as it applies to autistic and nonautistic, developmentally disordered individuals; in this study, clinician ratings of subtype showed good agreement, particularly with regard to autistic cases (kappa = 0.73; Cicchetti & Sparrow, 1981). For the purposes of the present discussion, Wing's social typologies will serve as a measure of outcome toward which the processes of social development in autism may be examined. Accordingly, each of the subtypes will be addressed in some detail.

5.1. *The "Aloof" Subtype*

The first group, described as "socially aloof," show general indifference to others and represent those most severely impaired in social interaction. As Wing (1983) notes, social aloofness is frequently associated with severe deficits in or complete absence of verbal and nonverbal communication. Some individuals in this group will make spontaneous approaches, though these tend to occur only with interest in gratifying immediate, personal needs (Wing & Gould, 1979). Further, aloof persons may take part in rough-and-tumble activities (e.g., tickling or chasing) with adults but show no interest in the purely social aspects of contact with others. Interestingly, aloof individuals are reported to show particularly marked indifference to interaction with other children (Wing & Gould, 1979). One might speculate that this relates directly to their tendency to interact exclusively for the purpose of meeting needs. A description of behavioral features of the "socially aloof" subtype is presented in Table 1.

As with each of the social typologies, a full range of intellectual functioning may be found across individuals. However, those represented in the aloof group tend to be severely or profoundly impaired,

TABLE 1
Behavioral Description of Wing and Gould's (1979) "Socially Aloof" Subtype

a. Aloof and indifferent in most situations (exceptions: having specific needs met)
b. Any interaction is primarily with adults through physical means (tickling, physical exploration)
c. Little apparent interest in social aspects of contact
d. Little evidence of verbal or nonverbal turn taking
e. Little evidence of joint activity or mutual attention
f. Poor eye contact, active gaze aversion
g. Repetitive, stereotypic behaviors may be present
h. May be oblivious to environmental changes (e.g., person entering room)
i. Moderate-to-severe cognitive deficiency

From "Facilitating Communication: Language Approaches" by B. M. Prizant and A. L. Schuler, 1987, *Handbook of Autism and Developmental Disorders* (p. 324) by D. J. Cohen and A. M. Donnellan (Eds.), 1987, New York: John Wiley & Sons. Copyright 1987 by John Wiley & Sons, Inc.

with better visuospatial than verbal skills as measured on standardized psychological tests (Wing & Attwood, 1987). Recent findings corroborate the relatively low IQ and mental age of individuals in the aloof group as compared to passive and active-but-odd persons (Volkmar *et al.*, 1989). Further, those autistic persons of low intellectual functioning (i.e., the aloof group) are reported to spend much time engaged in simple stereotyped activities (Wing & Attwood, 1987) that are generally self-directed (e.g., finger flicking, arm flapping, or body rocking) (Rutter & Lockyer, 1967; Shah, Holmes, & Wing, 1982). Moreover, Wing and associates (Wing & Gould, 1979; Wing & Attwood, 1987) indicate that an identifiable gross etiology is most likely to be found in a severely or profoundly retarded aloof autistic subject. Finally, aloofness and indifference to other persons is likely to persist throughout childhood and into adult life in the more severely and profoundly impaired of these individuals. In short, socially aloof children share much in common with the DSM-III and ICD-9 definitions of infantile autism; the higher functioning aloof individuals resemble those originally described by Kanner (1943) (Wing & Attwood, 1987).

5.2. *The "Passive" Subtype*

Similar to socially aloof persons, passive children and adults make social approaches only to have their immediate needs met; however, passive individuals accept initiations made by others and may even show some appearance of enjoyment in doing so (Wing & Attwood, 1987). Speech is generally better developed in passive than in the aloof persons, though the characteristic abnormalities (i.e., immediate and delayed echolalia, pronoun reversal) are present, and there is a lack of interpersonal communication for pleasure (Wing & Attwood, 1987). Further, there is evidence that passive individuals have higher levels of intellectual ability than those in the aloof group (Volkmar *et al.*, 1989), though they, too, show better visuospatial than verbal skills (Wing & Attwood, 1987). Children in the passive group are less likely than those in the aloof group to have an identifiable gross etiology related to their impairments (Wing & Gould, 1979). A description of the behavioral characteristics of the passive group are presented in Table 2. As Wing (1981; Wing & Attwood, 1987) has suggested, passive autistic children frequently have the ability to imitate others, and, thus, may appear to exhibit pretend play; however, the quality of their behavior (e.g., repetitiveness) indicates that they have little or no understanding of the copied actions. In summary, passive autistic persons tend to be the most amiable and easily managed of the three subtypes. They show less marked features of autism (e.g., less resistance to change, less stereotyped movement) and higher levels of intellectual and adaptive functioning than those in the aloof group.

Table 2
Behavioral Description of Wing and Gould's (1979) "Passive Interaction" Subtype

a. Limited spontaneous social approaches
b. Accepting of others' approaches
   Adult initiations
   Child initiations
c. Passivity may encourage interaction from other children
d. Little pleasure derived from social contact, but active rejection is infrequent
e. Child may be verbal or nonverbal
f. Immediate echolalia more common than delayed echolalia
g. Varying degrees of cognitive deficiency

From "Facilitating Communication: Language Approaches" by B. M. Prizant and A. L. Schuler, 1987, *Handbook of Autism and Developmental Disorders* (p. 324) by D. J. Cohen and A. M. Donnelan (Eds.), 1987, New York: John Wiley & Sons. Copyright 1987 by John Wiley & Sons, Inc.

TABLE 3
Behavioral Description of Wing and Gould's (1979) "Active-but-Odd Interaction" Subtype

a. Spontaneous social approaches are apparent
   Most frequently with adults
   Less with other children
b. Interaction may involve repetitive, idiosyncratic preoccupation
   Incessant questioning
   Verbal routines
c. Interaction may be communicative or noncommunicative (if verbal), delayed and immediate echolalia
d. Poor or deficient role-taking skills
   Poor perception of listener needs
   No modification of language complexity or style
   Problems in shifting topics
e. Interest in routine of interaction rather than content
f. May be very aware of other's reactions (especially extreme reactions)
g. Less socially acceptable than passive group (active violation of culturally determined social conventions)

From "Facilitating Communication: Language Approaches" by B. M. Prizant and A. L. Schuler, 1987, *Handbook of Autism and Developmental Disorders* (p. 324) by D. J. Cohen and A. M. Donnellan (Eds.), 1987, New York: John Wiley & Sons. Copyright 1987 by John Wiley & Sons, Inc.

5.3. *The "Active-but-Odd" Subtype*

The third subtype, "active, but odd interaction," is characterized by those individuals who make social approaches in the interest of indulging their own repetitive, idiosyncratic preoccupations (Wing & Gould, 1979). Accordingly, their social behavior has been described as one-sided (Wing, 1981; Wing & Attwood, 1987) and takes the form of talking *at* or repeatedly questioning another person (Wing & Attwood, 1987). Speech tends to be better than that in either of the other groups, though characterized by odd intonation and poor breath and volume control (Wing & Attwood, 1987). Moreover, active-but-odd children show the highest level of intellectual functioning of the three subtypes (Volkmar *et al.*, 1989). They differ from the others in that some show verbal abilities that are equal to or higher than their performance scores on the Wechsler scales; however, the verbal subtests on which they tend to excel require facility in rote memory rather than reasoning ability (Wing & Attwood, 1987). As with those in the passive group, identifiable gross etiologies are less frequently found than for persons in the aloof group. Many active-but-odd children show repetitive, stereotyped, "pretend" play, similar to that displayed by passive youngsters. Finally, behavior problems appear to be common in active-but-odd persons, presumably due in part to their socially imposing manner and accompanying sensitivity to criticism (Wing & Attwood, 1987). Descriptive characteristics of the active-but-odd subtype are presented in Table 3.

5.4. *Age-Related Changes in Social Behavior*

As Wing and Attwood (1987) indicate, the classification of autistic individuals by social impairment should not be taken as rigid. Rather, children can move from one group to another with age. Specifically, aloof children may become passive or active-but-odd as they grow older but rarely is there movement in the other direction (Wing & Attwood, 1987). Volkmar *et al.* (1989) provide some support for the notion of developmental progression (i.e., aloof → passive → active-but-odd) with their cross-sectional findings. Further, Rutter's (1970) follow-up study of autistic children into adulthood showed improvement in interpersonal relationships despite continued lack of "social knowhow." In contrast, Gillberg and Steffenburg (1987) found that about half of the autistic subjects in their population-based study maintained an aloof social style through adolescence and into the early adult years. Additionally, Mesibov, Schopler, Schaffer, and Michal (1989) failed to find any improvement in autistic children's relationships with others, using the Childhood Autism Rating Scale (CARS), before age 10 and after age 13. Thus the results are conflicting with regard to age-related improvement in the social relatedness of autistic persons. Clearly, caution should be exercised in interpreting the reported cross-sectional findings. Moreover, Rutter's (1970) work bears replication in an elaborated longitudinal design before any firm conclusions can be drawn regarding the suggested directional movement in social development.

As noted earlier, social subtype will be regarded as a measure of autistic outcome in the present developmental analysis. Therefore, discussion will be confined to those experiences that lead to reliable and predictable assignment to one of these subtypes. Wing and Attwood (1987) suggest that such assignment should be possible by school age on the basis of characteristic behavior (1) in response to unfamiliar adults and (2) in unstructured play activities. It should be appreciated that variability exists within the social behavior of autistic persons across settings (e.g., Lord, 1984) and that the social typologies are an attempt to capture the individual's characteristic or normative behavioral propensities. Moreover, the creation of social subtypes was an attempt to draw *clinically* meaningful distinctions between persons with varying degrees and types of social impairment (Wing & Gould, 1979). Thus important questions for future investigation relate to the stability of subtype with maturation (i.e., age) and change in social context (e.g., varying the number of interactants; in school or workshop as opposed to home) as well as the conditions under which the typologies are observed to be unreliable or malleable. Obviously, the former query has significant implications for assessment and the latter, for treatment. Moreover, given acceptable reliability, future investigations of social typologies should address their predictive validity.

6. *The Proposed Mechanism of Differentiation Leading to Social Subtypes*

Having reviewed the literature with regard to social subtypes in autism, the discussion will now turn to a possible mechanism through which individual differences in interactive style develop. As a starting point, constitutional differences between autistic and normal children and among individual autistic children will be detailed.

6.1. *Attentional and Response Deficits in Autism*

One of the more frequently observed characteristics of autistic individuals has been their abnormal response to sensory stimuli (e.g., DeMyer, 1976; Ornitz, 1974; Rutter, 1966). In fact, early unresponsiveness to speech may lead parents to wrongly suspect deafness or hearing impairment in their young autistic children (Wing & Attwood, 1987). Ornitz, Guthrie, and Farley (1978) indicate that absence of response to sounds occurred in the parental reports of over 70% of the autistic children sampled. However, paradoxically, many of these same children are reported to respond to less intense stimuli that may have meaning to them, such as the wrinkling of a candy wrapper (Wing & Attwood, 1987). Frith and Baron-Cohen (1987) note that autistic children are often described anecdotally as showing a tendency to *avoid* some types of stimulation on the one hand and to *seek* particular kinds of stimulation on the other. Such tendencies toward stimulation avoidance versus stimulation seeking, when considered in the social realm, may distinguish respectively those autistic persons who are aloof or passive from those who are active-but-odd.

6.2. *Stimulus Overselectivity*

Further evidence of attentional or response deficits in autistic persons is provided in the work of Lovaas and his colleagues on "stimulus overselectivity" or "overselective attention" (Lovaas & Schreibman, 1971; Lovaas, Schreibman, Koegel, & Rehm, 1971). Briefly, these investigators demonstrated that autistic children differed from normal and mentally retarded control children in that they responded to only one of the elements of a stimulus complex (Lovaas & Schreibman, 1971; Lovaas *et al.*, 1971); this phenomenon was observed for individuals responding to only one of several presented sensory features (e.g., visual as opposed to auditory or tactile) (Lovaas *et al.*, 1971; Lovaas & Schreibman, 1971) and when multiple stimulus features were presented within a single sense modality (Koegel & Wilhelm, 1973; Schreibman & Lovaas, 1973). Further, Schreibman and Lovaas (1973) showed that autistic children discriminated between male and female doll figures on the basis of only one stimulus component or on peculiar combinations of components (e.g., shoes); the authors concluded that their findings could have implications for the deviant development of social relatedness in autism.

Subsequent studies have shown that overselective attention or responding is not unique to autism but may also be found in nonautistic mentally retarded children (e.g., Anderson & Rincover, 1982; Koegel & Lovaas, 1978; Wilhelm & Lovaas, 1976). In the present context, overselective attention may be viewed as a constitutional tendency involved in the differentiation of autistic social subtypes. The observation that overselectivity is more common in lower functioning autistic persons (e.g., Schreibman & Lovaas, 1973) suggests that it may be a distinguishing characteristic of aloof as opposed to passive or active-but-odd persons.

6.3. *Infancy and Responsiveness to Stimulation*

As the earlier discussion of etiology suggests, nonspecific neurologic insult may serve as a postnatal starting point in the examination of social processes leading to distinct autistic outcomes. Moreover, the impact of such neurological damage, whether occurring pre-, peri-, or postnatally, is hypothesized to alter the functioning of the newborn's autonomic nervous system along a continuum from general hypo- to hyperresponsivity to stimulation. Porges (1976) outlined a model of autonomic imbalance in autism and other conditions that posited a phasic or chronic predominance of the adrenergic (sympathetic) or cholinergic (parasympathetic) branches of the autonomic nervous system (ANS); possible neurochemical mechanisms have been proposed (see Porges, 1976) but lie beyond the scope of the present discussion.

As noted behavioral parallels of the suggested atypical ANS activity are characteristic attentional or response deficits (Porges, 1976, 1984). Specifically, characteristics of the infant's orienting response or "reflex" may be taken as an index of reactivity to stimulation and as an early measure of attention (see Porges, 1984). Again, behavioral and physiological components may be identified in the orienting response, the former of which will be emphasized in the present analysis. As Finlay and Ivinskis (1987) state,

> The term attention is used to describe those behaviors that are directly ascribable to an infant's orientation toward, detection, and prolonged fixation of environmental stimuli. These behaviors include orientation of head and eyes toward a stimulus, habituation of head turning and visual fixation, together with changes in autonomic activity." (p. 45)

Moreover, Porges (1984) suggests that "behavioral constructs such as hypo- and hyperreactivity to environmental stimuli may be translated into 'weak' or 'strong' orienting responses" (p. 375).

6.4. *Individual Differences in Attention and Responsivity*

Individual differences in attention are suggested to be a direct manifestation of individual differences in nervous system functioning (Porges, 1984). James and Barry's (1980) review of the psychophysiological literature concludes that "no characteristic of ANS functioning can be unequivocally related to early onset psychosis" (p. 517) and that the impact of Central Nervous System (CNS) disability may take the form of overarousal or underarousal, with research supporting both positions. Further, Ornitz (1974, 1983) describes autistic children's "inadequate modulation of sensory input and motor output" and, similarly, concludes that its (behavioral) manifestation is either underreactivity or overreactivity to sensory stimuli. Finally, the American Psychiatric Association (DSM-III, 1980; DSM-III-R, 1987) has recognized hyper- and hyporesponsivity to sensory stimuli as at least an associated feature of all pervasive developmental disorders; the recent version of the *Diagnostic and Statistical Manual* (DSM-III-R, 1987) suggests that associated features as such are more likely to be present in younger and more severely impaired individuals.

In the present framework, extreme ANS reactivity (i.e., hyperreactivity) with corresponding impact on attention and responsivity is proposed to occur in infants who may become classified as socially aloof at school age. In contrast, the autonomic hyporeactivity of would-be passive and active-but-odd infants is reflected in deficient attention and, consequently, in lack of contingent responsiveness to stimulation. Porges (1984) indicates that the autonomic concomitants of the orienting response (e.g., heart rate) may be observed before the motor responses are clearly developed; however, the behavioral orientation and head turning of normal infants is observable within a few weeks of birth. As the present chapter's focus is on behavior, this observation raises another important issue that will now be considered.

6.5. *Infant Behavior in Autism*

The proposition that the differentiation of autistic social subtypes may be mediated by parent–infant transactions and the analysis that must follow rests on the observation of early behaviors. Unfortunately, accounts of autistic infant behavior are sorely lacking. Moreover, most of the available descriptions of early behavior in autistic individuals (e.g., DeMyer, 1979; Ornitz *et al.*, 1978) were derived from retrospective reports of parents, introducing the possibility of selective (i.e., unrepresentative) or distorted recall. It is further exasperating to note that a disturbance that is conceptually (e.g., Rutter & Schopler, 1988) and diagnostically (American Psychiatric Association, 1980, 1987) of early onset is rarely given clinical attention in the first 2 to 3 years of life. Ornitz *et al.* (1978) found that an average of between 2 and 2½ years passed from the time of parents' first serious concern about their child to the conclusive diagnosis of autism. Further, Volkmar, Cohen, and Paul (1986) reviewed case records and concluded that 54% of their sample were identified by parents in the first year of life and that another 34% were identified in the second year. These findings suggest problems in the early identification of autistic children that may not be accounted for by lack of parental concern and recognition (Zeanah, Davis, & Silverman, 1988). Nevertheless, Howlin and Rutter (1987) point out that the available empirical evidence does *not* weigh in favor of early diagnosis and intervention, adding that "it is not easy reliably to diagnose autism at that age and it may well be that some of the most dramatic changes occur in children who would not in any case have shown autistic handicaps" (p. 226). Consistent with this statement, it is proposed that individual differences in behavioral presentation may impede attempts at early identification and that infancy should become a period of emphasis to developmental analysis of autism. This point will be more fully addressed later.

Given the scarcity of research in this area, the behavioral characteristics of autistic infants will be "constructed" from the available parent- and clinician-reported accounts together with observations based on home movies (e.g., Massie, 1975, 1978a,b) and speculations based on social outcome and the behavior of normal infants. Ornitz (1983) has provided the most comprehensive description of autism in infancy, summarizing his own clinical observations and the parent-reported characteristics (Ornitz *et al.*, 1978) of newborn, 6-month-, and 12-month-old (autistic) children (see Table 4). As Oswald (1989) suggests, some of the reported early symptoms or features of autism lie at op-

TABLE 4
Early Symptoms of Autism

The newborn
Seems different from other babies
Seems not to need mother
Cries infrequently. Rarely fusses. "A very good baby"
Intensely irritable. Overreactive to stimulation
Indifferent to being held
Muscle tone may seem flaccid
The first 6 months
Undemanding. Fails to notice mother
Delayed or absent smiling, cooing, babbling and anticipatory response
Lack of interest in toys. Overreactive to sounds
The second 6 months
Unaffectionate. No interest in social games
Indifferent, limp, or rigid when held
Absent verbal and nonverbal communication
Toys cast away, flicked at, or dropped
Under- and overreactive to stimulation
Aversion to solid foods
Delayed or uneven motor milestones

Adapted from "The Functional Neuroanatomy of Infantile Autism" by E. M. Ornitz, 1983, *International Journal of Neuroscience, 19,* p. 87. Copyright 1983 by Gordon and Breach Science Publishers, Inc.

posite ends of a continuum and, as such, are not likely to be directly useful in early identification. Whereas this observation is quite correct, it should also be appreciated that divergent reports may reflect *real* differences in infant behavior that may be precursors to Wing's social subtypes. Specifically, Table 4 shows that autistic newborns have been variously described as "intensely irritable/overreactive to stimulation" and as "indifferent to being held" (Ornitz, 1983). Similarly, DeMyer's (1979) detailed interviews of the parents of 155 autistic children yielded reports of autistic infants as "too placid" and as "too irritable" (see Table 5). Within the present framework, such observations are taken as indices of variation in attention or reactivity to stimulation. In turn, these individual differences in behavior are proposed to reflect individual differences in ANS functioning. Thus, whereas infant behavioral variability may not aid in early identification efforts, it may well be helpful in explaining the differential development of subsequent social behavior (i.e., social subtype). Moreover, that variability exists in retrospective parent reports offers some, though clearly limited, argument against biased or distorted recall.

TABLE 5
Parent-Reported Symptoms during the First Year

Slow or unusual motor development
Unresponsive socially
Too placid
Too irritable
Eye muscle imbalance (squint)
Rocked/bounced excessively
Liked to be in one place always
Poor sleep

Adapted from *Parents and Children in Autism* (p. 26) by M. K. DeMyer, 1979, New York: John Wiley & Sons. Copyright 1979 by V. H. Winston & Sons.

Bearing at least the appearance of objectivity, Massie's (e.g., 1975, 1978a,b; Massie & Rosenthal, 1984) analysis of home movies of infants later diagnosed autistic provides further support for individual differences (i.e., extremes) in behavioral presentation and responsiveness. Zeanah *et al.* (1988) have summarized the work of Massie and others in table format, selected portions of which are presented in Table 6.

TABLE 6
Observational and Home Movie Studies of Autistic Infants

Massie (1975, 1978a). Analysis of home movies of five infants later diagnosed autistic found: flaccid body tone, uncoordinated movements, lack of molding to mother, predominantly somber or irritable mood, little smiling, self-absorption, vacant gaze, lack of visual pursuit of people, back arching, hand flapping, "plastic" facial expressions, and social unresponsiveness.

Massie (1978b). Analysis of home movies of 10 infants later diagnosed "psychotic" and 10 normal controls revealed that prepsychotic infants evidenced fewer infant-to-mother "attachment behaviors," more avoidance, and less reciprocity in interactions in the first 6 months.

Kubicek (1980). Analysis of brief mother–infant interaction with 4-month-old identical twins one of whom was later diagnosed autistic showed lack of eye contact, back-arching posture, and avoidance of mother's approaches.

Massie and Rosenthal (1984). Review of all previous home movie studies: "hallucinatory excitement," self-absorption, lack of visual pursuit of people, avoiding mother's gaze, resistance to being held, hand flapping, rocking, plastic facial expressions, fragmented and uncoordinated body movements, episodes of aimless and unmodulated hyperactivity.

Adapted from "The Question of Autism in an Atypical Infant" by C. H. Zeanah, S. Davis, & M. Silverman, 1988, *American Journal of Psychotherapy, 42*, p. 139.

7. The Development and Differentiation of Social Subtypes

Before proceeding with an account of the differentiation of social subtypes, it should be reiterated that the analysis will be limited to those processes occurring after delivery (i.e., postnatal influences). However, it is understood, nay emphasized, that the pre- and perinatal factors associated with autism are no less important or *social* as they relate to development. This point follows logically from the adoption of a systems perspective (e.g., Bertellanfy, 1933, 1962) and is consistent with the conceptual orientation described. Further, Gottlieb's (e.g., 1983) comparative research has demonstrated that prenatal experience (i.e., stimulation or function) may serve to maintain, facilitate, or induce the appearance of specific social behaviors postnatally. With regard to prenatal development in humans, Brazelton and Yogman (1986) cite unpublished work (Brazelton, 1981) that suggests the occurrence of fetal behavior that might be precursory to later social behavior. Specifically, fetuses in the last months of gestation seemed to "habituate" to unpleasant auditory and visual stimuli and to increase attention to "preferred" stimuli (Brazelton, 1981). Clearly, prenatal behavior offers promise as an area of future developmental research.

In the present effort, variable social outcomes are proposed to arise from variable processes (Valsiner, 1987). Accordingly, the development of each subtype will be considered independently. However, the probabilistic nature of development (Gottlieb, 1983) requires that there be some potential overlap in process and outcome. In fact, it is probable that postnatal insult of sufficient intensity could alter or reorganize an infant's ANS functioning, resulting in changes in responsivity to stimulation. Accordingly, the infant's behavior and, in turn, the parent's sensitivity to the infant could be changed. Lamb and Easterbrooks (1981) define parental sensitivity as "an adult's tendency to provide contingent, appropriate, and consistent responses to an infant's signals" (p. 127); the authors add that each of the defining characteristics is important.

That children may be appropriately and fruitfully regarded as stimuli to which parent's respond (Bell, 1968, 1971) has long been noted. Brazelton and Yogman (1986) capture the importance of this perspective to infancy with the following statement:

> Since a parent has invested in, and is likely to be deeply affected by, the newborn's behavioral reactions, an assessment of the infant's behavior becomes a window into the reactions of the parent's responses to him or to her. Thus, an infant's early behavioral reactions become important in understanding the infant as well as the parent's reactions to the infant. (p. 2)

In summary, no rigid boundaries are proposed to exist between the series of reorganizations or "pathways" by which one infant becomes aloof and another passive or active-but-odd. Moreover, the tendency toward development of particular social "style" or subtype is largely dependent on the pattern of parent–infant transactions and, therefore, primarily and jointly determined by the characteristics of both caregiver and child.

As emphasized, accounts of early behavior in autism are scarce as are attempts to understand the complex developmental processes that impact the expression of characteristic social deviance. Thus, whereas mechanisms for the emergence of autistic behaviors have been repeatedly proposed, their form has typically been on the order of simple main-effect solution (i.e., correlation with outcome) to the problem (see Cairns, 1986). A notable exception to this prevailing tendency is the developmental framework of Dawson and Galpert (1986). In their insightful explanatory model, autistic social development is considered with reference to the early behavior of normal infants. The following accounts of the early development of prototypical social subtypes will borrow liberally from this perspective maintaining its emphasis on the caregiver–autistic infant as a complex of mutual influences or system. Further, individual differences in infant attention and responsivity to (caregiver) stimulation will serve as a point of origin to the discussion. It is argued here that qualitative differences in infant social responding are amplified over time as a function of the enduring circumstances and influences in the social environment (i.e., caregiver responsiveness and consequent parent–infant transactions) (cf. Sameroff & Chandler, 1975). Further, the by-products of these deviant social relationships (e.g., deficits in reciprocity, synchrony, imitation, and attachment) (Cairns, 1986; Dawson & Galpert, 1986) are proposed to serve as the basis for relatively stable differences in autistic social outcomes or styles. As Dawson and Galpert (1986) indicate, infant social behavior is facilitated by caregivers under two conditions: (1) the infant must provide behavioral cues that guide and modulate their parents' actions and (2) the infant must be receptive to the stimulation provided (i.e., must be able perceptually to make sense of social stimuli). With respect to the first condition, these authors further note that young infants express themselves through gaze, motor activity, facial expressions (affect), and vocalizations (see Dawson and Galpert, 1986, for a review of relevant infancy literature). The current perspective asserts that individual differences are operative in both of these conditions. Accordingly, variations on each of these themes will be considered as they apply to the development of each respective subtype. Pertinent descriptions of autistic infant behavior will be abstracted from Tables 4 through 6.

7.1. *The Development of Aloofness*

Hyperresponsive to stimulation, those infants who would be subsequently classified aloof are proposed to exhibit "strong" orienting responses (see Porges, 1984) and to present as intensely irritable. Specifically, physical orientation to caregiver stimulation is likely to be exaggerated and uncoordinated with head turning. They are perceived by their parents as different (and difficult) relative to other babies, resisting all caregiver attempts to console their fussiness. In fact, parent approach is likely to exacerbate an already aroused state in the infant. Parents most often and generally most effectively attempt to terminate crying or distress in their infants by picking them up and holding them (e.g., Bell & Ainsworth, 1972). However, infants with a tendency toward hyperresponsivity ("aloof infants") assume a rigid, back-arching posture upon such initiation by caregivers. Thus infants in this group provide many cues to their parents, most of which are perceived as signals of distress and somber or irritable mood (e.g., crying, absence of smiling). Further, these infants are highly unreceptive of caregiver stimulation in response to their cues (e.g., poor sleep, food refusal) and may even escalate their irritable, aversive behavior. In short, parents of infants in this group are likely to perceive noncontingency between their nurturant behaviors and the infant's state of arousal or distress. Thus Seligman's (1975) learned helplessness theory may apply to the parent's behavior. Accordingly, it is probable that (1) they are likely to perceive noncontingency in future situations, even if "real" contingency does exist; (2) their motivation to respond to future infant signals will be reduced; and (3) their affect will be diminished with regard to caring for their infants (cf. Suomi, 1981). In this vein, parental responses to the infant, though appropriate, become less consistent and contingent over time and, therefore, would be construed as insensitive (Lamb & Easterbrooks, 1981). Parents are, thus, likely to develop a sense that their infants do not need them. Further, the lack of sensitivity on the part of caregivers results in failure for the infant and child to perceive contingent relationships or to develop social expectations (see Dawson & Galpert, 1986). In turn, these infants and children are severely impaired in their understanding of themselves as social agents (e.g., Dawson & Galpert, 1986). As noted earlier, the behavioral by-products of early relationships (e.g., reciprocity, synchrony, imitation, and attachment) are likely to be affected in children with attentional deficits (Cairns, 1986; Dawson & Galpert, 1986). Clearly, this charge is most applicable to aloof infants and children, given their early experiences.

The persistence of parent–infant transactions of this quality over time may take the broader form of reciprocal withdrawal. Bettleheim

(1967) proposed a similar behavioral course of withdrawal, though he ascribed perception of hostility, rejection, and resultant feelings of inner rage to very young children and attributed the outcome to psychological pathology in parents. In contrast, the pathology that might lead to social aloofness rests in the relationship between the parent and child and not in either party exclusively. Most fundamentally, aloof autistic children's failure to understand themselves as effective social agents is reflected in many of the outcome characteristics presented in Table 1. Specifically, they have little understanding or interest in the social aspects of contact, show little or no turn taking (reciprocity), and exhibit scant evidence of joint activity or mutual attention. However, with age, they may grow to understand their parents and others as effective agents for meeting their needs and, therefore, may interact with them as *objects* of effectance. Nonetheless, their behavior becomes increasingly inward (i.e., self-stimulatory, stereotypic) and directed toward minimizing stimulation or intrusion from the world without (cf. Wing, 1978). This is likely observed by parents, within the first year, as excessive rocking or bouncing and as a preference for being in one place always. Finally, the impact of their social and behavioral (e.g., stereotypies) deficits are likely to severely limit their opportunities for normalizing influences on cognitive and affective development (cf. Sroufe, 1979; Dawson & Galpert, 1986) and to exacerbate the extent to which they are constitutionally or organically mentally retarded. However, as noted earlier, the confluence of reciprocal and mutual determinants of developmental outcome preclude any clear statement of cause and effect.

7.2. The Development of Passive Interaction

In contrast to would-be aloof infants, those in the passive group are hyporesponsive to stimulation in accordance with their impaired autonomic functioning (i.e., parasympathetic dominance). This may be first observed in their "weak" orienting response (see Porges, 1984). Specifically, they are comparatively slow in their head turning to the onset of stimulation and may, in fact, be highly unresponsive to sounds. As noted earlier, this may lead parents to wrongly suspect hearing impairment (Wing & Attwood, 1987). Further, it is proposed that their deficient attention may be reflected in failure to habituate to continuous (e.g., visual) stimuli (Porges, 1984), objectively observed as sustained gaze. However, their gaze is likely perceived as vacant, with little tendency toward eye contact, and generally accompanied by "plastic" facial expression. In addition, passive infants are unlikely to show visual pursuit of people or other moving objects and exhibit constrained affect (e.g., little smiling). As newborns, their muscle tone may seem flaccid, and they are likely to appear indifferent to being held. Moreover, they are perceived by their parents as exceptionally "good" babies, crying infrequently and complying readily with imposed feeding schedules. Within the first 6 months, they continue to be undemanding and may seem oblivious to the presence or absence of others.

Importantly, the early development of social behavior in passive infants is impeded by their failure to provide behavioral cues or signals to their parents and their placid acceptance of caregiver stimulation (Dawson & Galpert, 1986). Given the absence of infant cues, it would seem unjustified to consider parental responsiveness insensitive. However, the delivery of noncontingent responses, regardless of their appropriateness and consistency, is likely to have deleterious effects on the infant's and child's social development. The infancy literature apparently has little to say regarding the effects of unresponsive or placid newborns on their parents' and, by association, their own behavioral development. However, Dawson and Galpert (1986) note that failure to display behaviors that typically elicit predictable caregiver responses may lead to failure in the development of social expectations and the general sense of effectance and intentionality (see Lamb, 1981). Whereas this is quite likely the case, it would seem, additionally, that passive infants become accustomed to noncontingent reward and attention from others. In this light, an increased emphasis is placed on their dependence upon the initiations of others, both in nonsocial and social realms.

With passage of time and the continued supportive transactions with parents, passive children become increasingly accepting of others' approaches, particularly as they lead to rewarding consequences (e.g., food). Moreover, their openness to inclusion in the activities of others distinguishes them from aloof persons in the degree to which they receive cognitive, affective, and social stimulation. Whereas their development in each of these areas remains markedly delayed and deviant, their deficits in any one of these areas is likely to be less than those of aloof children by virtue of experience (i.e., receptivity to stimulation). By school age, passive children may have developed the ability to speak, though such language use reflects lack of initiative and takes the predominant form of immediate echolalia. Moreover, their limited play behavior is similarly characterized by imitation of others and, therefore, lacks originality or initiation.

7.3. *The Development of Active-but-Odd Interaction*

Similar to passive individuals, those infants who would become active-but-odd are generally hyporesponsive to stimulation. However, their behavior differs in important ways that, as the current perspective holds, are likely to impact caregiver sensitivity (Lamb & Easterbrooks, 1981) and the consequent parent–infant transactions over time. Consistent with their proposed autonomic imbalance, active-but-odd infants exhibit "weak" orienting responses to early stimulation (see Porges, 1984). Specifically, both head turning and visual gaze are slow and uncoordinated; however, unlike passive infants, there is little tendency toward sustained visual attention. In fact, relatively continuous diversion of gaze is likely as the infant scans the environment in an apparently restless, aimless manner. As Wing (1978) has hypothesized, failure to use eye contact may reflect autistic children's absence of a mechanism for understanding the environment. Whereas this claim may be made with regard to those in each of the other groups to some extent, it is believed to be especially applicable to active-but-odd infants and children. Moreover, as suggested, fragmented and uncoordinated bodily movements are likely to pervade the wakeful states of these infants and to affect the use of visual gaze. In sum, the tendency toward aimless and unmodulated activity may indicate active stimulation seeking from the earliest months. Parents are likely to perceive and to respond to their infant's restlessness by picking them up (e.g., Bell & Ainsworth, 1972) and by showing other caretaking behaviors (e.g., feeding, talking to them). However, these infants are indifferent to their parent's stimulation, exhibiting little resistance, but failing to physically anticipate being picked up or to mold to their mother's arms. In addition, they may continue to restlessly scan the environment as if their caregiver were absent.

Within the explanatory framework of Dawson and Galpert (1986), as applied to each of the other subtypes, active-but-odd infants may be seen as providing many cues or signals to their parents. Specifically, their high motor activity and poor sleep may be interpreted as hunger or need for soothing. In fact, it is proposed that caregivers are highly responsive to these frequent signals, despite their ambiguity. In turn, the hyporesponsive infant and child responds to caregiver approach with indifference or passive acceptance. According to Lamb and Easterbooks (1981), sensitive responding on the part of parents depends not only on perception of need or signal from the infant but also on correct interpretation and the selection and implementation of an appropriate response. Clearly, the concept of sensitivity is difficult to apply with regard to parents of infants in this group. Where the hyporesponsive, stimulation-seeking infant and child is concerned, most caregiver approaches, independent of their nature or quality, are likely to be suitable to the expressed need. Namely, stimulation seeking on the infant's and child's part is largely indiscriminant. Therefore, to the extent that parents respond to the infant's ambiguous cues, they are fulfilling the "need" for environmental stimulation. However, the impact of repeated transactions of this one-sided character is likely to be strong development of infant social expectation (Lamb, 1981) and powerful sense of personal effectance. Infants and children in the active-but-odd group learn early to perceive themselves as social agents (see Dawson & Galpert, 1986). Moreover, their adherence to this pattern is independent of social or behavioral feedback. As noted, their response to stimulation is largely one of indifference. Thus, reciprocity of social interchange is markedly absent in active-but-odd individuals. As Dawson and Galpert (1986) note, early deficits in mother–infant interactions (e.g., synchronization, mutuality, reciprocity) are reflected in the autistic child's use of language "which shows an enduring impairment in its pragmatic aspects even when the formal elements have been mastered" (p. 248). Consistent with this view, active-but-odd children use language and social interaction in rigid, stereotypic ways that serve to elicit stimulation. Moreover, their activity is inflexible with regard to the attention and responsiveness of others and takes the form of repetitive "social" approach. Further, the content of their utterances reflects disregard for context or listener needs and may be limited to immediate and delayed echolalia. As suggested, these children exhibit the highest level of verbal and intellectual functioning of persons with autism. Their active seeking of stimulation may partially account for this, given that rote memory largely characterizes their acquisition in both areas. Imitation may also be observed, though it, too, reflects rote facility and pales in its pragmatic application (e.g., role taking). In short, the one-sided transactions that predominate the early relationships of active-but-odd infants undermine their development of reciprocity. In turn, deficits in the flexible use of social and communication rules (i.e., pragmatics) characterize much of their later behavior as they actively seek stimulation from others.

8. *Summary and Concluding Remarks*

In summary, we have identified proximate influences whereby variable infant and parent behavioral characteristics determine their early relationships with one another. Specifically, attentional and responsivity differences between autistic infants were proposed to impact caregiver sensitivity (see Lamb & Easterbrooks, 1981) and to modulate caregiver–infant transactions over time. Importantly, the enduring circumstance (i.e., repetition) of these early relationships was proposed to exacerbate the already deviant constitutional and behavioral characteristics of these infants and to result in variable expression of autistic social impairment. As Rutter (1983) observed: "More than anything else it is the reciprocity of social interchange that is missing in autism" (p. 525). Accordingly, several tenets of Dawson and Galpert's (1986) model for facilitating social behavior in autistic persons were applied to an examination of the processes impacting deficient development of reciprocal social interaction. Clearly, the foregoing accounts fall significantly short in explaining the array of deficits (i.e., the triad of social, cognitive, and language impairment; Wing, 1981) that characterize all persons with autism. Moreover, within the social domain alone, many gaps exist in understanding the specific connections between deficits in synchrony, mutuality, and reciprocity (e.g., Dawson & Galpert, 1986), for example, and individual differences in behavioral outcome. Deficiencies in attention and responsivity likely account for only a small piece of the puzzle. However, the intent of this chapter was mainly to make salient the heterogeneity, in both process (e.g., etiology) and outcome (e.g., expression of social deficits) that need to be addressed in conceptualization of autistic disturbances. Further, it is argued that an understanding of autism will come from intensive examination of the developmental processes that lead to individual differences in behavioral phenotype. It would seem that such examination must begin at the level of child–parent transaction. Accordingly, a descriptive account of early development could be attained in a naturalistic, longitudinal format. Such work has apparently been limited, to date, by problems in early identification. However, Zeanah *et al.* (1988) provide a detailed report of the assessment and follow-up of a less-than-a-year-old girl whose parents feared she was autistic. Their work is most interesting because the infant's sister was diagnosed autistic (increasing the likelihood that she would be autistic 50-fold) and because it raised many of the questions we posed in our review and that are likely to advance our understanding of autistic disturbances.

It is probable, given the earlier noted bias toward linear, main effect thinking (cf. Sameroff, 1975; Sameroff & Chandler, 1975) that many will prefer to attribute the social impairments in autism to IQ or mental age. In fact, the evidence to date suggests not only that IQ is stable and predicts educational achievement in autistic persons (e.g., DeMyer *et al.*, 1974), but that it is also a good predictor of outcome in such persons (e.g., Rutter & Garmezy, 1983). Further, as we noted earlier, Wing (1981; Wing & Gould, 1979) and others (e.g., Volkmar *et al.*, 1989) have observed a significant relationship between overall intelligence and qualitative differences in social impairment (i.e., social subtype). On the basis of these relationships, one might wonder whether a developmental analysis of social subtypes advances our understanding of autism any more than simple attention to IQ alone. On balance, however, Shah and Wing (1986) caution that many persons with severe or profound IQ deficits do not show the social deficits characteristic of autism, whereas others, of normal or superior intelligence, are markedly impaired in the social realm. In short, the present chapter has demonstrated that by endorsing simple main effect solutions to the perplexing social deficits of autistic children, information about development is discarded. Moreover, conceptual movement under such endorsement is in the direction of description (i.e., ultimate causation) and away from explanation (cf. Valsiner, 1987). Whereas accurate behavioral description may be an appropriate and necessary undertaking toward development of understanding, simple, linear accounts obscure such effort. The model outlined here is forwarded as the speculative beginnings of descriptive investigation in the former sense (i.e., toward explanation and understanding).

9. *References*

American Psychiatric Association. (1968). *Diagnostic and statistical manual of mental disorders* (2nd. ed.). Washington, DC: Author (1st ed., 1952).

American Psychiatric Association (1980). *Diagnostic and statistical manual of mental disorders* (3rd. ed.). Washington, DC: Author (1st ed., 1952; 2nd ed., 1968).

American Psychiatric Association (1987). *Diagnostic and statistical manual of mental disorders* (3rd. ed., rev.). Washington, DC: Author (1st ed., 1952; 2nd ed., 1968; 3rd ed., 1980).

Anderson, G. M., & Hoshino, Y. (1987). Neurochemical studies of autism. In D. J. Cohen & A. M. Donnellan (Eds.), *Handbook of autism and pervasive developmental disorders* (pp. 166–191). New York: John Wiley & Sons.

Anderson, N. B., & Rincover, A. (1982). The generality of overselectivity in developmentally disabled children. *Journal of Experimental Child Psychology, 34,* 217–230.

August, G. J., Stewart, M. A., & Tsai, L. (1981). The incidence of cognitive disabilities in the siblings of autistic children. *British Journal of Psychiatry, 138,* 416–412.

Baron-Cohen, S. (1988). Social and pragmatic deficits in autism: Cognitive or affective? *Journal of Autism and Developmental Disorders, 18,* 379–402.

Bartak, L., & Rutter, M. (1976). Differences between mentally retarded and normally intelligent autistic children. *Journal of Autism and Childhood Schizophrenia, 6,* 109–120.

Bell, R. Q. (1968). A reinterpretation of the direction of effects in studies of socialization. *Psychological Review, 75,* 81–95.

Bell, R. Q. (1971). Stimulus control of parent or caretaker behavior by offspring. *Developmental Psychology, 4,* 63–72.

Bell, R. Q., & Ainsworth, M. D. (1972). Infant crying and maternal responsiveness. *Child Development, 43,* 1171–1190.

Bertalanffy, L. V. (1962). *Modern theories of development: An introduction to theoretical biology.* New York: Harper. (Original work published 1933).

Bettleheim, B. (1967). *The empty fortress: Infantile autism and the birth of the self.* New York: Free Press.

Brazelton, T. B. (1981). *Fetal responses.* Unpublished manuscript.

Brazelton, T. B., & Yogman, M. W. (1986). Introduction: Reciprocity, attachment, and effectance: Anlage in early infancy. In T. B. Brazelton & M. W. Yogman (Eds.), *Affective development in infancy* (pp. 1–9). Norwood, NJ: Ablex Publishing Corporation.

Bregman, J. D., Leckman, J. F., & Ort, S. I. (1988). Fragile X syndrome: Genetic predisposition to psychopathology. *Journal of Autism and Developmental Disorders, 18,* 343–354.
Bryson, S. E., Smith, I. M., & Eastwood, D. (1988). Obstetrical suboptimality in autistic children. *Journal of the American Academy of Child and Adolescent Psychiatry, 27,* 418–422.
Cairns, R. B. (1979). *Social development: The origins and plasticity of interchanges.* San Francisco: Freeman.
Cairns, R. B. (1986). Social development: Recent theoretical trends and relevance for autism. In E. Schopler & G. B. Mesibov (Eds.), *Social behavior and autism* (pp. 15–33). New York: Plenum Press.
Cantwell, D. P., & Baker, B. L. (1984). Research on families of children with autism. In E. Schopler & G. B. Mesibov (Eds.), *The effects of autism on the family* (pp. 41–63). New York: Plenum Press.
Cantwell, D. P., Baker, B. L., & Rutter, M. (1978). Family issues. In M. Rutter & E. Schopler (Eds.), *Autism: A reappraisal of concepts and treatment* (pp. 269–296). New York: Plenum Press.
Cicchetti, D. V., & Sparrow, S. S. (1981). Developing criteria for establishing interrater reliability of specific items in a given inventory. *American Journal of Mental Deficiency, 86,* 127–137.
Courchesne, E., Yeung-Courchesne, R., Press, G. A., Hesselink, J. R., & Jernigan, T. L. (1988). Hypoplasia of cerebellar vermal lobules VI and VII in autism. *New England Journal of Medicine, 318,* 1349–1354.
Dawson, G. (1983). Lateralized brain function in autism: Evidence from the Halstead-Reitan neuropsychological battery. *Journal of Autism and Developmental Disorders, 13,* 369–386.
Dawson, G., & Galpert, L. (1986). A developmental model for facilitating the social behavior of autistic children. In E. Schopler & G. E. Mesibov (Eds.), *Social behavior in autism* (pp. 237–256). New York: Plenum Press.
DeLong, G. R. (1978). A neuropsychological interpretation of infantile autism. In M. Rutter & E. Schopler (Eds.), *Autism: A reappraisal of concepts and treatment* (pp. 207–241). New York: Plenum Press.
DeMyer, M. K. (1976). Motor, perceptual-motor, and intellectual disabilities of autistic children. In L. Wing (Ed.), *Early childhood autism* (2nd ed.; pp. 169–196). Oxford: Pergamon.
DeMyer, M. K. (1979). *Parents and children in autism.* Washington, DC: V. H. Winston & Sons.
DeMyer, M. (1987). The psychoses of childhood. In J. D. Call, R. L. Cohen, S. I. Harrison, I. N. Berlin, & L. A. Stone (Eds.), *Basic handbook of child psychiatry* (Vol. 5; pp. 362–374). New York: Basic Books.
DeMyer, M. K., Barton, S., DeMyer, W. E., Norton, J. A., Allen, J., & Steele, R. (1973). Prognosis in autism: A follow-up study. *Journal of Autism and Childhood Schizophrenia, 3,* 199–246.
DeMyer, M. K., Barton, S., Alpern, G. D., Kimberlin, C., Allen, J., Yang, E., & Steele, R. (1974). The measured intelligence of autistic children. *Journal of Autism and Childhood Schizophrenia, 4,* 42–60.
Deykin, E. Y., & MacMahon, B. (1979). The incidence of seizures among children with autistic symptoms. *American Journal of Psychiatry, 136,* 1310–1312.
Deykin, E. Y., & MacMahon, B. (1980). Pregnancy, delivery, and neonatal complications among autistic children. *American Journal of Disorders of Childhood, 134,* 860–864.
Eisenberg, L., & Kanner, L. (1956). Early infantile autism: 1943–1955. *American Journal of Psychiatry, 112,* 607–612.
Fein, D., Waterhouse, L., Lucci, D., & Snyder, D. (1985). Cognitive subtypes in developmentally disabled children. *Journal of Autism and Developmental Disorders, 15,* 77–95.

Fein, D., Pennington, B., Markowitz, P., Braverman, M., & Waterhouse, L. (1986). Toward a neuropsychological model autism: Are the social deficits primary? *Journal of the American Academy of Child Psychiatry, 25,* 198–217.

Ferster, C. B. (1961). Positive reinforcement and behavioral deficits of autistic children. *Child Development, 32,* 437–456.

Finegan, J., & Quarrington, B. (1979). Pre-, peri-, and neonatal factors and infantile autism. *Journal of Child Psychology and Psychiatry, 20,* 119–128.

Finaly, D., & Ivinskis, A. (1987). Cardiac change responses and attentional mechanisms in infants. In B. E. McKenzie & R. H. Day (Eds.), *Perceptual development in early infancy: Problems and issues* (pp. 45–63). Hillsdale, NJ: Lawrence Erlbaum Associates.

Folstein, S., & Rutter, M. (1977). Infantile autism: A genetic study of 21 twin pairs. *Journal of Child psychology and Psychiatry, 18,* 297–331.

Folstein, S., & Rutter, M. (1988). Autism: Familial aggregation and genetic implications. *Journal of Autism and Developmental Disorders, 18,* 3–30.

Frith, U., & Baron-Cohen, S. (1987). Perception in autistic children. In D. J. Cohen & A. M. Donnellan (Eds.), *Handbook of autism and pervasive developmental disorders* (pp. 85–102). New York: John Wiley & Sons.

Funderburk, S. J., Carter, J., Tanguay, P., Freeman, B. J., & Westlake, J. R. (1983). Parental reproductive problems and gestational hormonal exposure in autistic and schizophrenic children. *Journal of Autism and Developmental Disorders, 13,* 325–332.

Gaffney, G. R., Kuperman, S., Tsai, L. Y., Minchin, S. (1989). Forebrain structure in infantile autism. *Journal of the American Academy of Child and Adolescent Psychiatry, 28,* 534–537.

Gillberg, C. (1988). Annotation: The neurobiology of infantile autism. *Journal of Child Psychology and Psychiatry, 29,* 257–266.

Gillberg, C., & Gillberg, I. C. (1983). Infantile autism: A total population study of reduced optimality in the pre-, peri-, and neonatal period. *Journal of Autism and Developmental Disorders, 10,* 293–297.

Gillberg, C., & Steffenburg, S. (1987). Outcome and prognostic factors in infantile autism and similar conditions: A population based study of 46 cases followed through puberty. *Journal of Autism and Developmental Disorders, 17,* 273–287.

Gillberg, C., & Walstrom, J. (1985). Chromsome abnormalities in infantile autism and other child psychoses: A population study of 66 cases. *Developmental Medicine and Child Neurology, 27,* 293, 304.

Golden, G. S. (1987). Neurological functioning. In D. J. Cohen & A. M. Donnellan (Eds.), *Handbook of autism and pervasive developmental disorders* (pp. 133–147). New York: John Wiley & Sons.

Gottlieb, G. (1983). The psychobiological approach to developmental issues. In M. M. Haith & J. J. Campos (Vol. Eds.) & P. H. Mussen (Gen. Ed.), *Infancy and developmental psychobiology, Vol. 2: Handbook of child psychology* (pp. 1–26). New York: John Wiley & Sons.

Howlin, P., & Rutter (1987). *Treatment of autistic children.* New York: John Wiley & Sons.

James, A. L., & Barry, R. J. (1980). A review of psychophysiology in early onset psychosis. *Schizophrenia Bulletin, 6,* 506–525.

Johnston, T. D. (1987). The persistence of dichotomies in the study of behavioral development. *Developmental Review, 7,* 149–182.

Kanner, L. (1943). Autistic disturbances of affective contact. *Nervous Child, 2,* 217–250.

Kanner, L. (1949). Problems of nosology and psychodynamics of early infantile autism. *American Journal of Orthopsychiatry, 19,* 416–426.

Koegel, R., & Lovaas, O. I. (1978). Comments on autism and stimulus overselectivity. *Journal of Abnormal Psychology, 87,* 563–565.

Koegel, R., & Wilhelm, H. (1973). Selective responding to the components of multiple visual cues by autistic children. *Journal of Experimental Child Psychology, 15,* 442–453.

Konstantareas, E. M. (1986). Early developmental backgrounds of autistic and mentally retarded children: Future research directions. *Psychiatric Clinics of North America, 9,* 671–688.

Kubicek, L. F. (1980). Organization in two mother-infant interactions involving a normal infant and his fraternal twin brother who was later diagnosed as autistic. In T. Field (Ed.), *High-risk infants and children: Adult and peer interactions* (pp. 99–110). New York: Academic Press.

Lamb, M. E. (1981). The development of social expectations in the first year of life. In M. E. Lamb & L. R. Sherrod (Eds.), *Infant social cognition: Empirical and theoretical considerations* (pp. 155–176). Hillsdale, NJ: Lawrence Erlbaum Associates.

Lamb, M. E., & Easterbrooks, M. A. (1981). Individual differences in parental sensitivity: Origins, components, consequences. In M. E. Lamb & L. R. Sherrod (Eds.), *Infant social cognition* (pp. 127–154). Hillsdale, NJ: Lawrence Erlbaum Associates.

Lord, C. (1984). The development of peer relations in children with autism. In F. J. Morrison, C. Lord, & D. P. Keating (Eds.), *Applied developmental psychology* (pp. 165–229). New York: Academic Press.

Lotter, V. (1974). Factors related to outcome in autistic children. *Journal of Autism and Childhood Schizophrenia, 4,* 263–277.

Lovaas, O. I., & Schreibman, L. (1971). Stimulus overselectivity of autistic children in a two-stimulus situation. *Behaviour research and Therapy, 9,* 305–310.

Lovaas, O. I., Schreibman, L., Koegel, R., & Rehm, R. (1971). Selective responding by autistic children to multiple sensory input. *Journal of Abnormal Psychology, 77,* 211–222.

Massie, H. N. (1975). The early natural history of childhood psychosis. *Journal of the American Academy of Child Psychiatry, 14,* 683–707.

Massie, H. N. (1978a). Blind ratings of mother-infant interaction in home movies of prepsychotic and normal infants. *American Journal of Psychiatry, 135,* 1371–1374.

Massie, H. N. (1978b). The early natural history of childhood psychosis: Ten cases studied by analysis of home movies of the infancies of the children. *Journal of the American Academy of Child Psychiatry, 17,* 29–45.

Massie, H. N., & Rosenthal, J. (1984). *Childhood psychosis in the first years of life.* New York: McGraw-Hill.

Mesibov, G. B., Schopler, E., Schaffer, B., & Michal, N. (1989). Use of the childhood autism rating scale with autistic adolescents and adults. *Journal of the American Academy of Child and Adolescent Psychiatry, 28,* 538–541.

Mittler, P. (1971). *The study of twins.* Harmondsworth: Penguin.

Newsom, C., & Rincover, A. (1981). Autism. In E. J. Mash & L. G. Terdal (Eds.), *Behavioral assessment of childhood disorders* (pp. 397–439). New York: Guilford Press.

Newsom, C., Hovanitz, C., & Rincover, A. (1988). Autism. In E. J. Mash & L. G. Terdal (Eds.), *Behavioral assessment of childhood disorders* (2nd ed.; pp. 355–401). New York: Guilford Press.

Ornitz, E. M. (1974). The modulation of sensory input and motor output in autistic children. *Journal of Autism and Childhood Schizophrenia, 4,* 197–215.

Ornitz, E. M. (1983). The functional neuroanatomy of infantile autism. *International Journal of Neuroscience, 19,* 85–124.

Ornitz, E. M. (1987). Neurophysiologic studies of infantile autism. In D. J. Cohen & A. M. Donnellan (Eds.), *Handbook of autism and pervasive developmental disorders* (pp. 148–165). New York: John Wiley & Sons.

Ornitz, E. M., Guthrie, D., & Farley, A. J. (1978). The early symptoms of childhood autism.

In G. Serban (Ed.), *Cognitive defects in the development of mental illness* (pp. 24–42). New York: Brunner/Mazel.

Oswald, D. (1989). *Developmental course and prognosis of autistic disorder.* Unpublished manuscript.

Oyama, S. (1985). *The ontogeny of information: Developmental systems and evolution.* London: Cambridge University Press.

Pasamanick, B., & Knobloch, H. (1961). Epidemiologic studies on the complications of pregnancy and the birth process. In G. Caplan (Ed.), *Prevention of mental disorders in children* (pp. 74–94). New York: Basic Books.

Pauls, D. L. (1987). The familiality of autism and related disorders: A review of the evidence. In D. J. Cohen & A. Donnellan (Eds.), *Handbook of autism and pervasive developmental disorders* (pp. 192–198). New York: John Wiley & Sons.

Payton, J. B., Steele, M. W., Wenger, S. L., & Minshew, N. J. (1989). The fragile X marker and autism in perspective. *Journal of the American Academy of Child and Adolescent Psychiatry, 28,* 417–421.

Porges, S. W. (1976). Peripheral and neurochemical parallels of psychopathology: A psychophysiological model relating autonomic imbalance to hyperactivity, psychopathy, and autism. *Advances in Child Development and Behavior, Vol. 11.* New York: Academic Press.

Porges, S. W. (1984). Physiologic correlates of attention: A core process underlying learning disorders. *Pediatric Clinics of North America, 31,* 371–385.

Prechtl, H. F. R. (1968). Neurological findings in newborn infants after pre- and perinatal complications. In J. H. P. Jonxis, H. K. A. Visser, & J. A. Troelstra (Eds.), *Aspects of prematurity and dysmatuirty* (pp. 303–321). Leiden: H. E. Stenfert Kroese N. V.

Prechtl, H. F. R. (1980). The optimality concept (editorial). *Early Human Development, 4,* 201–205.

Prizant, B. M., & Schuler, A. L. (1987). Facilitating communication: Language approaches. In D. J. Cohen & A. Donnellan (Eds.), *Handbook of autism and pervasive developmental disorders* (pp. 289–300). New York: John Wiley & Sons.

Rapin, I. (1987). Searching for the cause of autism: A neurologic perspective. In D. J. Cohen & A. M. Donnellan (Eds.), *Handbook of autism and pervasive developmental disorders* (pp. 710–717). New York: John Wiley & Sons.

Rimland, B. P. (1964). *Infantile autism.* New York: Appleton-Century-Crofts.

Ritvo, E. R., Freeman, B. J., Mason-Brothers, A., Mo, A., & Ritvo, A. M. (1985). Concordance for the syndrome of autism in 40 pairs of afflicted twins. *American Journal of Psychiatry, 142,* 74–77.

Rutter, M. (1966). Behavioural and cognitive characteristics. In J. Wing (Ed.), *Early childhood autism: Clinical, educational and social aspects* (pp. 51–81). Oxford: Pergamon.

Rutter, M. (1968). Concepts of autism: A review of the research. *Journal of Child Psychology and Psychiatry, 9,* 1–25.

Rutter, M. (1970). Autistic children: Infancy to adulthood. *Seminars in Psychiatry, 2,* 435–450.

Rutter, M. (1978a). Diagnosis and definition. In M. Rutter & E. Schopler (Eds.), *Autism: A reappraisal of concepts and treatment* (pp. 1–25). New York: Plenum Press.

Rutter, M. (1978b). Diagnosis and definition of childhood autism. *Journal of Autism and Childhood Schizophrenia, 8,* 139–161.

Rutter, M. (1983). Cognitive deficits in the pathogenesis of autism. *Journal of Child Psychology and Psychiatry, 24,* 513–531.

Rutter, M., & Bartak, L. (1971). Causes of infantile autism: Some considerations from recent research. *Journal of Autism and Childhood Schizophrenia, 1,* 20–32.

Rutter, M., & Garmezy, N. (1983). Developmental psychopathology. In M. E.

Hetherington (Ed.), *Handbook of child psychology* (Vol. 4; pp. 775–911). New York: John Wiley & Sons.

Rutter, M., & Lockyer (1967). A five to fifteen year follow-up study of infantile psychosis: I. Description of the sample. *British Journal of Psychiatry, 113,* 1169–1182.

Rutter, M., & Schopler, E. (1987). Autism and pervasive developmental disorders: Concepts and diagnostic issues. *Journal of Autism and Developmental Disorders, 17,* 159–186.

Rutter, M., & Schopler, E. (1988). Autism and pervasive developmental disorders. In M. Rutter, A. H. Tuma, & I. S. Lann (Eds.), *Assessment and diagnosis in child psychopathology* (pp. 408–434). New York: Guilford Press.

Sameroff, A. J. (1975). Early influences on development: Fact or fancy? *Merrill-Palmer Quarterly, 21,* 267–294.

Sameroff, A. J., & Chandler, M. J. (1975). Reproductive risk and the continuum of caretaker casualty. In F. D. Horowitz, M. Hetherington, S. Scarr-Salapatek, & G. Siegel (Eds.), *Review of child development research* (Vol. 4; pp. 187–244). Chicago: University of Chicago.

Schopler, E. (1983). New developments in the definition and diagnosis of autism. In B. B. Lahey & A. E. Kazdin (Eds.), *Advances in clinical child psychology* (Vol. 6; pp. 93–127). New York: Plenum Press.

Schopler, E., & Mesibov, G. B. (1986). Introduction to social behavior in autism. In E. Schopler & G. B. Mesibov (Eds.), *Social behavior in autism* (pp. 1–11). New York: Plenum Press.

Schopler, E., & Mesibov, G. B. (Eds.). (1987). *Neurobiological issues in autism.* New York: Plenum Press.

Schopler, E., Brehm, S. S., Kinsbourne, M., & Riechler, R. J. (1971). Effects of treatment structure on development in autistic children. *Archives of General Psychiatry, 20,* 174–181.

Schreibman, L. (1988). *Autism.* Newbury Park, CA: Sage Publications.

Schreibman, L., & Lovaas, O. I. (1973). Overselective response to social stimuli by autistic children. *Journal of Abnormal Child Psychology, 1,* 152–168.

Seligman, M. E. P. (1975). *Helplessness: On death, depression, and development.* San Francisco: Freeman.

Shah, A., Holmes, N., & Wing, L. (1982). Prevalence of autism and related conditions in a mental handicap hospital. *Applied Research in Mental Retardation, 3,* 303–317.

Shah, A., & Wing, L. (1986). Cognitive impairments affecting social behavior in autism. In E. Schopler & G. B. Mesibov (Eds.), *Social behavior in autism* (pp. 153–169). New York: Plenum Press.

Siegel, B., Anders, T. F., Ciaranello, R. D., Bienenstock, B., & Kraemer, H. C. (1986). Empirically derived subclassification of the autistic syndrome. *Journal of Autism and Developmental Disorders, 16,* 275–293.

Sroufe, L. A. (1979). Socioemotional development. In J. D. Osofsky (Ed.), *Handbook of infant development* (pp. 462–516). New York: John Wiley & Sons.

Suomi, S. J. (1981). The perception of contingency and social development. In M. E. Lamb & L. R. Sherrod (Eds.), *Infant social cognition* (pp. 177–203). Hillsdale, NJ: Lawrence Erlbaum Associates.

Torrey, E. F., Hersh, S. P., & McCabe, K. D. (1975). Early childhood psychosis and bleeding during pregnancy. *Journal of Autism and Childhood Schizophrenia, 5,* 287–297.

Valsiner, J. (1987). *Culture and the development of children's action.* New York: John Wiley & Sons.

Volkmar, F. R., Cohen, D. J., & Paul, R. (1986). An evaluation of DSM-III criteria for infantile autism. *Journal of the American Academy of Child and Adolescent Psychiatry, 25,* 190–197.

Volkmar, F. R., Cohen, D. J., Bregman, J. D., Hooks, M. Y., & Stevenson, J. M. (1989). An examination of social typologies in autism. *Journal of the American Academy of Child and Adolescent Psychiatry, 28,* 82–86.

Wilhelm, H., & Lovaas, O. I. (1976). Stimulus overselectivity: A common feature in autism and mental retardation. *American Journal of Mental Deficiency, 81,* 26–31.

Wing, L. (1978). Social, behavioral, and cognitive characteristics: An epidemiological approach. In M. Rütter & E. Schopler (Eds.), *Autism: A reappraisal of concepts and treatment* (pp. 27–46). New York: Plenum Press.

Wing, L. (1981). Language, social, and cognitive impairments in autism and severe mental retardation. *Journal of Autism and Developmental Disorders, 11,* 31–44.

Wing, L. (1983). Social and interpersonal needs. In E. Schopler & G. B. Mesibov (Eds.), *Autism in adolescents and adults* (pp. 337–354). New York: Plenum Press.

Wing, L., & Attwood, A. (1987). Syndromes of autism and atypical development. In D. J. Cohen & A. M. Donnellan (Eds.), *Handbook of autism and pervasive developmental disorders* (pp. 3–19). New York: John Wiley & Sons.

Wing, L., & Gould, J. (1978). Systematic recording of behaviors and skills of retarded and psychotic children. *Journal of Autism and Childhood Schizophrenia, 8,* 79–97.

Wing, L., & Gould, J. (1979). Severe impairments of social interaction and associated abnormalities in children: Epidemiology and classification. *Journal of Autism and Developmental Disorders, 9,* 11–30.

World Health Organization. (1978). *international classification of diseases* (9th ed.). Geneva: Author.

Zeanah, C. H., Davis, S., & Silverman, M. (1988). The question of autism in an atypical infant. *American Journal of Psychotherapy, 42,* 135–150.

Zeskind, P. S., & Ramey, C. T. (1978). Fetal malnutrition: An experimental study of its consequences on infant development in two caregiving environments. *Child Development, 49,* 1155–1162.

Zeskind, P. S., & Ramey, C. T. (1981). Preventing intellectual and interactional sequelae of fetal malnutrition: A longitudinal, transactional, and synergistic approach to development. *Child Development, 52,* 213–218.

4 Psychobiological Approaches to Personality and Their Applications to Child Psychopathology

KEITH MCBURNETT

1. Introduction

This chapter will survey some theoretical advances in understanding personality differences, and the extension of these models to psychopathology that is related to extremes of personality dimensions. These theories have important implications for the study and treatment of child psychopathology, as will be shown. If we can predict individual differences in learning, cognition, attention, and motivation on the basis of differences in psychobiological personality dimensions, we can better describe and understand child disorders and ultimately gain precision in matching them with appropriate treatment. Although he was writing in a different context, Eysenck (1982) pointed out the perils of ignoring individual differences in personality dimensions:

> Extraverted and introverted children behave differently in their reactions to different methods of teaching, and to average them all simply loses the important information that the experiment can provide. To design the experiment on the old-fashioned formula A = (f) B in fact ensures that we have a nonsignificant main effect and a very large error variance term. Instead, we should write: A = (f) B, P, where B is the method of teaching used, and P is the personality variable extraversion-introversion; when this is done the looked-for effect comes out as an *interaction* between method of teaching and

---

KEITH MCBURNETT • Child Development Center, Department of Pediatrics, University of California, Irvine, California 92715, and State Developmental Research Institutes, 2501 Harbor Boulevard, Costa Mesa, California 92626.

Advances in Clinical Child Psychology, Volume 14, edited by Benjamin B. Lahey and Alan E. Kazdin. Plenum Press, New York, 1992.

> personality. In that way we can save a great deal of the variance from being relegated to the error term, and we achieve insight into the dynamics of the situation, as well as the practical reward of now being able to adjust our teaching method to the personality of the pupil. (pp. 3–4)

One of the goals of a psychobiological approach to psychopathology is to reconcile clinical diagnostic categories and subtypes with biopsychologically relevant personality dimensions, so that categorical diagnosis does not "average" meaningful and extreme dimensional differences that tie behavioral variation to biological variation. This approach has important treatment implications because the poles of psychobiological dimensions are associated with differential response to drugs and to schedules of reinforcement.

All of the scientists whose work is discussed herein—Eysenck, Cloninger, Gray, Newman, Quay, and Zuckerman—have been selected because their work assumes that biological differences underlie differences in learning and motivational styles that in turn underlie the stability of behavioral propensities that we call traits. Furthermore, the work of these scientists has been applied to child psychopathology, generally with the results that would be predicted from a rational understanding of the theory under test. A disproportionate amount of this chapter is devoted to the work of Gray, because Gray has provided the most detailed psychobiological model of behavior and because some of the more detailed discussion of brain–personality relationships fit best under Gray's section in the chapter. This allocation should not be taken as an effort to give Gray's work preeminence or to diminish the importance of the contributions of other scientists, either from those discussed herein or from others whose work is omitted because of space limitations.

2. *Eysenck's Tridimensional Personality System*

Most of the work described in this chapter can be traced to theories originally advanced by H. J. Eysenck. Eysenck developed an integrated biopsychosocial theory of personality and psychopathology that still stands as a major achievement in integrating diverse empirical observations about human behavior. Eysenck proposed a typology of behavioral propensities that is based on three dimensions of personality.

2.1. *Personality Theory*

According to Eysenck (1969), historical antecedents of his approach to personality types can be found in ancient Greek civilization. These are the classical four categories of Sanguine, Melancholic, Choleric, and Phlegmatic temperaments, which were reiterated by Immanuel Kant in the late eighteenth century. An important development to this four-category approach appeared at the beginning of this century, when Wilhelm Wundt proposed that these four categories result from the intersection of two dimensions of emotional reactivity: the *strength* (on a dimension of strongly emotional to nonemotional) and the *speed of change* (on a dimension of changeable to unchangeable) of emotional reaction. This latter dimension corresponds to the personality dimension popularized by Carl Jung, that of *introversion–extroversion*. Thus, Wundt's contribution provided the basis for a model of personality types that placed individuals in one of four quadrants but allowed for individual variation within a quadrant based on how that person's traits deviated along two orthogonal continuous dimensions. Jung added the interesting observation that persons differing along the extraversion–introversion dimension were prone to develop different psychopathological complications. Introverts, thought Jung, were more susceptible to dysthymia, whereas extroverts were more likely to develop hysterical reactions.

Eysenck's early factor analyses of rating scale data from neurotics yielded two strong, relatively independent factors, which he termed *E* (Extroversion–Introversion) and *N* (Neuroticism). Eysenck also took items from the questionnaires of both Cattell and Guilford and extracted these same independent dimensions. These analyses, along with replications from different countries and different cultures, led Eysenck to consider *E* and *N* as *superfactors* that emerge from any personality assessment system that adequately samples the domain of personality variables. These superfactors encompass several other personality traits that are less reliably derived and more intercorrelated. (In Eysenck's [1947] own hierarchical model of personality, *E* and *N* are the dimensions that characterize the overarching personality *types*. Branching down under each type variable are the various *traits* or subfactors that comprise the type, derived on the basis of trait intercorrelation. In the case of *E*, these traits are "Sociability," "Impulsiveness," "Activity," "Liveliness," and "Excitability." Branching down from each trait are *habitual responses*, which, by virtue of their intercorrelation, give rise to a particular trait. In the case of Sociability, these habitual responses are such activities as going to parties, liking to talk to people, having many friends, and so forth. Finally, each habitual response is supposedly based on a number of specific observable responses, such as repeated occasions of attending parties.)

One of the main qualities of individuals who score high on the *E* dimension is preference for the stimulation provided by groups of other people. An important quality of individuals who score high on the *N*

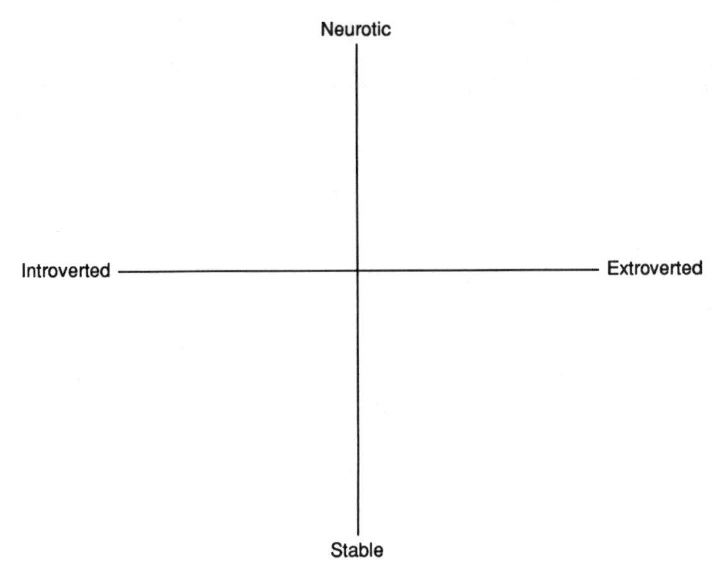

FIGURE 1. Graphic representation of Eysenck's *E* and *N* superfactors.

dimension is emotional reactivity to stimuli. "Pure" introverts and "pure" neurotics therefore might both avoid large parties but for different reasons. Introverts would prefer the reduced stimulation of a small group or a solitary activity, whereas emotionally labile neurotics would likely feel fearful or anxious (yet excited) at the thought of encountering a large group.

These orthogonal dimensions, when gradually displayed as intersecting lines, produce quadrants of stable–introverted, stable–extroverted, neurotic–introverted, and neurotic–extroverted (see Figure 1). A great deal of research has documented consistent differences on various indicators of external validity among groups of people, based on the *E–N* coordinates of the groups. For the present purpose of comparing personality dimensions with psychopathology, it should be noted that sociopaths and criminals (as groups) have long been found to be extremely extroverted, whereas depressives, obsessives, phobics, and anxiety-prone persons have been located in the neurotic–introvert quadrant (e.g., Corah, 1964). Among patients high on neuroticism, those who are also high on extraversion tend to express anxiety through somatic symptoms; those neurotics who are highly introverted tend to exhibit cognitive anxiety symptoms (Corah, 1964). This distinction between somatic and cognitive anxiety as expressed by patients differing along personality dimensions was later recast by Cloninger (1986) in terms of his three-factor biosocial theory.

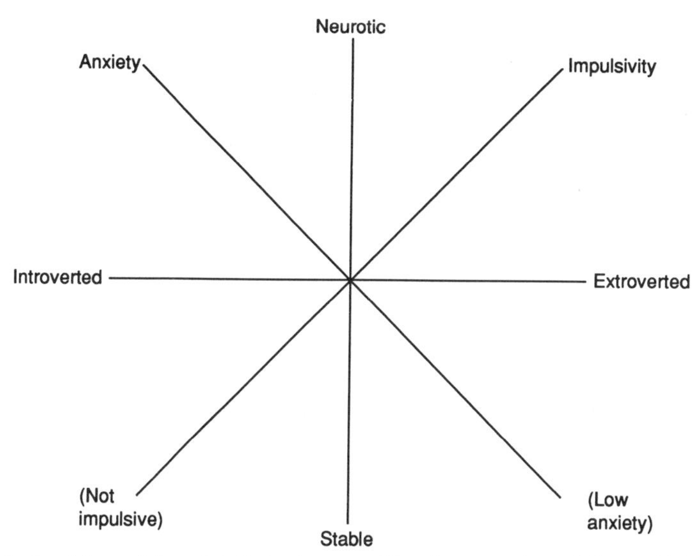

FIGURE 2. Anxiety and Impulsivity factors resulting from rotation of Eysenck's *E* and *N* dimensions.

Kassebaum, Couch, and Slater (1959) conducted a factor-analytic study of the MMPI that was portentous in two ways. First, they extracted *three* primary factors. The first two factors, which they labeled Ego Weakness versus Ego Strength and Introversion–Extroversion, were similar to Eysenck's *N* and *E* factors and accounted for much more of the variance than did the weaker third factor (see below). The third factor, Tender-Minded Sensitivity, was similar to the Psychoticism factor that Eysenck added to his theory. Secondly, Kassebaum, Couch, and Slater (1959) extracted two "fusion factors" that they labeled Impulsivity–Intellectual Control and Social Withdrawal–Social Participation. When drawn on top of the two intersecting primary factors (like placing an "X" over a "+" sign), these fusion factors ran diagonally from the upper-left quadrant to the lower-right quadrant and from the upper-right quadrant to the lower-left quadrant. This procedure had the same effect as *rotating* the original primary factors 45 degrees, and redrawing new vertical and horizontal coordinates. This is exactly the configuration that was later proposed by Gray (1970, 1973). Gray termed these rotated dimensions Impulsivity and Anxiety (see Figure 2).

Eysenck's programmatic research in personality scaling convinced him that a simple two-dimensional scheme was insufficient. A weaker third factor, Psychoticism, was developed (Eysenck, 1952; Eysenck & Eysenck, 1976b). The Psychoticism dimension, or *P*, has also been called Tough-Mindedness–Tender-Mindedness. This dimension discriminates diagnosed psychotics from normals and neurotics, but it is more a measure of emotional detachment than of thought disorder. Individuals exhibiting certain qualities of leadership or creativity, as well as sociopaths and criminals, have been found to score above the mean on *P*. High *P* scorers tend to be aloof, egocentric, aggressive, impersonal, impulsive, lacking in empathy, and unconcerned about the rights and well-being of others.

2.2. *Biological Substrates of Eysenck's Dimensions*

Eysenck (1967) proposed that two aspects of arousal underlie individual variations in *E* and *N*. The biological basis of *N* is the lability or sensitivity of the limbic system and the associated autonomic nervous system. Individuals high on *N* have a limbic–autonomic system that tends to be highly responsive to environmental and psychological stimuli and that tends to maintain autonomic arousal for a relatively long period after the initial stimulus is no longer present. The biological basis of *E* is more closely (but inversely) related to the tonic level of arousal in the neocortex, as modulated by the ascending reticular activating system. Individuals high on *E* have a characteristically low level of cortical arousal, whereas those low on *E* tend toward high cortical arousal. Because a primary function of the neocortex is to inhibit its own stimulation from lower centers and to inhibit output from lower centers, *low* cortical arousal is associated with distractability, high motor activity level, and extroverted social behavior. Differences in cortical and limbic–autonomic activity among persons differing on *N* and *E* have been found in a number of paradigms. For example, the EEG alpha rhythm in introverts tends to be higher in frequency and lower in amplitude (indicating higher arousal) than that of extroverts (Eysenck, 1981). Individual differences in cortical and limbic–autonomic activity, which may be inferred from scores on the *E* and *N* dimensions, have important implications for predicting learning and conditioning, response to medication, and social behavior.

Eysenck invoked Pavlov's law of "transmarginal inhibition" as the neural explanation for the relationship of *E* with cortical arousal. This explanation begins with the observation that increases in the strength of stimuli are linearly related to increases in responses (Pavlov's law of strength). According to the law of transmarginal inhibition, stimulation can reach a saturation point at which it overwhelms neurons. Inhibition then occurs, and responding reaches an asymptote and begins to decline. This results in the quadratic, "U-shaped" function that is often observed between arousal and performance (the Yerkes–Dodson curve).

Because of their differences in tonic cortical arousal, this neural asymptote for optimal level of stimulation will occur at lower levels for introverts than for extroverts. This not only means that introverts may function better at lower (and extroverts better at higher) levels of stimulation—it also implies that introverts and extroverts may seek different levels of environmental stimulation in order to maintain their optimal level of arousal. As is discussed later, this is the explanation for the trait of sensation seeking as developed by Zuckerman.

High arousal generally facilitates conditioning, and one of the most theoretically important tenets of Eysenck's theory is that introverts condition more readily than extroverts. In terms of associated psychopathology, therefore, introverts should be prone to developing specific phobias and other conditioned emotional responses of the anxious–depressive variety. Extroverts, who are less conditionable, should be less able to benefit from aversive conditioning, less sensitive to conditioned stimuli for punishment (threats, warnings, prohibitions, etc.) and more prone to exhibiting antisocial behavior. Sociopaths, particularly primary sociopaths, should also show less conditioned arousal and poorer learning in avoidance conditioning and less ability to benefit from punishment (Schmauk, 1970). However, when extremely strong unconditioned stimuli are used, or other conditions operate to over-arouse introverts and trigger neural inhibition, extroverts should condition better than introverts.

Also associated with arousal is vigilance. A somewhat repetitive task may elicit a comfortable level of cortical arousal in an introvert, enabling that person to maintain vigilance for extended periods. The same task may provide an intolerable underaroused state of cortical excitation in an extrovert, resulting in performance that is easily distracted by competing off-task stimuli or internally generated off-task thoughts and behaviors. Eysenck (1981) reviewed numerous studies that support similar generalizations.

The biological substrate of *P* is more problematic for Eysenck. Because males score higher on *P* than females and because sociopathy, criminality, and schizophrenia are more prevalent in males, Eysenck and Eysenck (1976b) proposed that *P* may be related in some way to androgens. Other evidence has suggested that *P* may be associated in some way with serotonin. Eysenck (1982) cites unpublished data suggesting that *P* scores may vary inversely with metabolites of serotonin. The importance of individual differences in serotonergic systems is discussed later in this chapter.

Drug effects are relevant to any psychobiological system of personality. Drugs that affect the proposed biological mechanism underlying a particular personality dimension should produce predictable changes in correlates of that dimension. Aside from the theoretical importance of validating the biological–dimensional relationship, this approach has direct implications for clinical management. In Eysenck's system, *E* should be affected by drugs that act on cortical arousal. Stimulants (e.g., amphetamine) should increase vigilance, conditioning, and introverted behavior, whereas depressants (alcohol, sodium amytal) should have the opposite effect. *N*, according to Eysenck, should be modulated by drugs that involve the limbic–autonomic system; that is, adrenalin should increase emotional reactivity and benzodiazapines and bromides should decrease emotional reactivity. Numerous studies have provided general support for these relationships, although the complexities of psychopharmacology are beyond such a simple model. There is evidence that extroverts and hysterics (by virtue of their lower cortical arousal) have a lower sedation threshold than do ambiverts, introverts, and dysthymics; for example, they require less sodium amytal to reach sedation (Eysenck, 1982). Pharmaceutical validation of Eysenck's theory is much less clean, and less supported, for the *P* dimension. Eysenck (1982) speculated that LSD should cause normal subjects to behave similarly to high *P* scorers and that phenothiazines and other antipsychotics should have the opposite effect. One of several inconsistencies with this speculation is that the putative antipsychotic mechanism of phenothiazines involves postsynaptic dopamine receptor blockade, rather than alterations in the serotonergic system.

Because the major dimensions of a psychobiological personality system are based on biological mechanisms and show remarkable stability across time, they would appear to be innate or fixed early in life. Eysenck has attempted to determine the relative contributions of nature and nurture to the expression of the major traits. The variance of a particular trait can be partitioned into genetic factors, within-family environmental factors (e.g., birth order), and between-family environmental factors (e.g., SES, neighborhood environment, etc.). In Eysenck's (1982) review of genetic analyses, he concluded that approximately two-thirds of the true variance in personality dimensions is contributed by heredity. The remaining true variance that is contributed by the environment is almost wholy attributable to within-family factors, and almost no variance is due to between-family variables. By way of contrast, the environmentally related variance in general intelligence appears related mostly to between-family variance such as SES.

2.3. *Early Applications of Eysenck's Theory to Child Psychopathology*

The bidimensional approach using *N* and *E* has been fairly well validated in children as young as 4 to 5 years old, although reliability of measurement at that age places statistical limits on validation attempts.

Reliability is improved greatly by the age of 8–9. Factor analyses and longitudinal studies cited by Rachman (1969) and by S. B. G. Eysenck (1969) suggest that *E* and *N* can be assessed reliably in children, that these dimensions tend to be stable and resemble the dimensions observed in adults, and that activity and rapidity in infancy are related to extroversion in childhood. Gender differences on the major dimensions first appear in childhood. According to Rachman (1969) and S. B. G. Eysenck (1969), girls tend to be more emotional (higher on *N*), and boys tend to be more extroverted.

In its predictions regarding behavior and emotional disorders of childhood and adolescence, Eysenck's theory has received mixed support. Factor-analytic studies of specific child behaviors, such as items on behavior checklists or rating scales, have generally produced two (or three) factors that are roughly analogous to *E* and *N* (and sometimes *P*). An early study by Hewitt and Jenkins (1946) of 500 clinic-referred children identified three behavior problem clusters: unsocialized aggressive behavior (cruelty, aggression), socialized delinquency (gang activities, covert behavior problems such as truancy and stealing), and overinhibited behavior (shyness, sensitivity). The question arises, do these clusters of problems correspond to psychobiological dimensions of personality? Personality measures were not available on this sample, but under Eysenck's system, the unsocialized aggressives should score high on *P*, the socialized delinquents should score high on *E*, and the overinhibited children probably should score low on *E*. However, it is not clear what Eysenck's system would predict for these groups on the *N* factor. Clearly, the overinhibited children would be predicted to score high on *N*, but is this their definitive personality characteristic, or are they more precisely described by a combination of low *E* and high *N*? And is *N* a general marker of maladjustment and instability, leading to the prediction that all three clinical cluster groups should score high on *N*?

Other analyses of child behavior problems have yielded only two groupings (possibly, as Quay, 1986, has suggested, because of an insufficient number of *P* behavior items): conduct problems and personality or emotional problems (e.g., Himmelweit, 1952, cited in Rachman, 1969; Peterson, 1961). Rachman (1969) compared these factors to those obtained in Eysenck's (1967) analyses of adult behavior problems, stating that children with conduct problems resembled adult hysterics, psychopaths, and criminals, whereas children with personality problems resembled adult dysthymics. Peterson (1961) equated his two factors to *N* and *E*.

In adults, dysthymia and anxiety disorders rather consistently have been found to be related to high *N* but also have been related often to low scores on *E*. Adult sociopaths mostly have been found to score above the mean on *E*, but sometimes at the mean on N (Corah, 1964), and more often well above the mean on *N* (Eysenck, 1969). A simple one-to-one relationship between Eysenck's dimensional *genotype* and the observed *phenotypes* of behavioral symptom groupings is too problematic to be tenable (as Cloninger has pointed out; see later discussion). Empirical studies linking either the dimensions of *N* and *E* or their interactions (quadrants) to clinical problem groups in children and adolescents have only partially supported the predicted associations, and there are many instances of negative findings. Delinquents, according to a review of studies by Morris (1979), consistently fail to show an extroversion effect. In a longitudinal study, West and Farrington (1973) found that neurotic extroverted children were at no greater risk for delinquency than normal children (and they found little association of Eysenckian dimensions with delinquency). Some studies have suggested that child conduct problems, especially the more serious ones, are more related to the *P* dimension than to *E* (Allsop & Feldman, 1974; Saklofske, 1977), or are related to both P and E (Allsop & Feldman, 1976).

3. *Zuckerman and the Sensation-Seeking Trait*

Zuckerman (e.g., 1979, 1983b) has accumulated a number of interesting links between biological processes and the personality dimension of sensation seeking. Sensation seeking (Zuckerman, 1971) is considered to be the expression of a need for varied, novel, and complex sensations and experiences and a willingness for risk taking in pursuit of such experiences. The application of sensation seeking, as a behavioral attempt to "correct" low cortical activity, to the clinical syndrome of psychopathy was proposed by Quay (1965).

3.1. *Relation to Behavior and Personality Problems*

Sensation seeking is believed to have behavioral correlates in an individual's variety of sexual and drug experiences; consumption of cigarettes, alcohol, and stimulating foods; gambling behavior, speeding, and other disregard of risk or danger; engaging in high levels of physical and social activities; choice of exotic over commonplace alternatives, and so forth. It appears to be related to a tendency toward liberal social and political attitudes and values. It is uncorrelated with the Eysenck *N* dimension but positively correlated with *P* and *E* (more with the Impulsivity factor than the Sociability factor of the *E* dimension; see Farley & Farley, 1970) dimensions, with the Hypomania scale of the MMPI, and with traits of adventurousness and social dominance. The trait of sensation seeking is currently considered to comprise four factors: Thrill and Adventure Seeking, Experience Seeking, Disinhibition, and Boredom Susceptibility. Among clinical populations, primary sociopaths, delinquents, and polydrug users score high on sensation seeking, especially on the Disinhibition factor. This factor (Disinhibition) is also the one most associated with aggressiveness (Zuckerman, 1983a). Disinhibition and Thrill and Adventure Seeking are higher in males than in females and show the greatest decline with advancing age (Zuckerman, Eysenck, & Eysenck, 1978).

3.2. *Biological Correlates of Sensation Seeking*

Zuckerman has reviewed evidence for a biological basis of sensation seeking (1983a). Although Zuckerman has placed emphasis on monoamine oxidase levels as important correlates of sensation seeking, several different biological processes have been related to this trait. Sensation seeking may be associated with a stronger orienting reflex and weaker defensive responses in psychophysiological reactions to stimuli of moderate intensity. High sensation-seeking males exhibit a stronger orienting response than normals to novel stimuli, as indicated by changes in electrodermal skin conductance (Feij, Orleberke, Gazendam, & van Zuilen, 1985; Neary & Zuckerman, 1976) and heart rate (Orleberke & Feij, 1979; Ridgeway & Hare, 1981). Plasma dopamine-beta-hydroxylase (which has been found to be very low in undersocialized delinquents) and CSF norepinephrine (NE) appear inversely related to sensation seeking (Ballenger, Post, Jimerson, Lake, Murphy, Zuckerman, & Cronin, 1983; Zuckerman, Ballenger, & Post, 1984). Levels of the NE metabolite, MHPG, in urine have been positively correlated with sensation seeking (Buchsbaum, Muscettola, & Goodwin, 1981). Sensation seeking, particularly the factor of Disinhibition, is related to an augmenting rather than a reducing slope in the average evoked potential (AEP) recorded from the cortex in response to high intensity stimuli.

This tendency toward AEP augmentation, as well as other relevant variables such as criminal convictions, chronic alcoholism, familial suicide attempts, bipolar (but not unipolar) depression, time spent in social activities, male gender, younger age, and the psychometric trait of sensation seeking, have all been correlated with low levels of platelet monoamine oxidase (MAO). Presumably, the amount of MAO in the central nervous system and its relationship to brain monoamine levels would be the important biological substrate, but investigators are generally limited to measuring peripheral levels of MAO. The MAO in peripheral blood platelets has been found to be inversely related to general sensation seeking (Murphy, Belmaker, Buchsbaum, Martin, Ciaranello, & Wyatt, 1977; Schooler, Zahn, Murphy, & Buchsbaum, 1978; von Knorring, Oreland, & Winblad, 1984). Platelet MAO is highly reliable within subjects, giving test–retest reliability of .86 over 8 to 10 weeks (Murphy, 1976) and may be related to the amount of MAO in the brain (Zuckerman, 1979).

The subfactor of Disinhibition has been found to be positively related to the levels of sex hormones (testosterone, estradiol, and estrone) in both males and females (Daitzman & Zuckerman, 1980; Daitzman, Zuckerman, Sammelwitz, & Ganjam, 1978). Zuckerman (1979) believes that this is at least partly an indirect effect because androgens and especially estrogens are potent inhibitors of MAO. By decreasing central MAO, sex hormones increase central catecholamines, thereby increasing brain excitability and behavioral activation. In Zuckerman's model, sensation seeking is in some part a function of the level of NE and dopamine in the reward areas of the limbic system. Central MAO is very high in limbic structures compared with the rest of the brain. Sex hormones may affect the availability of limbic MAO and alter the catabolism of limbic catecholamines. Limbic effects on the cortex and reticular activating system would then alter the orienting response and the augmentation of the averaged evoked potential.

Zuckerman's biological theory of sensation seeking is able to account for a great deal of the relationships between psychometric and biological data. Also the theory is consistent with findings that psychometrically-measured sensation seeking, platelet MAO, and average evoked response augmenting-reducing patterns all show high degrees of genetic heritability (Fulker, Eysenck, & Zuckerman, 1980; Zuckerman, 1979). However, the theory is based on a number of assumptions that have varying degrees of support; for example, that peripheral MAO is a reliable measure of central MAO; that levels of central NE can be estimated from peripheral levels of the NE metabolite, MHPG; and that levels of central MAO and central NE are inversely related. Further clarification is needed to resolve Zuckerman's postulate of high limbic catecholamine levels with the postulate of underarousal in high sensation seekers. Also, Zuckerman's theory needs to be expanded to account for relationships among sensation seeking, serotonin, and endorphins. For example, endorphins, which correlate positively with Neuroticism and negatively with Disinhibition and Boredom Susceptibility, are high in AEP reducers and low in AEP augmenters (Zuckerman, 1983a). Firm conclusions regarding the amine basis of sensation seeking await additional study.

3.3. *Application of Sensation Seeking to Child and Adolescent Psychopathology*

As noted earlier, sensation seeking is positively related to *E* in adults. Sensation seeking has been repeatedly linked to adult sociopathy, whether identified by personality tests or by diagnosis (Blackburn, 1969; Emmons & Webb, 1974; Gorman, 1970; Zuckerman & Neeb, 1979). Although underarousal and high sensation seeking have been proposed as a basis for hyperactivity in children (Rosenthal & Allen, 1978; Satterfield, 1976; Zentall & Zentall, 1983), very little research has been conducted on sensation seeking in child or adolescent clinical populations. This may be in part because of difficulty in measuring sensation seeking in children. In a study using the adult Sensation Seeking Scale (SSS), Wallbank (1985) found that juvenile delinquents scored higher than nondelinquents on the overall SSS and on the Disinhibition, Experience Seeking, and Boredom Susceptibility subscales. Using an early child version of the SSS, Kafry (1982) found that sensation seeking was related to endorsement of delinquent behaviors in children. Russo, Lahey, Christ, Frick, McBurnett, Walker, Loeber, Stouthamer-Loeber, and Green (1991) administered a newly developed child SSS to normal and clinic-referred children. The obtained test–retest reliability indicated that this trait can be reliably measured in elementary-school-aged children. A factor analysis yielded only two factors—Boredom Susceptibility and Thrill and Adventure Seeking. In the clinic-referred sample, children with Conduct Disorder (CD) scored significantly higher than children with Attention-deficit Hyperactivity Disorder (ADHD). Control children and those with both CD and ADHD obtained intermediate scores. When CD children with and without an accompanying anxiety disorder were compared, those free of anxiety scored higher (Russo *et al.*, 1991; Walker, Lahey, Russo, Frick, Christ, McBurnett, Loeber, Stouthamer-Loeber, & Green, 1991). Children's total SSS and Boredom Susceptibility scales were correlated significantly but modestly with their biological mothers' total score on the adult SSS (r = .29 and .33, respectively).

4. *Gray's Theories of Personality and Nervous System Function*

Jeffrey Gray has integrated findings from learning, psychometric, pharmacological, neurophysiological, and other areas of research into a general model of personality and functional neuropsychology. Gray has drawn from widely diverse paradigms, ranging in scope from Eysenck's personality model to Amsel's frustration–counterconditioning theory (Amsel, 1962, 1990) to support a general theory of emotions and behavior. The more comprehensive presentations of Gray's work are book-length (Gray, 1975, 1982, 1987). Basic principles can be summarized more briefly here, although some detail will be required in order to adequately present Gray's abstraction of a mechanistic "conceptual nervous system" from the empirical knowledge base of the working biological nervous system. Many readers may prefer to skim over the details of the conceptual nervous system and to concentrate more on Gray's personality theory as it relates to the most important modular components of the conceptual nervous system: the behavioral activation system and the behavioral inhibition system.

One of the most important aspects of Gray's writings has been his extrapolation from the behavior of animals with discrete surgical lesions to the septum or hippocampus, to the behavior of animals and humans who are extroverted or disinhibited. Animals with lesions in the system comprised by the medial septum, hippocampus, and orbital–frontal cortex, and humans with disinhibitory syndromes (especially typified by psychopathy), appear to share abnormalities in avoidance learning, anticipation of noxious events, classical aversive conditioning, inhibition of appetitive responding, and mediation of temporal events. They also share a greater propensity to seek out sensation and stimulation than their normal conspecifics. These behavioral differences may be interpreted as stemming from a deficit in avoidance or self-inhibition, from a heightened appetite for reward and novel stimulation, or from a combination of both. An overactive septal–hippocampal system in Gray's theory is responsible for anxiety, whereas underactivity of the system results in impulsivity. The biological underpinnings of these behavioral traits suggested to Gray that fundamental personality factors may be best described in terms related to variations in septal–hippocampal function. The validity of this approach is strengthened by pharmaceutical evidence. Drugs that have anxiolytic properties, such as ethanol and the benzodiazepines, not only reduce anxiety in humans—they also produce changes in experimental animal behavior that are qualitatively similar to changes secondary to septal–hippocampal lesions (Gray, 1982, 1987).

4.1. *Personality Theory*

Gray (1970, 1973) proposed that a rotation of the axes of dimensions extracted in Eysenck's factor-analytic studies of personality (cf. Eysenck, 1967; Eysenck & Eysenck, 1969) leads to an important modification that fits some experimental data better than Eysenck's original model. In Eysenck's original two-factor model, the dimension of *E* (introversion–extroversion) was set orthogonally against the dimension of *N* (stability–neuroticism). These intersecting axes produced quadrants of stable–introverted, stable–extroverted, neurotic–introverted, and neurotic–extroverted (Figure 1). Reasoning from learning experiments and other experimental findings, Gray proposed that these same dimensions could be derived on the basis of *sensitivity to conditioned reward and conditioned punishment*. According to Gray, the *E* dimension represents a relative responsivity to signals (conditioned stimuli) of punishment or frustrative nonreward (for introversion) or to signals of reward or relief/nonpunishment (for extroversion). The *N* dimension corresponds to secondary lability, or the absolute susceptibility to conditioned stimuli. Gray's rotated axes resemble those earlier proposed by Kassebaum, Couch, & Slater (1959) in their factor analysis of the MMPI. An axis drawn from the neurotic–introverted quadrant to the stable–extroverted quadrant becomes the dimension of anxiety, going from the highest level to the lowest. An axis drawn from the stable–introverted quadrant to the neurotic–extroverted quadrant corresponds to impulsivity, again running from the highest level to the lowest. The dimensions of *E* and *N* then become derivatives of the primary dimensions of anxiety and impulsivity (Figure 2).

This approach generates predictions that differ from those arising from the original arrangement of *E* and *N* (Gray, 1981). One difference that has direct relevance for the study of antisocial behavior concerns individual differences in conditionability. In Eysenck's system, this is a fundamental difference between introverts and extroverts. Introverts should condition more easily than extroverts. Gray views the relative sensitivity to punishment versus reward as the critical difference. Gray's system thus makes the important distinction that introverts should condition more readily when reinforcers are aversive (punishment or nonreward) but that extroverts should condition more readily than introverts when reinforcers are appetitive (reward or relief). Gray (1987) cites several studies in which the findings are more explicable under his model than under that of Eysenck. The findings of Newman, Widom, and Nathan (1985) also fit Gray's revision of Eysenck's model somewhat better than the original model. Newman *et al.* (1985) found that errors on a passive avoidance task by introverts and extroverts were equal when a single valence incentive was used. When the incentives were mixed, that is, when there was a reward for correct responses and a penalty for incorrect responses, extroverts made significantly more errors of commission than did introverts on all four experiments reported. A close examination of Newman *et al.*'s (1985) data shows also that introverts made more errors of omission under conditions of mixed incentives in all four experiments, although these differences were not statistically significant.

Gray has acknowledged that qualifications may be needed for some applications of his personality theory (Gray, Owen, Davis, & Tsaltas, 1983). For example, correlates and subfactors of the third Eysenckian dimension (*P*) and of sensation seeking are difficult to resolve with the simple model. Extreme scores on measures of sensation seeking and impulsivity tend to be associated with high scores on psychoticism measures, leading Gray (1973) to speculate that individual differences on the psychoticism dimension may correspond to susceptibility to the effects of unconditioned reward or punishment, or primary lability. The dimension of impulsivity in *humans* may be more complex than a simple extrapolation from Gray's animal model would suggest. Eysenck and Eysenck (1977) found that impulsivity in humans is comprised of the following subfactors: a narrowly conceived impulsive behavior factor, a risk-taking factor, a nonplanning factor, and a liveliness factor. Highly impulsive individuals, who are high on both *E* and *P*, can be divided into those high on *N* (and thus high on "impulsiveness") and those low on *N* (and thus high on "venturesomeness," similar to sensation seeking). A full resolution of these complexities with Gray's model awaits further research.

4.2. *Functional Anatomical Substrates of Motivated Behavior: The Conceptual Nervous System*

Gray has provided an extremely detailed account of the specific neuroanatomical and functional bases of his Conceptual Nervous System. An overview of Gray's model, with some discussion of serotonergic and other neurotransmitter involvement, is provided for readers with an interest in neuropsychological aspects of personality. Those readers with less interest in neuroanatomy and neurochemistry may wish to skim the following sections and pick up the discussion at section 4.3.

4.2.1. *Arousal Mechanism*

Although Gray has written extensively (cf., 1982) on the functional neuroanatomical system subserving behavioral inhibition (the Behavioral Inhibition System, BIS) the BIS is but one component of his biobehavioral theory. Gray (1987) outlined a theoretical model specifying the neuroanatomical foci of each of the various components of what he termed the *conceptual nervous system*. The *arousal mechanism* corresponds to the ascending noradrenergic fibers. These are comprised of two major pathways. Cell bodies in the locus coeruleus project to all cortical areas of the brain. Along the way, the dorsal bundle arising from these cells innervates areas of the amygdala and anterior hypothalamus and branches into the stria terminalis before going on the cerebral cortex. A ventral noradrenergic bundle arises from cell groups spread throughout the brainstem and projects to the lateral mamillary nuclei, the lateral and ventral hypothalamus, and to large areas of the limbic system, including the anterior medial amygdaloid complex, the ventral medial septum, and the cingulum. The ventral hypothalamus in turn projects to the median eminence and the infundibulum, thereby influencing the endocrine system. While this system normally functions to modulate arousal in accordance with environmental demands, there is good evidence that mood disorders can result from changes in the arousal system. Stress of any kind initially tends to increase neurotransmission in all the biogenic amine systems. When stress is prolonged and uncontrollable (as in animal paradigms of depression or learned helplessness; Seligman, 1975), there is an eventual fall in the levels of norepinephrine in the locus coeruleus (Weiss, Bailey, Goodman, Hoffman, Ambrose, Salman, & Charry, 1982), with membrane potential changes secondary to reduced occupation of the alpha-2 noradrenergic autoreceptors.

4.2.2. Control of Unconditioned Fight or Flight

A second component of Gray's conceptual nervous system is that providing *control of unconditioned fight or flight.* As discussed previously, Gray has hypothesized that individual variation in this system may underlie differences in psychometric measures of psychoticism, and in behavioral responses of anger or aggression to unconditioned punishment or nonreward. The neuroanatomical substrate begins with the amygdala, which sends an inhibitory projection via the diffuse ventral amygdalofugal pathway to the medial hypothalamus. The medial hypothalamus is in turn inhibitory on the central gray region of the midbrain, via the dorsal longitudinal bundle of Schutz. Therefore, stimulation of the amygdala increases the activity in the central gray, heightens aversive sensation, and stimulates the autonomic nervous system and fight-or-flight behavior. The central gray also receives a major input from spinal afferents involved in pain.

Bilateral damage to the temporal lobes, including the amygdala, produces the classic Kluver–Bucy syndrome, with the result (among others) of lack of fear and indiscriminate approach behavior (Kluver & Bucy, 1937). Subsequent classical conditioning is disrupted, as amygdalectomized animals appear not to discriminate the reinforcement significance of various unconditioned stimuli and, if extensive damage is involved, may exhibit "psychic blindness" (visual agnosia) of objects.

Thus, disruption of conditioning following damage to the amygdala may be related to failure to appreciate the significance of a novel UCS, rather than failure to appreciate previously learned CS–UCS associations. Learning experiments by Hencke (1977) have shown that discrete lesions to the amygdala eliminate the normal frustration effect (of increased running speed in the second half of a double runway experiment after experiencing frustrative nonreward at the end of the first half) but do not impair the partial reinforcement extinction effect (resistance to extinction, which is controlled by secondary frustrative cues). Following Gray's argument that unconditioned frustrative nonreward is functionally equivalent to unconditioned pain, this dissociation of effects in learning paradigms supports Gray's contention that the amygdala mediates responses to *unconditioned* aversive stimuli (fight-or-flight behavior), but not responses to *secondary* aversive stimuli (which are mediated by the behavioral inhibition system).

4.2.3. *Behavioral Inhibition System (BIS) and Comparator for Novelty/Familiarity*

The *BIS*, as a functional system, is activated by novel or fear-related stimuli, and it responds with outputs that inhibit ongoing behavior, increase arousal, and increase attention and information processing. The functioning of the BIS is itself inhibited by drugs such as ethanol and benzodiazapines. A commonplace example of BIS activity might be a driver who hears a siren and sees a highway patrol car in the rear-view mirror. These conditioned signals of punishment may cause the driver to cease accelerating and thinking about the destination; to respond with increased heart rate, perspiration, and respiration; and to devote attention to the patrol car while racking short-term memory for instances of traffic violations. Gray considers the BIS to consist primarily of the septum and the hippocampus, but other limbic structures are also involved. The functional components of the BIS include a neural circuit in the hippocampus with a gating mechanism; direct biasing mechanisms on this circuit gate such as the medial septum and indirect biasing influences such as the locus coeruleus and the raphe nuclei; and a mechanism (the subiculum) that compares relatively direct sensory information with representative information traveling around the three-synapse, gated hippocampal circuit.

4.2.3.1. Structure and Neurochemical Control of Hippocampal Gate Mechanism. The structures of the hippocampal formation that are functionally most important in BIS operation are the entorhinal cortex, the dentate gyrus, the subiculum, and areas CA1 and CA3 of the hippocampus proper. The major input to the hippocampus is the entorhinal cortex, and the major output is to the subiculum. Highly processed, multimodal sensory information enters the BIS through the entorhinal cortex. The information then takes two different routes to the subiculum. One of these is direct from entorhinal cortex to subiculum. The other is a trisynaptic route (the circuit) running from the entorhinal cortex to the granule cells of the dentate gyrus, then along the axons of the granule cells to the pyramidal cells in area CA3 of the hippocampus, then along the Schaffer collaterals to pyramidals in area CA1 of the hippocampus and finally to the subiculum. Between the dentate granule cells and area CA3 of this circuit, there appears to be a *functional gate.* This dentate/CA3 gate is opened wider with presentation of a biologically relevant conditioned stimulus, theoretically by way of noradrenergic fibers traveling in the dorsal bundle from the locus coeruleus. Noradrenergic activity in this system has the effect of *decreasing* spontaneous or resting firing rate of neurons, but *increasing* firing reactivity to a stimulus. In signal theory terms, the signal-to-noise ratio for important or biologically significant stimuli is increased.

The locus coeruleus–dorsal bundle complex contains GABA (gamma amino butyric acid, the principal inhibitory transmitter in the CNS) receptors in the cell bodies and on the hippocampal terminals. It is thought to be a primary site of action of the anxiolytic drugs. Anxiolytics indirectly reduce release of norepinephrine to the hippocampus and affect activity in the gated trisynaptic circuit (and affect noradrenergic "biasing" of the hippocampal theta rhythm; see below).

4.2.3.2. "Theta" and Its Modulation by the Septum. The septum functions as a "pacemaker" for hippocampal processing. The important functional distinctions of the septum are the medial and lateral areas. In addition to its facilitative effects on the dentate-CA3 gate, noradrenergic input from the locus coeruleus affects a pacemaker function situated in the medial septum, probably mediated by cells in the diagonal band of Broca within the medial septum (Wilson, Motter, & Lindsley, 1976). The medial septal area sends cholinergic projections to the hippocampus that control the *hippocampal theta rhythm.*

Most of what we know about theta comes from studies with the laboratory rat. "Theta" refers to synchronous, rhythmic, slow-wave electrical activity that can be recorded from electrodes implanted in the hippocampus. This rhythm consists of peaks of electrical activity with wave durations around 80–160 msec. Thus, the hippocampal theta rhythm is not a single frequency, but a range of frequencies, ranging from 6 to 12 Hz in free-moving rats. Theta itself appears to adjust the *time of passage* of sensory information around the trisynaptic hippocampal circuit. In the absence of theta, the electrical activity in the hippocampus is fast, low in amplitude, and desynchronized.

In the rat, theta above 7 Hz is related to movement, and faster movement tends to be accompanied by faster theta. Theta below 8 Hz is related to immobilization. This immobility theta can be elicited by stimulation of serotonergic activity in the raphe nuclei in the brainstem. Gray has theorized that *these two ranges of theta correspond to operations of the septo-hippocampal system.* More rapid movement theta is seen when the septo-hippocampal system is in a *checking mode,* monitoring the fit between sensory and predictive information (the subiculum performs this comparator function; see below). Slower immobility theta is seen when the system is in a *control mode.* This occurs when the BIS is activated to take control of behavior, and the animal engages in more intensive information processing and problem solving. The lesser frequencies of this immobility theta reduce the speed of circuit transmission in the hippocampal and Papez loops, permitting a greater load of information processing.

In addition to its permissive effects on the dentate/CA3 gate, noradrenergic input to the septo-hippocampal system seems to bias the hippocampal theta rhythm toward a frequency of 7.7 Hz in rats. This bias effect means that less energy is required for theta at 7.7 Hz than at other frequencies. Gray considers 7.7 Hz to be *the fastest speed of information processing that the septo-hippocampal system can permit while still remaining in the control mode.*

When animals are implanted with chronic septal electrodes, electrical pulses of one-half millisecond duration can be delivered and will result in recordable theta in the hippocampus. Different frequencies of hippocampal theta have been found to require different thresholds of this driving current. In free-moving male rats, the current needed to drive theta is lowest when theta is 7.7 Hz (interval between pulses = 130 msec). Theta frequencies deviating from 7.7 Hz (in both directions) require more current, and frequencies more distant from 7.7 Hz require substantially more current (the bias is toward 7.7). This minimal threshold value is changed when barbituates, benzodiazepines, or ethanol is administered, and 7.7 Hz theta becomes no longer the frequency requiring the least amplitude to be driven. Rats that are low in fearful behavior, including female and experimental strains bred to be nonfearful, do not show the 7.7 Hz minimum in theta-driving. (It should be pointed out that females show the least fear of the two rodent sexes on behavioral measures of fear, in contrast to humans.) Castration of normal male rats eliminates the 7.7 minimum, and injection of testosterone restores it (Drewett, Gray, James, McNaughton, Valero, & Dudderidge, 1977). Circulating testosterone does not appear to be the cause of the 7.7 minimum, but testosterone receptors in the locus coeruleus may be sensitive to testosterone variation and may modulate norepinephrine output accordingly. The two important points here are that there are *strain, gender, and individual differences in the 7.7 theta bias,* and that *anxiolytic substances* (alcohol, barbituates, benzodiazapines) *reduce this bias.*

4.2.3.3. Serotonergic Effects on the BIS. Anchel and Lindsley (1972) described two pathways in the cat brain (extending from the brainstem and midbrain through the hypothalamus and septum to the hippocampus) that when stimulated, produced different effects on hippocampal activity. They used these to stimulate different sections of the hippocampus and they found that stimulation of the medial hypothalmus produced theta, while stimulation of the lateral hypothalmus (which is continuous with the medial forebrain bundle; see below) produced desynchronized fast activity. Later studies have shown that stimulation to the locus coeruleus, the nucleus reticularis pontis oralis, the ventrolateral periaqueductal gray, or either the central superior nucleus or the nucleus linearis intermedius (LIR) of the raphe results in theta rhythm in the hippocampus, although the central superior raphe appears to affect hippocampal activity differently and may in some circumstances increase frequency and desynchronize rhythm (Wilson, Hirasuna, & Lindsley, 1988). Stimulation of these sites disrupts ongoing operant behavior, with the locus coeruleus being least disruptive and the raphe most disruptive. LIR stimulation produces complete motor freezing and unresponsiveness to sensory stimulation except pain for up to several seconds. Behavioral responses to stimulation of the other sites include scanning and orienting, although the central superior raphe also produces brief arrest of behavior or fixed gaze, often accompanied by high-amplitude, low-frequency (3–4 Hz) theta.

The neurotransmitter involved in the raphe nuclei excitation of the BIS and the amygdala is serotonin. Serotonergic fibers arise from the dorsal and, more importantly, the median raphe nuclei and innervate the BIS extensively but diffusely (similar to the characteristics of noradrenergic innervation). Like those of norepinephrine, serotonin's effects on the BIS are antagonized by anxiolytics. For example, electrical stimulation of the raphe nuclei suppresses operant behavior, and this behavioral suppression can be reversed by injections of benzodiazepines (Stein, Wise, & Berger, 1973).

Although serotonin and norepinephrine both appear to stimulate BIS function and to be antagonized in this process by anxiolytics, there are important differences in the two neurotransmitter system effects, especially regarding the output of the BIS. Ascending noradrenergic fibers are more involved in increasing general arousal and attention (the "biasing" effects), whereas ascending serotonergic fibers enhance BIS inhibition of motor behavior. Experimental destruction of serotonergic afferents to the hippocampus has been shown to produce motor disinhibition proportional to the loss of serotonin in the hippocampus.

4.2.3.4. "Comparator" Role of the Subiculum. As described above, the subiculum is the primary output of the hippocampal formation. The subiculum is in a nodal position between the trisynaptic hippocampal circuit and the circuit of Papez. A loop in Papez's circuit branches from the subiculum to the anteroventral thalamus and to the mammillary bodies, which in turn also project to the anteroventral thalamus. The anteroventral thalamus then sends projections back to the subiculum as well as to the cingulate gyrus. The cingulate gyrus projects back to the subiculum as well as back to the entorhinal cortex, and it also provides output to motor systems. The hippocampal theta rhythm generated by the medial septal area also appears to adjust the passage time around the Papez loop. The Papez loop has access to information (perhaps stored in the temporal neocortex) involving stimulus–stimulus regularities via the anteroventral thalamus and involving both response–response regularities and current motor plans via the cingulate cortex (which receive motor plan information from the prefrontal cortex).

The subiculum has been purported by Gray to operate as a prediction generator and *comparator*. The direct signal of sensory information from the entorhinal cortex to the subiculum is acted upon only if accompanied by an enabling signal from the ungated trisynaptic hippocampal circuit. As described previously, this gate is widened by noradrenergic input from the locus coeruleus, so that the functioning of the circuit is biased toward biologically significant stimuli. The subiculum compares the direct sensory information against predictions returning from the Papez loop, with its memory and motor plan access. A mismatch between the direct and circuitous sensory signals may be detected by the subiculum if a stimulus is high in novelty or is a conditioned signal for punishment.

It can be seen from this discussion that a combination of low serotonin or low raphe activity, and the ingestion of ethanol or benzodiazepines, may be particularly unfavorable to the operation of the BIS. This combination may be especially predisposing to unreflective acting out of behavioral impulses. Thus, the theory would predict a significant drinking (ethanol ingestion) by personality (low anxiety, high impulsivity) interaction on impulsive, disinhibited behavior.

It is not necessary to understand fully the inner workings of the BIS in order to understand its role in determining behavior. If the BIS is considered as a black box, the inputs and outputs permit a simplified but well-summarized model of its operation. Typically, the BIS operates in "checking" mode, monitoring incoming sensory information for excessive novelty or predictiveness of punishment. Innate fear stimuli, novel stimuli, and conditioned stimuli signaling either punishment or frustrative nonreward can activate the BIS and cause it to shift to "control" mode. The output results are behavioral inhibition (in the extreme, "freezing"), increased general arousal, and increased attention to the stimuli. These effects are ameliorated by barbituates, benzodiazepines, ethanol, and other antianxiety drugs. Ascending noradrenergic pathways are more critical for increasing the arousal and attentional functions of the BIS, whereas serotonergic pathways are more critical for motor inhibition and restraint of impulsive responding.

4.2.4. *Further Relevance of Serotonergic Systems*

Because of the growing evidence that serotonin is strongly linked to personality dimensions and to psychopathological symptoms such as impulsivity and anxiety, some digressive discussion of this neurotransmitter is included here.

4.2.4.1. Distribution of Serotonin. Serotonin appears to exert an inhibitory action on a diversity of targets. Destruction of serotonin neurons, inhibition of serotonin synthesis, or blockade of serotonin receptors in experimental animals reliably results in hypersensitivity to virtually all environmental stimuli and hyperactivity in virtually all situations (Carpenter & Sutin, 1983). The midbrain raphe serotonergic neurons share with the locus coeruleus noradrenergic neurons the characteristic of extensive distribution of projections throughout the CNS. Deprivation of serotonin produces total insomnia, although the raphe activity decreases with sleep onset and stops during REM (Carpenter & Sutin, 1983). The suprachiasmatic nuclei and the dorsal raphe control the circadian organization of REM sleep, slow wave sleep, and cortisol secretion through serotonergic mechanisms (Mouret, 1982). Serotonin has been shown to stimulate the hypothalamic–pituitary axis in a number of species, including humans, as well as to increase beta-endorphin release (Muller & Nistico, 1989). In normal humans, both serotonergic precursors and receptor agonists elevate serum cortisol, and the serotonin and cortisol responses to stress appear to covary (Muller & Nistico, 1989).

Earlier the serotonergic input from the raphe nuclei to the BIS was described. This input is part of a group of fibers from dorsal and medial raphe nuclear groups to midbrain and forebrain structures. The raphe projections also affect several other structures, including the substantia nigra. This effect is borne by a tract which arises from (a) the dorsal and dorsal tegmental raphe nuclei and (b) the superior central nucleus (another raphe nucleus, also called the median raphe nucleus), passes through the ventral tegmental area and medial fields of Forel, and enters the medial forebrain bundle at the lateral hypothalamus. The most rostral terminals of these projections are in the frontal lobes, whereas the earliest projections emerge medially to the hypothalamus and laterally through the internal capsule to the corpus striatum (the caudate and the putamen) and the amygdaloid nuclear complex. Between these branchings, serotonin fibers in the medial forebrain bundle project into the stria medullaris to the thalamus, the stria terminalis to the amygdala, the fornix to the hippocampus, and the medial olfactory stria to the olfactory bulb. The projections to the septo-hippocampal system are associated with the superior central nucleus, whereas the striatal projections are associated with the dorsal group. Some fibers from the dorsal raphe nuclear group innervate the substantia nigra, which runs the length of the midbrain into the caudal diencephalon and is the largest nuclear group in the midbrain. The substantia nigra is the source of a major dopaminergic tract that projects to the corpus striatum. The serotonergic projections are inhibitory on single neurons in the substantia nigra, particularly those in the pars compacta, which is the source of the nigrostriatal pathway (Carpenter & Sutin, 1983). The dopaminergic nigrostriatal pathway in turn is inhibitory on the corpus striatum and the globus pallidus.

The dorsal raphe nucleus also projects to the locus coeruleus. Segal (1979) has shown that the increased firing in locus coeruleus neurons in response to noxious stimuli can be blocked by electrical stimulation of the dorsal raphe or by direct injection of serotonin into the locus coeruleus. The inhibition of the locus coeruleus by the raphe is blocked by a variety of pharmacological disruptions of serotonin mechanisms. This mechanism, among others, may mediate variations in behavioral responsivity to punishment. Serotonin activity in the raphe, in turn, is elevated by increased noradrenergic activity and decreased by GABA. The anxiolytic properties of benzodiazepines have been ascribed to their facilitative effects on GABA hyperpolarization of neuron membranes (Paul, Marangos, & Skolnick, 1981). Stein and associates have implicated serotonin in the benzodiazepine inhibition of anxiety (Stein, Belluzi, & Wise, 1977; Stein, Wise, & Berger, 1973).

4.2.4.2. Serotonergic Involvement in Pain and Irritability. Serotonin is one of three modes of inhibition (the others being GABA and opioids) in the central gray of the midbrain, that area described above as playing a major role in the experience of pain and in activating fight-or-flight behavior. While drugs that antagonize serotonergic action reduce motor suppression by the BIS, they increase the aversive properties of stimulation in the fight/flight system. Direct stimulation of the nucleus raphe magnus inhibits the activity of spinal tracts associated with nociceptive sensory input, and the terminals of these projections closely correspond to opiate-binding sites (Carpenter & Sutin, 1983).

These relationships suggest that an individual with low central serotonergic activity might exhibit excess motor behavior and impulsiveness, and also be irritable and prone to aggressive or otherwise unreflective behavior upon encountering primary frustration or punishment. An impressive number of studies have found low levels of 5-hydroxyindoleacetic acid (5-HIAA), the principal metabolite of serotonin, in the cerebrospinal fluid (CSF) of persons with disinhibited behaviors such as suicide attempters and completers, borderline personalities, arsonists, murderers, and other violent offenders (e.g., Brown, Ebert, Goyer, Jimerson, Klein, Bunney, & Goodwin, 1983; Lidberg, Asberg, & Sundquist-Stensman, 1984; Linnoila, Virkhunen, Scheinin, Nuutila, Rimon, & Goodwin, 1983; Roy, DeJong, & Linnoila, 1989a; Virkhunen, DeJong, Bartko, Goodwin, & Linnoila, 1989; Virkhunen, DeJong, Bartko, & Linnoila, 1989).

A problem with drawing conclusions about serotonin function in the brain from CSF measures is that most of the 5-HIAA in the CSF comes from the spinal cord rather than the brain. But other indices of brain serotonin activity also have been studied. One such index is the degree of imipramine binding in neural tissue or blood platelets. Imipramine binding sites are located next to serotonin reuptake sites on presynaptic serotonergic nerve terminals (Stoff, Pollock, Vitiello, Behar, & Bridger, 1987). These sites bind exogenously administered tritiated imipramine and theoretically bind an endogenous ligand involved in regulation of serotonin reuptake. Reduced numbers of imipramine-binding sites relative to controls have been found in the prefrontal cortex of suicide completers (Perry, Marshall, Blessed, Tomlinson, & Perry, 1983; Stanley, Virgilio, & Gershon, 1982). In a sample of prepubertal children with comorbid DSM-III Conduct Disorder and Attention Deficit Disorder, the imipramine-binding sites on blood platelets in the psychiatric group were reduced by 29% relative to controls (Stoff *et al.*, 1987). The imipramine-binding site measure inversely correlated significantly with the Externalizing ($r = -0.42$) and Aggressive ($r = -0.48$) factors of the Child Behavior Checklist—Parent Version (Achenbach & Edelbrock, 1983).

A means of investigating the functional integrity of the brain's serotonin system is to measure the prolactin response to fenfluramine hydrochloride. Serotonergic fibers from the dorsal raphe stimulate the hypothalamus to release prolactin releasing factors, and in response, acidphil cells in the anterior pituitary release prolactin. (Fenfluramine has both direct and indirect serotonergic agonistic properties. The direct postsynaptic action is a result of its active metabolite, norfenfluramine, occupying receptor sites and facilitating membrane depolarization. Presynaptically, fenfluramine both stimulates the release of serotonin from storage vessicles and inhibits reuptake, thereby extending the duration of activity in the synapse.) A recent study compared the raphe–hypothalamic–pituitary axis response to fenfluramine among normal controls, depressives, and borderline personalities (Coccaro, Siever, Klar, Maurer, Cochrane, Cooper, Mohs, & Davis, 1989). Blunted prolactin response was associated with history of suicide attempt, and it distinguished both patient groups from controls. Among the borderline patients, peak prolactin response was significantly and inversely correlated with clinician ratings of aggression (Brown–Goodwin Aggression scale, $r = -.57$) and with self-report of aggression (Buss–Durkee Hostility Inventory Motor Aggression scale, $r = -.52$) and of impulsiveness (Barratt Impulsiveness scale, Total Impulsiveness, $r = -.48$; Barratt Motor Impulsivity subscale, $r = -.54$). No significant correlations were obtained with the Spielberger State-Trait Anxiety Inventory, the Zuckerman Sensation-Seeking Inventory, or any scales from the Minnesota Multiphasic Personality Inventory, suggesting a specificity of association for aggression and impulsivity. Two of the subscales of Buss–Durkee Motor Aggression were even more specifically related to prolactin response. These were the subscales tapping Assault ($r = -.65$) and Irritability ($r = -.68$). A stepwise regression found that these two subscales together accounted for 59% of the variance in prolactin response in the borderline group (combined $r = -.77$).

These findings are consistent with the hypothesis that reduced serotonergic activity in the CNS produces two important biobehavioral effects: (a) impairment of the BIS with consequent behavioral disinhibition, and (b) lessened inhibition of central gray activity, causing a heightened response to pain and an overly reactive fight-or-flight system, and therefore behavioral irritability or explosiveness. The results of Coccaro *et al.* (1989) support the notion that lowered CNS serotonergic activity impairs the BIS and disinhibits the fight-or-flight system, with specific behavioral effects of irritability, impulsivity, and especially impulsive aggression, in a personality disorder characterized by unpredictable behavior.

Deficiencies in serotonin activity would also have implications for differential reactions to warnings (conditioned cues) versus actual punishment and frustration in Gray's theory. As previously outlined, conditioned cues of punishment or frustration create arousal and inhibition by activating the BIS, whereas primary punishment and frustration create arousal by activating the fight-or-flight system. The independence of the neural systems subserving these two classes of phenomena has been demonstrated in a variety of experiments cited by Gray (1987). For example, anxiolytics have different effects on two intermittent reinforcement paradigms from double runway operant experiments (Amsel, 1962). The *frustration effect* applies to the increase of speed in the second half of a double runway after encountering an empty first goalbox that had been previously associated with reward. The explanation is that primary frustration has activated the fight-or-flight system and increased arousal in the second half of the runway. The *partial reinforcement acquisition effect* applies to the rapid increase in running speed of rats trained under partial reinforcement schedules, that is, the observation in early trials of acquisition that partially reinforced rats run faster than continuously reinforced rats. In a double runway paradigm with partial reinforcement in the first goalbox, rats also run faster in the first leg of the runway owing to conditioned frustration activation of the BIS and increased arousal. Sodium amobarbital (Gray, 1969) and ethanol (Nelson & Wollen, 1965), which impair the BIS more than the fight/flight system, abolish the partial reinforcement acquisition effect but not the frustration effect. This dissociation of conditioned vs. primary frustration and punishment provides an explanation for the observation that many antisocial individuals do not respond to warnings of punishment or frustration, but respond violently to actual punishment or frustration. An individual with low central serotonin activity, and therefore an impaired BIS and possibly an overreactive fight/flight system, would hypothetically show both (a) poor response to warnings of frustration and punishment, but (b) aggressive outbursts in response to frustration or punishment. This is in fact what is often seen in some conduct–disordered children.

Blood levels of serotonin in juvenile offenders with CD have been reported to be higher than depressed or anxious controls without CD (Pliszka, Rogeness, Renner, Sherman, & Broussard, 1988), but this apparent paradox may be explained by the observation that there appears to be an inverse relation between whole blood serotonin and central serotonin activity. (Speculatively, this might occur with reductions in serotonin receptor number or sensitivity—the inverse of the serotonin hypersensitivity hypothesis in anxiety; see later discussion.)

4.2.4.4. Pharmacological Treatment of Serotonergically Mediated Internalizing Symptoms. Alterations in serotonin activity have been proposed as mechanisms for anxiety and depressive disorders. Extensive research into behavioral suppression in animals has lead to a model of depression based on postsynaptic serotonergic receptor hypersensitivity in the CNS, thought to account for a subgroup of unipolar depressives (Aprison & Hingtgen, 1986). A similar mechanism has been proposed for anxiety and obsessive–compulsive disorders, supported by a growing number of treatment studies.

The tricyclic antidepressants vary in their effects on the different monoamine systems. Imipramine and amitryptyline are more potent inhibitors of serotonin uptake than their desmethyl derivatives, desipramine and nortriptyline, and the greatest efficacy in blocking uptake belongs to chlomipramine (3-chloroimipramine) (Muller & Nistico,

1989). Studies have consistently shown chlomipramine to be effective in treating obsessive–compulsive disorder (OCD), in contrast to lesser or no efficacy for other tricyclics (Kahn *et al.*, 1988). A correlate of chlomipramine clinical efficacy may be its reduction of 5-HIAA in the CSF (Thoren, Asberg, Bertilsson, & Traskman, 1980). Both chlomipramine and serotonin agonists often initially exacerbate symptoms of panic disorder (PD), but ameliorate symptoms with continued administration (Kahn *et al.*, 1988) and down-regulation of 5-HT2 ligand binding (see later discussion of receptor subtypes). Buspirone, which has both agonistic and antagonistic effects on the 5-HT1a receptor and decreases raphe firing, is effective in generalized anxiety disorder, as is ritanserin, a selective 5-HT2 antagonist (Kahn *et al.*, 1988). The efficacy of serotonin agonists in OCD and PD is consistent with the hypothesis of postsynaptic serotonergic receptor hypersensitivity or proliferation, and subsequent down-regulation with treatment. This would account for the biphasic treatment effects seen in PD. Receptor hypersensitivity could also account for the finding of low CSF 5-HIAA in depressed patients with prominent anxiety. In this case, changes in receptor sensitivity or number might result in less turnover and lower amounts of the metabolite (Kahn *et al.*, 1988).

4.2.4.3. Specificity of Serotonin Receptor Subtypes. Increased interest is being devoted to the role of different types of serotonergic receptors in the pathophysiology of psychiatric disorders. The major distinction is between 5-HT1 and 5-HT2 receptors. The latter are found in high concentrations in the hippocampus and frontal cortex and display a high affinity for classical serotonin antagonists and neuroleptics. In humans, three subtypes of 5-HT1 receptors are found. The hippocampus and frontal cortex also host 5-HT1a receptors, which appear to be involved in regulating the activity of the raphe nuclei. The 5-HT1c receptor is found in choroid plexus and cortex. The 5-HT1d receptor, which appears to be the predominant variety of 5-HT1 receptor, displays a high affinity for tryptamines, ergots, and yohimbine (Kahn, van Praag, Wetzler, Anis, & Barr, 1988). The role of the various receptor types in normal and abnormal neural processes is not well understood, although progress is being made. For example, Lindgren and Kantak (1987) found a dose-dependent decrease in aggressive behavior in mice using 5-methoxytryptamine (5-MT), a selective 5-HT1 receptor agonist, and for quipazine, which preferentially (but less strongly so than 5-MT) binds to 5-HT1 sites. Mianserin, a 5-HT2 antagonist, also decreased aggression in a dose-dependent manner. This suggests that blockade of the 5-HT2 site and stimulation of the 5-HT1 site both inhibit aggressive behavior. The various types of aggression—predatory, defensive, and offensive—respond in the same direction to most manipulations of serotonergic activity (Lindgren & Kantak, 1987).

Recently, a serotonin receptor imbalance model has been proposed to account for serotonin's role in human internalizing disorders (Deakin, 1988). Because anxiety and depressive symptoms often co-occur in humans, it has been difficult to reconcile the theory that anxiety is related to excessive serotonin activity with the theory that some forms of depression are related to insufficient serotonin activity. The imbalance model proposes that affective disturbance results from excessive 5-HT2 and 5-HT1c activity relative to 5-HT1a and 5-HT1d. The 5-HT2 receptor family is believed to mediate anxiety, and deficient 5-HT1a function is believed to mediate depressive symptoms. Inappropriate anxiety is conceived to result from serotonergic activation of the dorsal raphe by conditioned fear stimuli. The dorsal raphe then projects to 5-HT2 receptors in the amygdala and other forebrain areas. The model received experimental support in a study that compared the effects of ritanserin, a selective 5-HT2/5-HT1c antagonist, to placebo on aversive classical conditioning and extinction in normal human adults (Hensman, Guimarães, Wang, & Deakin, 1991). There was no difference between ritanserin and placebo groups on habituation of skin conductance response (SCR) to tone signals or on the SCR to a single trial in which the tone was paired with aversive white noise. On subsequent trials of tone only, SCR in the ritanserin group replicated the habituation curve, whereas SCR in the nonritanserin group showed much less decline (evidence of a conditioned emotional response).

4.2.5. Reward Mechanism for Approach Behavior

A classic line of research into reward mechanisms was initiated by Olds and Milner (1954). The paradigm they pioneered involved studying neural self-stimulation by providing animals access to a Skinner bar which delivered electric current to electrodes chronically implanted in specific brain regions. This paradigm permitted the mapping of brain regions that would support high rates of bar pressing, and it permitted study of how drugs affected the rate of bar pressing. Electrodes implanted in the hypothalamus and all along the medial forebrain bundle into the limbic and olfactory forebrain were found to support self-stimulation. As described at the beginning of this chapter, the medial forebrain bundle contains noradrenergic, dopaminergic, and serotonergic pathways. One of the two somewhat intertwined dopamine pathways here is the nigrostriatal pathway, running from the substantia nigra to the basal ganglia. This pathway is involved in motor control, partially by inhibitory adjustment of the action of the globus pallidus. When unopposed, the globus pallidus excites an ascending pathway through the ventral anterior and ventral lateral nuclei of the thalamus and on to motor cortex, producing a tremor at rest. Disruption or blockade of the dopamine pathways appears to be part of the pathogenetic mechanism of Parkinson's disease and of the extrapyramidal side effects associated with phenothiazines (Pincus & Tucker, 1985).

The other dopamine tract in the medial forebrain bundle is the mesolimbic pathway. This arises from cell groups in the ventral tegmental area of the brainstem and projects to the nucleus accumbens, olfactory tubercule, lateral septal area, and frontal cortex. Gray considers this route to be responsible for conveying information concerning the availability of reward. Striatal neurons are then responsible for the initiation of appropriate motor approach. The ascending dopaminergic fibers, along with the targeted dorsal and ventral striatum, are considered to constitute the *reward mechanism for approach behavior.*

Stein (1978) challenged the aspect of Gray's theory that attributes reward processes largely to dopamine systems and that considers norepinephrine to be concerned for the most part with alarm and with the arousal and attentional aspects of the BIS. Drawing on a large body of research in self-stimulation and drug self-administration, Stein (1978) argued that reward processes subserved by dopaminergic pathways are complemented by roles of the three ascending noradrenergic systems in reward: the dorsal pathway from the locus coeruleus to the cortex, cerebellum, hippocampus, and thalamus; the ventral pathway from the brainstem cell groups to the hypothalamus and ventral limbic system; and the periventricular pathway from the central gray to the medial thalamus and hypothalamus. Pharmaceutical inhibitors of DBH (the enzyme that converts dopamine to norepinephrine) maintain brain levels of dopamine while permitting norepinephrine to be exhausted. DBH inhibitors stop self-stimulation and eliminate increase in rate of self-stimulation normally produced by amphetamine; intraventricular norepinephrine reverses these effects (Wise & Stein, 1969; Wise, Belluzi, & Stein, 1977). As disruption of either the dopamine or norepinephrine systems results in termination of self-stimulation, Stein has concluded (1983) that the two catecholamines work jointly in mediating operant behavior. Dopamine is thought to be more related to the incentive aspects of activating approach behavior, whereas norepinephrine is considered to be related to reinforcement valence and to guide response selection.

Because animals will work for and self-administer drugs that have opposite effects on arousal, two types of reward may be distinguished (Belluzi & Stein, 1977). The neurochemical substrates of incentive reward, typified by cocaine or amphetamine ingestion and arousal increases, are the catecholamines. The substrate of satisfaction reward, typified by morphine ingestion and arousal decrease, is hypothesized to be enkephalin or a related opioid peptide.

4.2.6. *Reciprocal Inhibition between BIS and Reward Systems*

The reward system and the BIS interact at several points. Terminals of the mesolimbic dopaminergic pathway in the lateral septal area inhibit the behavioral effects of the cholinergic signal from the medial septum to the hippocampus (Galey, Durkin, Sitakis, Kempf, & Jaffard, 1985). Projections from the subiculum to the cingulate cortex may inhibit motor plans, and projections from the lateral septal area to the hypothalamus may inhibit fixed action patterns of consummatory behavior (Albert & Chew, 1980). A large projection from the subiculum to the nucleus accumbens and other regions of the ventral striatum may be the mechanism by which the BIS inhibits rewarded instrumental behavior.

4.2.7. *Decision Mechanism*

The final common pathways for reward approach (the medial forebrain bundle) and for pain–fight/flight (the dorsal longitudinal bundle of Schutz, also termed the periventricular system of fibers) connect to the midline system of hypothalamic nuclei and descend into the midbrain. These structures receive inputs from the amygdala, the septohippocampal system, and the lateral hypothalamus, thus providing the inhibitory links necessary for final determinations of unconditioned consummatory and fight/flight behavior and responses to conditioned aversive stimuli. Whereas stimulation of the medial forebrain bundle is positively reinforcing, and stimulation of the periventricular fibers is punishing, stimulation of the midline hypothalamic nuclei yields mixed approach and escape/avoidance behaviors. One of the midline hypothalamic nuclei, the ventromedial nucleus, appears to specifically mediate the decision selection between defensive attack and escape, in response to input from the amygdala.

4.3. *Simplified Modular Framework for Gray's Theory*

Gray's theory can be greatly simplified by referring to three biological subsystems that influence behavior: the BIS (behavioral inhibition system), the BAS (behavioral activation system), and the fight-or-flight system. Table 1 summarizes the types of stimuli, behavioral responses, learning functions, and personality dimensions associated with each of these modules of Gray's conceptual nervous system.

TABLE 1
Stimuli and Responses Associated with BAS, BIS, and Fight-or-Flight System

	BAS	BIS	Fight/flight
Activated by	CS for reward, CS for relief or non-punishment	CS for punishment, CS for nonreward, novel stimuli, innate fear stimuli	UCS
Behavioral functions	Approach, predatory aggression	Inhibition or "freezing"	Defensive aggression, withdrawal
Learning functions	Escape learning, active avoidance	Passive avoidance, extinction	
Personality dimensions	Impulsivity	Anxiety	Unclear; aspects of *P*?

The BIS regards conditioned signals of nonreward as functionally equivalent to conditioned signals of punishment. Primary nonreward (frustration in the face of expected reward) activates the fight-or-flight system, resulting in an "extinction burst" or initial increase in vigor of responding when reward is no longer available. As trials continue, activation of the BIS by secondary nonreward (conditioned signals of frustration) cause inhibition of responding, resulting in extinction. To the BAS, conditioned signals of reward are functionally equivalent to those of escape or avoidance, all of which cause the BAS to activate a motor response.

4.4. *Extension of Gray's Theory by Fowles to Psychophysiological Measures*

Fowles (1980) applied Gray's theory to psychophysiological measures of heart rate (HR) and electrodermal activity (EDA). After a review of studies in which HR was found to increase in incentive situations (for both reward and active avoidance) beyond the rate accounted for by nonoperant somatic activity, Fowles concluded that HR in these situations reflected the activity of the central reward system in Gray's theory—the Behavioral Activation System (BAS). BAS excitation of HR has two related aspects: the response to incentives and the activation of overt behavioral responses or cardiac–somatic coupling. Experimentally, these can be somewhat dissociated. The correspondence between increase in HR and increase in incentive or drive in several studies led Fowles to the conclusion that HR is a more accurate index of BAS activity than is somatic activity.

Fowles (1980) stated that EDA is a measure of BIS activation, although he acknowledged that EDA also responds nonspecifically to a variety of stimuli, some of which may not activate the BIS. Conditions of threat or danger increase the frequency of nonspecific fluctuation (electrodermal responses, EDR, that occur "spontaneously" with no discernible trigger). Conditioned aversive stimuli reliably elicit EDRs, and the magnitude of EDRs is generally proportional to the "emotionality" or "attention-getting" characteristics of the stimuli (these characteristics being defined *a priori* without reference to the EDR). Conditioned aversive stimuli presented on an operant schedule (the conditioned emotional response paradigm) suppresses both lever pressing and nonrewarded general activity, decreases HR, and increases skin conductance and skin potential (Roberts, 1974). Skin conductance or electrodermal level, according to Fowles, also increases to stimuli that activate the BIS. However, measurement of the skin conductance response to discrete stimuli is contaminated by skin hydration from sweat and electrolyte and reaches a ceiling under conditions of moderate to high threat.

Thus Fowles (1980) states that under differing incentive conditions, HR and EDA can show "directional fractionation," or change in opposite directions, predictable on the basis of hypotheses of differential activation of the BIS or BAS. A nonincentive activation of the BIS by novel stimuli would elicit HR slowing and EDA increase, which are in fact the empirical concomitants of the classical orienting response.

Fowles (1980) proposed that the clinical features and psychophysiological studies of psychopaths suggest that this disorder is largely the manifestation of an underactive BIS, although an overactive BAS and other undetermined factors may also play a role. Hare (1978) summarized the psychophysiological results of aversive conditioning studies with psychopaths. Compared with controls, psychopaths condition more poorly and show lesser EDA in anticipation of aversive stimuli. In contrast to normals, who show no change or deceleration of HR in anticipation of aversive stimuli, psychopaths show cardiac acceleration, perhaps reflecting a coping response. Fowles (1980) interpreted this difference as a tendency for BAS preparation for active avoidance, which overshadows a deficient BIS tendency toward passive acceptance, when psychopaths are faced with punishment. Harpur and Hare (1990) have recently discussed the cognitive aspects of Newman's model (see section 6) in interpreting the psychopathic response of cardiac acceleration.

According to this interpretation, cardiac acceleration is part of an active coping response that includes changes in attention that help "tune out" signals of aversive stimuli. The reduced EDA in anticipation of aversive stimuli is therefore, at least in part, an effect of the successful active coping response. An attentional bias against negative cues would have important implications for the clinical features of "impeturbability," shallow affect, and lack of guilt and remorse that are often reported in psychopathy (Cleckley, 1976).

5. *Application of Gray's Theory to Children and Adolescents by Quay and Colleagues*

Some 25 years ago, Quay proposed that the psychobiological trait underlying psychopathy was low cortical arousal, which led to excessive stimulation seeking. Quay has recently specified that the stimulation preferred by psychopaths is that which energizes the BAS (Quay, 1990). In contrast to Fowles's (1980) assertion that the predominant problem in psychopathy was an underactive BIS, Quay (1988b) hypothesized that an overactive reward system (that is, the BAS) characterizes Undersocialized Conduct Disorder (UCD), whereas an underactive BIS is the pathogenetic process in Attention-Deficit Disorder with Hyperactivity (ADD-H). Children high on the trait of anxiety-withdrawal were proposed to have an overactive BIS. Quay (1987) recommended that behavioral treatment be based on cognizance of alterations in these systems and resulting deficits in passive avoidance learning by rewarding nonprohibited behavior instead of punishing prohibited behavior.

5.1. *Quay's Predictions*

The hypothesis that ADD-H is related to an underactive BIS generates several corollaries. If, as Quay (1988a) suggested, children with ADD-H are indeed characterized by relative impairment of the BIS, they should show:

1. Greater resistance to extinction (because conditioned signals of nonreward would not readily activate the BIS into extinguishing responding).
2. Higher rates of responding under fixed interval, fixed ratio, and differential reinforcement of low rates of responding (DRL) schedules (because the signals of temporary nonreinforcement inherent in those reinforcement schedules would not readily engage BIS inhibition).

3. A less perseverative partial reinforcement extinction effect, and less behavioral contrast and peak shift in response to frustration.

Quay (1988a) also made predictions concerning HR and galvanic skin response under incentive conditions, derived from Fowles's (1980, 1983) work extending Gray's theory to psychophysiological variables.

Quay's hypotheses have implications for children who have comorbid psychiatric disorders. First, children with CD and ADD-H, having an underactive BIS and an overactive BAS should be especially prone to disinhibition in the face of signals of both possible punishment and possible reward. This hypothesized double bias toward disinhibition is consistent with the poorer functioning and outcome of children who have both disorders (cf. Hinshaw, 1987). Second, children with CD and an anxiety disorder, having overactivity of both the BAS and the BIS, may have their BAS impulsivity mitigated by the restraint of the BIS. This depiction is supported by a recent study by Walker, Lahey, Russo, Frick, Christ, McBurnett, Loeber, Stouthamer-Loeber, and Green (1991). In that study, children with CD and an anxiety disorder were nominated by classmates less often for "fights most" and "meanest," had fewer police contacts and school suspensions, and scored lower on the Boredom Susceptibility subscale of the child SSS (Russo *et al.*, 1991) than children with CD but without an anxiety disorder. Lastly, Quay's hypotheses are more difficult to apply in the case of comorbid ADD-H and anxiety. This combination of disorders purportedly involves both underactivity and overactivity of the BIS. This means that either (a) children with ADD-H cannot possibly have an anxiety disorder; (b) the BIS of children diagnosed with anxiety and ADD-H is poorly regulated, vacillating between underactivity and overreactivity; (c) some *component* of the BIS is overactive, whereas another component is underactive; or (d) when anxiety is present, the disorder diagnosed as comorbid ADD-H is an atypical expression of these symptoms, partially secondary to the arousal associated with anxiety.

5.2. *Empirical Studies*

In at least two studies, Quay and associates have used a test of response perseveration and a test of delayed responding (i.e., differential reinforcement of low-rate responding, DRL) to evaluate disinhibition in child behavior disorders. In the first of these, Shapiro, Quay, Hogan, and Schwartz (1989) had teachers of seriously emotionally disturbed (SED) children and adolescents rate their students' behavior on the Revised Behavior Problem Checklist (RBPC, Quay & Peterson, 1987; Lahey & Piacentini, 1985). Two groups were formed: children with extreme ratings on the CD factor of the RPBC and children with relatively low ratings of CD (not-CD, NCD). (These groups also differed, to a lesser extent, on the Attention Problems–Immaturity factor, AP, of the RBPC, reflecting the well-established association of attention problems and aggression/conduct problems in children.) The groups were administered a card-playing task originated by Siegal (1978) and adapted by Newman, Patterson, and Kosson (1987), along with a DRL task (McClure & Gordon, 1984). Trials on the card-playing task were rewarded by tokens or punished by loss of reinforcement according to a preprogrammed sequence in which early trials were successful 90% of the time. Probability of success decreased as the task progressed, until it reached 0% near the end of the task. Subjects were permitted to quit at any time and keep their winnings. The dependent measures of the card-playing task were (a) the number of cards a subject chose to play and (b) the total amount of money or reinforcement earned. Shapiro *et al.*'s (1989) CD group performed much worse on the card-playing task, and this difference was significant despite statistical adjustment for the group difference in AP. Thus the card-playing task results strongly supported the notion that SED children with CD, compared to SED children without CD, are overly sensitive to reward and fail to inhibit responding in mixed incentive situations. On the DRL task, the CD group made more total responses and fewer correct responses than the NCD group, but these differences were not statistically significant. The correct responses were divided by the total responses to produce an efficiency ratio (ER). The CD group had a marginally lower ER than the NCD group across the entire DRL task ($p = .06$) and a significantly lower ER than the NCD group in the fourth and final block of DRL trials. These mixed results on the DRL task weakly supported the hypothesis that this paradigm is more difficult for CD children. Shapiro *et al.* (1989) assumed that these (the card-playing task and the DRL task) would tap similar processes, but none of the correlations between the card-playing dependent variables (number of cards played, money earned) and the DRL dependent variables (total responses, total correct, total ER, fourth block ER) were significant. Furthermore, according to Gray's theory, performance on a DRL task should depend on the hippocampal enabling circuit controlled by the dentate/CA3 gate and a fully functioning BIS. The dependence on the BIS for DRL performance is substantiated by findings that septal lesions, hippocampal lesions, and anxiolytics all disrupt DRL performance (Gray, 1987). Empirical findings of poorer performance of ADD children on the DRL task (McClure & Gordon, 1984) are more consistent with Quay's (1988a) assignment of BIS impairment and DRL inefficiency to that diagnostic group rather than to CD. Perplexingly, the DRL variables were uncorrelated with the AP dimension in the Shapiro *et al.* (1989) sample, but the card-playing variables were weakly correlated with AP (money earned, $r = -.41$, $p < .08$; cards played, $r = .45$, $p > .05$). Partial correlations of AP (with the CD dimension as the covariate) with the card-playing and DRL measures were not reported but would be helpful in evaluating the relationship between problem behavior dimensions and these experimental tasks.

In a second experiment, Daugherty and Quay (1991) administered the RBPC to public schoolteachers of third- through sixth-grade children. Children who received an extreme rating on one RBPC dimension were assigned to either a CD group (high CD score), and ADD group (high AP score), or an AW group (high AW score). Children rated high on the CD, AP, and Motor Excess (ME) factors formed a CD/ADDH group, and children without any factor elevations formed a normal control (NC) group. These groups were given a computer-presented response perseveration task, consisting of a series of 100 doors that subjects could choose to open. Early in the series, the probability of reward (by token reinforcement) for a single door was 90%; this probability decreased by 10% after each tenth door and reached 0% by the last 10 doors. Opening a losing door was punished by loss of a token. Thus the door-opening task was highly similar to the card-playing task in that the probability of reward declined as the task progressed, and the probability of punishment increased. After completing the door-opening task, children were given a DRL task similar to that used by Shapiro *et al.* (1989). Consistent with Quay's (1988a) hypotheses, the CD and CD/ADDH groups were predicted to be more perseverative for reward on the card-playing task than the NC and AW groups. On the DRL task, the ADD and CD/ADDH groups were predicted to perform less efficiently than the NC and AW groups, as suggested by Quay (1988a), but the CD group was also predicted to perform less efficiently. The AW group was predicted to make fewer responses than the NC group on the DRL task, but another relationship derivable from Quay (1988a)—that AW children should be especially sensitive to the increasing nonreward and punishment posed by the door-opening task and therefore should terminate earlier than the other groups—was not predicted. As predicted, the CD and CD/ADDH groups opened more doors than the NC and AW groups. No differences in DRL total responses or ER emerged among any of the groups. Consistent with Quay's (1988a) hypothesis, the majority of the CD and CD/ADDH subjects (65%) perseverated well beyond the range of door-opening trials that is optimal for total winnings. The majority of AW subjects (78%) were overcautious, and they inhibited responding prior to reaching the optimal range.

6. Disinhibitory Psychopathology Model of Newman and Colleagues

Gorenstein and Newman (1980) laid out a theoretical framework relating behavioral propensities observed in extroversion and disihibitory syndromes including psychopathy, hysteria, hyperactivity, antisocial and impulsive personality, and alcoholism. The theory drew analogies from Meehl's (1962) diathesis-stress model of schizophrenia and built upon Gray's (1970, 1972) animal model of disinhibition stemming from septal–hippocampal dysfunction. Extroversion and the various categories of disinhibitory psychopathology (psychopathy, hysteria, etc.) were proposed to share a common biological diathesis that exhibits heritable variation. The heritable biological propensity was hypothesized to produce differing behavioral expressions according to its interaction with different modifying variables (generally environmental-experiential). The *disinhibitory diathesis* was described as leading to perceptual, motivational, learning, and behavioral similarities to animals given experimental lesions of the septal–hippocampal formation, although septal dysfunction was explicitly regarded as analogous rather than causal in human syndromes. Over the last 10 years, Newman and his colleagues have tested and substantially revised the original theory of disinhibitory personality.

6.1. Empirical Development of Disinhibitory Model

Newman and colleagues have used rather ingenious tasks to tease out individual differences in response to reinforcement. One of these tasks is called Passive-Avoidance with Loss of Reward (PALR) In this task, half of a set of items (for example, numbers) are arbitrarily designated as positive discriminative stimuli, and half are designated as negative. The items then are presented repeatedly to a subject, who is instructed to respond (for example, touch the item or press a key) to positive items and withhold responding to negative items. The subject must respond in order to learn whether an item is positive or not. Responses to positive items earn rewards. Responses to negative items are considered passive-avoidance errors (commission errors) and lose rewards. Withheld responses to positive and to negative stimuli produce no consequences and no information as to the status of the item; however, withheld responses to positive items are tallied as "omission errors." Often a control condition is used that involves *only reward* of correct responses, whether active or passive (Reward of Response Inhibition; RRI); or alternatively, *only punishment* of incorrect responses. In the typical PALR experiment, the "disinhibited" group (extroverts, psychopaths, etc.) has learned and performed equally as well as the control group on the RRI or punishment-only condition but has made more passive-avoidance (commission) errors on the PALR (Newman, Widom, & Nathan, 1985; Newman & Kosson, 1986). These experiments substantiate the hypothesis that disinhibited persons, as typified by extroverts and psychopaths, are deficient in learning to inhibit goal-directed behavior in the presence of cues for reward. In a study that used the PALR but did not include a reward-only or punishment-only condition, Scerbo, Raine, O'Brien, Chan, Rhee, and Smiley (1990) found that adolescent psychopaths made fewer errors of omission but did not differ from nonpsychopaths on errors of commission.

In another study of responses to mixed incentives, a computerized card-playing task was programmed to reduce the odds of winning from 90% to 10% over the course of 100 trials (Newman, Patterson, & Kosson, 1987). A mixed incentive schedule paid players five cents for winning trials and penalized them five cents on losing trials, and subjects could chose to continue or stop at any point and keep their winnings. Psychopaths played longer but kept less winnings than controls, in keeping with the hypothesis of disinhibition. These results have been replicated using school-age children with Conduct Disorder (Shapiro *et al.*, 1989, described in detail in section 5.2). Recently, the card-playing task was adapted for use with a small sample of preschool children in Iran (Kalantari, Yule, & Gardner, 1990), with a mean age of 4 years 6 months. Six children with persistent behavior problems (temper tantrums, disrupting others, fighting, difficult to control, destructive, unpopular, overactive, poor concentration) were compared to matched controls. All six of the behavior-disordered children played all the cards and thereby lost all of their candy rewards. Of the six normal children, four stopped before the end, and two played all the cards. The group difference in cards played was significant.

6.2. *Refinement of Disinhibitory Model*

Patterson and Newman (1989) outlined a theory of abnormal cognitive processing and response modulation associated with disinhibitory syndromes. The theory accounts for the activating effect that punishment can produce in psychopaths and the relation of this effect to poor passive-avoidance learning (Newman, 1987). *Disinhibition* in this theory is the outcome of four component processes. The first component involves the adoption and maintenance of a *dominant response set* (under conditions of reward opportunity) of ongoing goal-directed behavior that takes motivational precedence over competing behavioral sets. There is attentional overfocusing on signals of reward opportunity, and other information may not be apprised. Approach behaviors are activated, accompanied by HR acceleration driven in part by the awareness of reward availability. Individuals who are characteristically disinhibited tend to maintain this goal-approach set more vigorously and to anticipate reward more keenly than nondisinhibited persons when reward appears available.

The second component involves the *cognitive and physiological responses to frustration* of reward-seeking behavior, or such responses to any aversive event that may disrupt the response set. In all individuals, this results in a need for additional information processing, with a possible shift in attention and an increase in arousal. The difference between disinhibited and normal individuals is the tendency to maintain the approach behavior (first component) with increased vigor in the face of punishment or frustration. Thus the third component of disinhibition is that the *dominant response set of the disinhibited individual is facilitated rather than suppressed by punishment or frustration.* Instead of reflectively gathering and processing additional information, the frustrated–disinhibited individual adopts a more impulsive cognitive style.

The fourth component is an *associative deficit that is a consequence of the impulsive, reward-focused style.* If the cues associated with punishment are not processed adequately, they will not be learned. If behavior is impulsively energized rather than suppressed in the service of reflection, the immediate retrospective reflection on cues that predict aversive consequences suffers, along with subsequent memory-based prospective reflection or judgment in future similar situations. In some instances, impulsive reactivation of the goal-directed behavior set may be conditioned to the context in which the aversive event occurs.

Disinhibited persons may thus differ from their nondisinhibited counterparts in reliance on a global rather than an analytic approach to problem solving and in preference for active rather than passive coping. They may learn from their impulsive mistakes, but because of a paucity of negative affective–inhibitory associations, this learning is less likely to occur than with nondisinhibited persons. Patterson and Newman (1989) view impulsive behavior as secondary to the disinhibition construct, and it is the predilection for disinhibition that is the heritable diathesis. They hypothesized that a developmentally early expression of the disinhibitory diathesis, aside from psychopathy at a young age, may be one of the etiologies among the attention deficit–hyperactivity spectrum.

Consistent with this model, Derryberry (1987) found that extroverts responded more quickly after negative outcomes than after positive outcomes (active disinhibition). Introverts responded more slowly after negative outcomes than after positive outcomes (activation of the BIS). Gray's theory would have predicted this latter effect, but Newman's theory can specifically account for the increased speed of responding by extroverts following negative outcomes. Similar results supporting the disinhibition hypothesis were reported by Nichols and Newman (1986). In the Derryberry experiment (1987, Experiment 1) extroverts made more errors of impulsive responding on "catch trials" (neutral, no-target trials) than introverts, consistent with both a general temperamental theory of impulsiveness in extroversion and a specific disinhibition theory involving a temperament by negative cue interaction. These findings are consistent with the neurochemical theory that extroverts have lower serotonergic activity than introverts. Low serotonin activity would be associated with lower anxiety. More relevantly, it would result in less motor inhibition, but no group difference in arousal increase, when the BIS is activated.

6.3. *Further Application of Cognitive Processes Associated with Disinhibition*

One of the major contributions of Newman's model has been the focus on differences in cognitive as well as behavioral responses to contingencies as a function of personality dimensions. Important cognitive features of psychopathy (impeturbability, lack of guilt, etc.) and extroversion (optimism) can be explained to some extent in terms of perseveration in a dominant response set and reduced associative learning of negative signals when both positive and negative information coexist. Furthermore, the cognitive response to punishment or loss appears to differ among introverts and extroverts. Pearce-McCall and Newman (1986) exposed introverts and extroverts to a computer game in which the schedule of successful trials versus unsuccessful trials was fixed. The manipulation was whether subjects began with $5.00 and ended up with $2.50 (50% punishment schedule), or whether they began with $0 and ended up with $2.50 (50% reward schedule). The dimension of *E* was found to significantly interact with the loss versus reward schedule. Following punishment, extroverts slightly increased their perceived control over the task, whereas introverts sharply decreased their perceived control. The implications of this finding for an increased susceptibility to cognitively induced, learned-helplessness depression for introverts is obvious. Also following punishment, extroverts reported that they expected their luck to improve, and they increased their subsequent betting. Introverts, following punishment, *lost* confidence in their success, and they decreased their subsequent betting. A possible biological substrate for this model is suggested by the results of Roy, DeJong, and Linnoila (1989b). Those investigators reported that among a group of hospitalized pathological gamblers, the *E* dimension was positively correlated with CSF, plasma, and urine indexes of noradrenalin (NA) function. (Cloninger has accounted for the association of noradrenaline with pathological gambling in terms of his noradrenergic theory of reward dependence. Pathological gamblers are expected to have inherited low basal rates of NA firing, and hence postsynaptic NA hypersensitivity. This facilitates conditioning of reward signals and may facilitate development of a dominant reward-driven response style; see Cloninger, 1988.)

As discussed in section 4.4, sociopaths may emit an adaptive coping response that enables them to deny, "tune out," or otherwise dissociate negative cues (Harpur & Hare, 1990). This may result from the overengaging effects of reward cues on information processing in psychopaths (Newman, Patterson, Howland, & Nichols, 1990). When motivated by a money-rewarding task or by the presence of a female experimenter, persons high on psychopathy or low on socialization may allocate less attention to unrewarded tasks (Kosson & Newman, 1986, 1989). The attentional processes of introverts or persons with anxiety disorder, on the other hand, are hypervigilant and may promote greater awareness of negative cues. Derryberry (1987) found that in a chronometric covert orienting task, introverts allot more attention to negative cues than extroverts, and a similar interaction of cue negativity and personality was found by MacLeod, Mathews, and Tata (1986) with clinically anxious subjects. A logical extension of this approach would be to test child clinical groups using chronometric paradigms. Children with CD, for example, may respond more quickly after negative outcomes than after positive outcomes in chronometric studies, similar to Derryberry's (1987) results with extroverts. Similarly, children with anxiety disorders may perform like anxious or introverted adults. However, research using this approach must take into account possible structural differences in the components of attention (Posner, 1988) in children with ADHD. Experimental work with this group by Swanson and associates (Swanson, Posner, Potkin, Bonforte, Youpa, Cantwell, & Crinella, 1991; Swanson, Shea, McBurnett, Potkin, Fiore, & Crinella, 1990) has documented *lateralized* differences in covert orienting of attention in a rigorously selected subgroup of ADHD children (with clear early onset of syndrome and extreme teacher ratings of inattention and overactivity) *without* using positive/negative cues or feedback in the experimental task. Without elaboration, Quay's hypothesis of an underactive BIS in hyperactive children does not readily account for a lateral difference in attentional functions. The underactive BIS hypothesis could be tested in future research by comparing the variables associated with arousal following punishment in a chronometric paradigm between ADD groups and other children.

7. Cloninger's Biobehavioral Theory of Personality

Cloninger (1987a) has proposed a system of personality and psychopathology that has deceptively simple underpinnings. Similar to that of Gray, Cloninger's system begins with behavioral dimensions that are based on brain systems. These dimensions are *novelty seeking,* based on the behavioral activation system and operating principally within dopaminergic circuits; *harm avoidance,* based on the behavioral inhibition system and operating within serotonergic circuits; and *reward dependence,* based on the behavioral maintenance system and operating within norepinephrine systems. Each of these three systems responds in particular fashion to stimuli that are most relevant to the system (but, as discussed below, overt behavior is the result of the integration of the responses of all three systems to any given stimulus). The behavioral activation system responds to novel stimuli with exploratory pursuit, to potential rewards with appetitive approach, and to potential relief from punishment or monotony with active avoidance or escape responses. The behavioral inhibition system responds to conditioned signals of punishment, novelty, or frustrative nonreward with passive avoidance or extinction of other responses. The behavioral maintenance system responds to conditioned signals for reward or for relief of punishment by providing resistance to extinction of the responses to these stimuli.

7.1. Personality Theory

Cloninger has emphasized that the three personality dimensions are related to observed patterns of behavior as genotypes are related to phenotypes. Although particular personality characteristics are associated with each of the three independent dimensions, the complexities of normal and disordered behaviors can only be explained in terms of the interaction of these dimensions and the interaction of the dimensions with individual learning history. If the strength or activity of each of the three dimensions is given two possible values (high or low), there are six possible combinations of polar extremes in three-dimensional space, or personality clusters. The possible combinations of high or low novelty seeking (NS) and harm avoidance (HA) yield a hyperthymic (both low) versus hypothymic (both high) "cluster" dimension and an impulsive (high NS-low HA) versus rigid (low NS-high HA) cluster. Similarly, personality clusters of scrupulous versus opportunistic, narcissistic versus self-effacing, passive-avoidant versus oppositional, and gullible versus alienated are generated by the other permutations of the basic stimulus–response typology. These are termed *second-order clusters* in

Cloninger's system. When the possible values of the third basic stimulus–response dimension are added in, there become eight possible nonoverlapping third-order personality clusters. These correspond closely to traditional conceptions of antisocial, histrionic, passive–aggressive, explosive, obsessional, schizoid, cyclothymic, and passive-dependent personality disorders. To illustrate, antisocial personality is the result of high NS, low reward dependence (RD), and low HA; or opportunistic (high NS-low RD), impulsive (high NS-low HA), and oppositional (low RD-low HA) traits. An advantage of this kind of classification system for personality disorders, according to Cloninger, is a balance between the descriptive value and comprehensiveness of the diagnostic criteria on the one hand and the discriminative power of the criteria on the other.

Cloninger developed a clinical interview (the Tridimensional Interview of Personality Style, or TIPS) based on his theory. More importantly for validation of his basic personality dimensions in normal populations, he developed a brief true–false self-report questionnaire, the Tridimensional Personality Questionnaire (TPQ; Cloninger, 1987a, 1988). In a sample of medical students, the TPQ dimensions of HA, NS, and RD were normally distributed, reliable over a 1-week interval, and largely independent.

Some important differences between his theory and other theories have been emphasized by Cloninger (1988). In Cloninger's system, observable personality traits are not the same as the underlying neuroadaptive dimensions but result from the interaction of the multiple opponent processes. A single environmental stimulus can affect all three neuroadaptive systems, whereas for Gray and Eysenck, individual personality dimensions are more associated with separate, mutually exclusive sets of stimuli. Cloninger's system makes less of a distinction between primary and conditional stimuli, especially for punishment. Cloninger divides the process of extinction between the BIS (which facilitates extinction) and the behavioral maintenance system (which facilitates resistance to extinction), whereas Gray's theory attributes extinction to the BIS. Cloninger (1988) argues that the distinctions made by his theory are better able to account for clinical phenomena such as sensitivity to pain and the development of cognitive versus somatic anxieties. These distinctions (and others not listed here) lead to important testable hypotheses regarding the validity of the different theories. Cloninger himself (1988) has modified aspects of his theory based on empirical findings that did not square with early developments of the theory. A comprehensive, integrated presentation of the theory and its empirical validation awaits publication (Cloninger, in press).

7.2. *Biological Correlates of Personality Dimensions*

Cloninger's model of brain–behavior relationships is based on functional organization (as opposed to neuroanatomical organization) of three "chemically-coded neural networks that are regulated by independent genetic determinants but interact in response to interoceptive or exteroceptive stimulation" (Cloninger, 1988, p. 86). Individual variations in the responsiveness of each of the three monoamine networks regulate the activation, maintenance, and inhibition of behavioral responses to novel, appetitive, and aversive stimulations. Individual differences in monoamine system functioning are the biological basis of individual differences in sensitization, habituation, classical and operant conditioning, and attentional and other cognitive mechanisms. Environmental events, that is, individual learning histories, can modify the functioning of the monoamine systems. Cloninger therefore emphasizes that the interactive functional organization cannot be understood without a "dynamic developmental perspective." At present, the developmental aspect of Cloninger's theory focuses on modifications of biochemical function by learning history. Work on the theory remains to be done in the area of developmental adaptation that is specific to ranges of the life span.

Two important aspects of the biological mechanisms of Cloninger's theory are *basal or spontaneous rate of neuronal firing* and *receptor sensitivity.* One of the basic principles of neurophysiology is that the nervous system is regulated, not by onset or offset of individual neuronal action potentials, but by changes in the rate of spontaneous neuronal firing in response to cumulative polarization and depolarization events. Long-term changes in the tonic or base rate of synaptic discharge is often followed by adaptations in the number or sensitivity of postsynaptic receptors, that is, *up-regulation* or *down-regulation* of the receptors. Cloninger has assumed that extreme individual differences in the base firing rate of a monamine system is accompanied by differences in the reverse direction of postsynaptic sensitivity. For example, persons with low spontaneous dopaminergic firing are expected to need and to seek extraordinary thrills (novelty, cues to reward) in order to feel pleasant and to be highly avoidant of monotony and susceptible to boredom. When they do encounter excitement, the postsynaptic dopamine receptor (especially the D2 receptor) supersensitivity in these persons is expected to result in more intensely thrilling and exhilarating subjective experience and in facilitated acquisition of operant conditioning to the rewarding stimuli. On the other extreme, individuals with high spontaneous rates of firing of midbrain dopaminergic neurons should have correspondingly less sensitive postsynaptic receptors. These persons should be relatively pleased and content in a variety of circumstances, slower to acquire conditioned responses to rewards, less seeking of extraordinary sensation, and more tolerant of monotony and aversive stimulation. In localizing the NS-behavioral activation system, Cloninger has emphasized dopaminergic nuclei in the midbrain and their ascending projections to the prefrontal cortex, central amygdala, lateral septum, bed nucleus of the stria terminalis, habenula, nucleus accumbens, hypothalamic nuclei around the median eminence, and the locus coeruleus. Dopaminergic and nondopaminergic interconnections among these structures provide a positive-feedback neural network that integrates and coordinates behavioral activation, although different components of the network are differentially regulated by various neuropeptides and hormones.

The localization of the HA-behavioral inhibition system is similar to the BIS-serotonergic system in Gray's theory, discussed before in detail. The structures that receive terminal projections from the midbrain serotonergic neurons have serotonergic and cholinergic interconnections and are also modulated by GABA and various neuropeptides and hormones, forming a neural network that modulates inhibition of behavior by its widespread opposition to catacholaminergic (dopaminergic and noradrenergic) input. A clear departure from Gray's theory lies in Cloninger's categorization of stimuli that activate this system: unconditioned punishment and unconditioned rewards and conditioned signals of punishment and nonreward. Activation of the system results in behavioral inhibition and in cortisol release and other "stress" responses. Possible relationships between serotonergic receptor sensitivity and anxiety/depression symptoms have been discussed. Cloninger has also emphasized the impact of individual learning history on the development of chronic anxiety states. For example, a person with a high basal rate of serotonergic firing and superior passive avoidance learning may not develop chronic cognitive anxiety unless the individual is exposed to chronic inescapable or recurrent unpredictable punishment, leading to a sensitized state.

The localization of the RD-behavioral maintenance system begins with the noradrenergic cell bodies in the locus coeruleus. The widespread ascending projections from this nucleus provide a neural network that modulates "cortical tone," or more specifically, leads to an increased "signal-to-noise ratio" in its postsynaptic targets, sharpening the contrast between relevant and irrelevant stimuli (Tucker & Williamson, 1984). Noradrenergic projections are thought to be involved in the formation of conditioned signals of reward and relief and to increased resistance to extinction, but not in the acquisition of positively reinforced behavior, whereas dopaminergic projections are thought to be involved in the acquisition of positively reinforced behavior and in the activation of learned approach in response to already-learned conditioned signals of reward/relief but not in resistance to extinction (Cloninger, 1988; Stein, 1983). Persons with low basal firing rates of the locus coeruleus are expected to have high RD, facilitation of classical appetitive conditioning and identification of signals of reward/relief, resistance to extinction and persistance in the face of nonreward, development of positive sentiments, and enhanced sensitivity to social and verbal cues that signal personal preferences or the preferences of other people.

7.3. Applications to Child Psychopathology

Initial applications of Cloninger's theory to child psychopathology attempted to validate the theory by conducting retrospective assessment of the three dimensions and examining their relationship with later outcome. Obtaining measures of RD, NS, and HA necessitated development of child scales for these dimensions and applying these scales to existing records. The child scales for RD, NS, and HA appear in Sigvardsson, Bohman, and Cloninger (1987) and in Cloninger, Sigvardsson, and Bohman (1988).

Sigvardsson, Bohman, and Cloninger (1987) factor-analyzed teacher ratings of 431 Swedish children (233 boys, 198 girls) at age 11 and obtained three personality factors. These factors, Impulsivity, Diligence, and Neuroticism, were felt to correspond to Eysenck's factors of Extroversion, Psychoticism (with reverse scoring), and Neuroticism. The teacher ratings and narratives were also used to obtain scores for each child for NS, HA, and RD. These scores were then correlated with the personality factors. NS was positively related to Impulsivity and Negatively related to Diligence. HA was negatively associated with Impulsivity and positively associated with Neuroticism. RD was positively associated with Diligence and Neuroticism. Scores on HA, NS, and RD were predictive of adult outcome for these children, including criminal behavior. The proportion of variance explained was small, but noteworthy considering the limitations imposed by the measures and retrospective longitudinal design of this study.

The association of hyperactivity in childhood with particular patterns of alcoholism in adulthood has been of interest for some time (e.g., Tarter, McBride, Buonpane, & Schneider, 1977). Cloninger (1987b) linked two patterns of alcoholism, primarily distinguished as to whether drinking problems began before the age of 25 (Type 2) or after that age (Type 1), to patterns of personality traits. Type 1 alcoholics are thought to be low on NS but high on HA and RD. Type 2 alcoholics are thought to have the opposite pattern, that is, to be high on NS but low on HA and RD. The Type 2 drinking pattern was associated with high heritability (independent of environmental influences) and criminality in biological fathers. Similar associations, along with greater propensity to violence, depression, and suicide attempts, have been found in Type 2 alcoholism when an age of onset of 20 years is used to divide the alcoholic groups (Buydens-Branchey, Branchey, & Noumair, 1989). Cloninger, Sigvardsson, and Bohman (1988) used retrospective assessments of 431 Swedish children at age 11 to measure their placement on the RD, NS, and HA dimensions. Independent evaluations of alcohol abuse were obtained at age 27. Those identified as having alcohol problems were considered to be primarily Type 2 alcoholics. Although extremes on any dimension in childhood tended to be associated with increased risk of alcoholism in adulthood, high NS and low HA was extremely predictive of alcoholism.

8. *Summary*

The common theme underlying psychobiological theories of personality is the attempt to explain individual differences in terms of permutations of a few basic personality traits—traits which are linked to genetically influenced biological processes that can be modified by drugs and by learning history. This chapter surveyed some of the major theoretical and empirical advances in linking personality, psychopathology, learning and affective styles, and biological processes. Some brief summarizations can be stated, although admittedly these are gross oversimplifications. Eysenck's pioneering theory linked the personality dimensions of *E*, *N*, and *P* to specific biological processes that underlie differences in conditioning and socialization. Psychopathological syndromes such as psychopathy and anxiety–depression were associated with extreme variations in the basic personality syndromes. Zuckerman's work has focused on the trait of sensation-seeking and on the concept of an optimal level of arousal that individuals seek to maintain. The theories of Gray and of Newman and colleagues were heavily influenced by the syndrome exhibited by rats with septal-hippocampal lesions. Gray made the critical rotation of Eysenck's *E* and *N* factors and related the resulting factors of Anxiety and Impulsivity to specific components of a conceptual (modular) nervous system. Newman and his group have explored individual differences in response bias and cognitive style that are elicited by rewards and punishments. Cloninger has proposed that three basic personality traits are associated with the activity of the monoamine systems, and proposed that the gamut of personality disorders could be related to combinations of extremes of these basic traits and their interactions with learning history.

Except for some early work applying Eysenck's traits of *E* and *N* to children, the applications of these psychobiological theories to childhood psychopathology has begun only recently. Quay has provided an important impetus to this endeavor by applying Gray's theory and making specific predictions about different child diagnostic groups. The implications of this kind of approach are far-reaching. The notion of individual differences in response to reward and punishment may lead to some "shift" in the prevailing behavior modification paradigm that views children as homogeneous black boxes and child behaviors as having equipotentiality for influence by consequences. The biological basis of reward and punishment sensitivity and of other basic personality traits has direct implications for understanding genetic contributions to child psychopathology, for the rational investigation of drug treatment (and other treatments) of pathological personality extremes, and for refining diagnostic and subtyping strategies. Research activity in this area on psychopathy and conduct disorder is shedding new light on the incorrigibility aspect of chronic antisocial behavior.

One of the important themes in this area is that behavioral phenomena are produced by *interactions* of psychobiological systems. This emphasis on considering interactive as well as main effects is perhaps most explicitly expressed in Cloninger's theoretical system. Experimentally, Newman's group has repeatedly demonstrated that reward systems and inhibitory systems underlying motivated behavior cannot be fully understood in isolation, and that important individual differences in disinhibited behavior emerge only when reward systems and inhibitory systems are competitively activated. The importance of considering the interaction of appetitive dimensions (reward-driven or aggressive behaviors) and inhibitory dimensions (anxiety) in child psychopathology is demonstrated for Conduct Disorder in behavioral validation (Walker *et al.*, 1991) and biological validation (McBurnett, Lahey, Frick, Risch, Loeber, Hart, Christ, & Hanson, 1991) studies, and by a review of biological findings in CD (Lahey, McBurnett, Loeber, & Hart, in press).

We are far from understanding completely how individuals who are extreme on psychobiological dimensions either do or do not develop psychopathology. Not all impulsive, low-anxiety extroverts develop or maintain antisocial behavior, and not all reactive introverts develop anxiety disorders. The relative contribution of biological and environmental determinants may be different for individuals near the mean, compared to individuals at the extreme of psychobiological dimensions. One of the most challenging and exciting aspects of applying these theories to the development of psychopathology will be the investigation of factors leading to prosocial versus antisocial expressions of the same extremes of psychobiological traits.

ACKNOWLEDGMENTS

The author wishes to thank the following colleagues for their comments on an earlier version of this chapter: Francis M. Crinella, Benjamin B. Lahey, Joseph P. Newman, Herbert C. Quay, James M. Swanson, and Tim Wigal. However, any inaccuracies or other shortcomings in the text are the fault of the author and not of these commentators.

9. *References*

Achenbach, T. A., & Edelbrock, C. S. (1983). *Manual for the Child Behavior Checklist.* Burlington: University of Vermont School of Medicine.

Albert, D. J., & Chew, G. L. (1980). The septal forebrain and the inhibitory modulation of attack and defence in the rat: A review. *Behavioral and Neural Biology, 30,* 357–388.

Allsop, J. F., & Feldman, M. P. (1974). Extraversion, neuroticism, psychoticism, and antisocial behavior in school-girls. *Social Behavior and Personality, 2,* 140–149.

Allsop, J. F., & Feldman, M. P. (1976). Personality and antisocial behavior in school boys: Item analysis of questionnaire measures. *British Journal of Criminology, 16,* 337-351.

Amsel, A. (1962). Frustrative nonreward in partial reinforcement and discrimination learning: Some recent history and a theoretical extension. *Psychological Review, 69,* 306–328.

Amsel, A. (1990). Arousal, suppression, and persistence—Frustration theory, attention, and its disorders. *Cognition and Emotion, 4,* 239–268.

Anchel, H., & Lindsley, D. B. (1972). Differentiation of two reticulo-hypothalamic systems regulating hippocampal activity. *Electroencephalography and Clinical Neurophysiology, 32,* 209–226.

Aprison, M. H., & Hingtgen, J. N. (1986). A hypersensitive serotonergic receptor theory of depression: The role of stress. In R. C. A. Frederickson, H. C. Hendrie, J. N. Hingtgen, & M. H. Aprison (Eds.), *Neuroregulation of autonomic, endocrine, and immune systems* (pp. 443–460). Boston: Martinus Nijhoff.

Ballenger, J. C., Post, R. M., Jimerson, D. C., Lake, C. R., Murphy, D., Zuckerman, M., & Cronin, C. (1983). Biochemical correlates of personality traits in normals. *Personality and Individual Differences, 4,* 615–625.

Belluzi, B. L., & Stein, L. (1977). Enkephalin may mediate euphoria and drive-reduction reward. *Nature, 266,* 556–558.

Blackburn, R. (1969). Sensation seeking, impulsivity, and psychopathic personality. *Journal of Consulting and Clinical Psychology, 33,* 571–574.

Brown, G. L., Ebert, M. H., Goyer, P. F., Jimerson, C. D., Klein, W. J., Bunney, W. E., & Goodwin, F. K. (1983). Aggression, suicide, and serotonin: Relationships to CSF amine metabolites. *American Journal of Psychiatry, 139,* 741–746.

Buchsbaum, M. S., Muscettola, G., & Goodwin, F. K. (1981). Urinary MHPG, stress response, personality factors and somatosensory evoked potentials in normal subjects and patients with affective disorders. *Neuropsychobiology, 7,* 212–224.

Buydens-Branchey, L., Branchey, M. H., & Noumair, D. (1989). Age of alcoholism onset: I. Relationship to psychopathology. *Archives of General Psychiatry, 46,* 225–230.
Carpenter, M. B., & Sutin, J. (1983). *Human neuroanatomy* (8th ed.). Baltimore: Williams & Wilkins.
Cleckley, H. (1976). *The mask of sanity* (5th ed.). St. Louis: Mosby.
Cloninger, C. R. (1986). A unified biosocial theory of personality and its role in the development of anxiety states. *Psychiatric Developments, 3,* 167–226.
Cloninger, C. R. (1987a). A systematic method of clinical description and classification of personality variants: A proposal. *Archives of General Psychiatry, 44,* 573–588.
Cloninger, C. R. (1987b). Neurogenetic adaptive mechanisms in alcoholism. *Science, 236,* 410–416.
Cloninger, C. R. (1988). A unified biosocial theory of personality and its role in the development of anxiety states: A reply to commentaries. *Psychiatric Developments, 2,* 83–120.
Cloninger, C. R. (in press). *Personality and psychopathology: Neuroadaptive processes.* New York: Oxford University Press.
Cloninger, C. R., Sigvardsson, S., & Bohman, M. (1988). Childhood personality predicts alcohol abuse in young adults. *Alcoholism: Clinical and Experimental Research, 12,* 494–505.
Coccaro, E. F., Siever, L. J., Klar, H. M., Maurer, G., Cochrane, K., Cooper, T. B., Mohs, R. C., & Davis, K. L. (1989). Serotonergic studies in patients with affective and personality disorders: Correlates with suicidal and impulsive aggressive behavior. *Archives of General Psychiatry, 46,* 587–599.
Corah, N. L. (1964). Neuroticism and extraversion in the MMPI: Empirical validation and exploration. *British Journal of Social and Clinical Psychology, 3,* 168–174.
Daitzman, R., & Zuckerman, M. (1980). Disinhibitory sensation seeking, personality, and gonadal hormones. *Personality and Individual Differences, 1,* 103–110.
Daitzman, R., Zuckerman, M., Sammelwitz, P., & Ganjam, V. (1978). Sensation seeking and gonadal hormones. *Journal of Biosocial Science, 10,* 401–408.
Daugherty, T. K., & Quay, H. C. (1991). Response perseveration and delayed responding in childhood behavior disorders. *Journal of Child Psychology and Psychiatry and Allied Disciplines, 32,* 453–461.
Deakin, J. F. W. (1988). 5HT2 receptors, depression, and anxiety. *Pharmacology, Biochemistry, and Behavior, 29,* 819–820.
Derryberry, D. (1987). Incentive and feedback effects on target detection: A chronometric analysis of Gray's model of temperament. *Personality and Individual Differences, 8,* 855–865.
Douglas, V. I., Barr, R. G., O'Neill, M. E., & Britton, B. G. (1986). Short term effects of methylphenidate on the cognitive, learning, and academic performance of children with attention deficit disorder in the laboratory and the classroom. *Journal of Child Psychology and Psychiatry, 27,* 191–211.
Drewett, R. F., Gray, J. A., James, D. T. D., McNaughton, N., Valero, I., & Dudderidge, H. J. (1977). Sex and strain differences in septal driving of the hippocampal theta rhythm as a function of frequency: Effects of gonadectomy and gonadal hormones. *Neuroscience, 2,* 1033–1041.
Emmons, T. D., & Webb, W. W. (1974). Subjective correlates of emotional responsivity and stimulation seeking in psychopaths, normals, and acting-out neurotics. *Journal of Consulting and Clinical Psychology, 42,* 620.
Eysenck, H. J. (1947). *Dimensions of personality.* London: Routledge & Kegan Paul.
Eysenck, H. J. (1952). *The scientific study of personality.* London: Routledge & Kegan Paul.
Eysenck, H. J. (1967). *The biological basis of personality.* Springfield, IL: C C Thomas.
Eysenck, H. J. (1969). Nature and history of human typology. In H. J. Eysenck & S. B. G.

Eysenck (Eds.), *Personality structure and measurement* (pp. 3–140). London: Routledge & Kegan Paul.

Eysenck, H. J. (1981). *A model for personality.* New York: Springer Verlag.

Eysenck, H. J. (1982). *Personality, genetics, and behavior: Selected papers.* New York: Praeger.

Eysenck, H. J., & Eysenck, S. B. G. (Eds.) (1976a). *Personality structure and measurement.* London: Routledge & Kegan Paul.

Eysenck, H. J., & Eysenck, S. B. G. (1976b). *Psychoticism as a dimension of personality.* London: Hodder & Stoughton.

Eysenck, H. J., & Eysenck, S. B. G. (1977). The place of impulsiveness in a dimensional system of personality description. *British Journal of Social and Clinical Psychology, 16,* 57–68.

Eysenck, H. J., & Zuckerman, M. (1978). The relationship between sensation-seeking and Eysenck's dimensions of personality. *British Journal of Psychology, 69,* 483–487.

Eysenck, S. B. G. (1969). Personality dimensions in children. In H. J. Eysenck & S. B. G. Eysenck (Eds.), *Personality structure and measurement* (pp. 265–316). London: Routledge & Kegan Paul.

Farley, F. H., & Farley, S. V. (1970). Impulsiveness, sociability, and the preference for varied experience. *Perceptual and Motor Skills, 31,* 47.

Feij, J. A., Orlebeke, J. F., Gazendam, A., and van Zuilen, R. W. (1985). Sensation seeking: Measurement and psychophysiological correlates. In J. Strelau, F. H. Farley, & A. Gale (Eds.), *The biological bases of personality and behavior: Vol. 1, Theories, measurement techniques, and development* (pp. 195–210). Washington, DC: Hemisphere.

Fowles, D. C. (1980). The three arousal model: Implications of Gray's two-factor learning theory for HR, electrodermal activity, and psychopathy. *Psychophysiology, 17,* 87–104.

Fowles, D. C. (1983). Motivational effects on HR and electrodermal activity: Implications for research in personality and psychopathology. *Journal of Research in Personality, 17,* 48–71.

Fulker, D. W., Eysenck, S. B. G., & Zuckerman, M. (1980). A genetic and environmental analysis of sensation seeking. *Journal of Research in Personality, 14,* 261–281.

Galey, D., Durkin, T., Sitakis, G., Kempf, E., & Jaffard, R. (1985). Facilitation of spontaneous and learned spatial behaviors following 6-hydroxydopamine lesions of the lateral septum: A cholinergic hypothesis. *Brain Research, 340,* 171–174.

Gorenstein, E. E., & Newman, J. P. (1980). Disinhibitory psychopathology: A new perspective and a model for research. *Psychological Review, 87,* 301–315.

Gordon, M. (1979). The assessment of impulsivity and mediating behavior in hyperactive and nonhyperactive boys. *Journal of Abnormal Psychology, 6,* 317–326.

Gorman, B. S. (1970). 16PF correlates of sensation-seeking. *Psychological Reports, 26,* 741–742.

Gray, J. A. (1969). Sodium amobarbital and effects of frustrative nonreward. *Journal of Comparative and Physiological Psychology, 69,* 55–64.

Gray, J. A. (1970). The psychophysiological basis of introversion-extroversion. *Behaviour Research and Therapy, 8,* 249–266.

Gray, J. A. (1972). The psychophysiological basis of introversion-extroversion: A modification of Eysenck's theory. In V. D. Nebylitsyn & J. A. Gray (Eds.), *The biological bases of individual behavior* (pp. 372–399). New York: Academic Press.

Gray, J. A. (1973). Causal theories of personality and how to test them. In J. R. Royce (Ed.), *Multivariate analysis and psychological theory* (pp. 409–463). London: Academic Press.

Gray, J. A. (1975). *Elements of a two-process theory of learning.* London: Academic Press.

Gray, J. A. (1981). A critique of Eysenck's theory of personality. In H. J. Eysenck (Ed.), *A model for personality* (pp. 246–276). Berlin: Springer.

Gray, J. A. (1982). *The neuropsychology of anxiety: An enquiry into the functions of the septo-hippocampal system.* Oxford: Oxford University Press.

Gray, J. A. (1987). *The psychology of fear and stress* (2nd ed.). Cambridge: Cambridge University Press.

Gray, J. A., Owen, S., Davis, N., & Tsaltas, E. (1983). Psychological and physiological relations between anxiety and impulsivity. In M. Zuckerman (Ed.), *Biological bases of sensation seeking, impulsivity, and anxiety* (pp. 181–217. Hillsdale, NJ: Lawrence Erlbaum.

Hare, R. D. (1978). Electrodermal and cardiovascular correlates of psychopathy. In R. D. Hare & D. Schalling (Eds.), *Psychopathic behavior: Approaches to research* (pp. 107–143). New York: Wiley.

Harpur, T. J., & Hare, R. D. (1990). Psychopathy and attention. In J. T. Enns (Ed.), *The development of attention: Research and theory* (pp. 429–444). Amsterdam: Elsevier–North-Holland.

Hencke, P. G. (1977). Dissociation of the frustration effect and the partial reinforcement effect after limbic lesions in rats. *Journal of Comparative and Physiological Psychology, 91,* 1032–1038.

Hensman, R., Guimarães, F. S., Wang, M., & Deakin, J. F. W. (1991). Effects of ritanserin on aversive classical conditioning in humans. *Psychopharmacology, 104,* 220–224.

Hewitt, L. E., & Jenkins, R. L. (1946). *Fundamental patterns of maladjustment.* Springfield, IL: State of Illinois.

Hingtgen, J. N., Shekhar, A., DiMicco, & Aprison, M. H. (1988). Response suppression in rats after bilateral microinjection of 5-hydroxytryptophan in lateral hypothalamus. *Biological Psychiatry, 23,* 711–718.

Hinshaw, S. P. (1987). On the distinction between attention deficits/hyperactivity and conduct problems/aggression in child psychopathology. *Psychological Bulletin, 101,* 443–463.

Kafry, D. (1982). Sensation seeking of young children. *Personality and Individual Differences, 3,* 161–166.

Kahn, R. S., van Praag, H., Wetzler, S., Anis, G. M., & Barr, G. (1988). Serotonin and anxiety revisited. *Biological Psychiatry, 23,* 189–208.

Kalantari, M., Yule, W., & Gardner, F. (1990). Oversensitivity to reward in preschool conduct disordered children. Unpublished manuscript, University of Esfahan, Iran.

Kassebaum, G. G., Couch, A. S., & Slater, P. E. (1959). The factorial dimensions of the MMPI. *Journal of Consulting Psychology, 23,* 226–236.

Kluver, H., & Bucy, P. C. (1937). "Psychic blindness" and other symptoms following bilateral temporal lobectomy in rhesus monkeys. *American Journal of Physiology, 119,* 352–353.

Kosson, D. S., & Newman, J. P. (1986). Psychopathy and the allocation of attentional capacity in a divided-attention situation. *Journal of Abnormal Psychology, 95,* 257–263.

Kosson, D. S., & Newman, J. P. (1989). Socialization and attentional deficits under focusing and divided attention conditions. *Journal of Personality and Social Psychology, 57,* 87–99.

Lahey, B. B., & Piacentini, J. C. (1985). An evaluation of the Quay-Peterson Revised Behavior Problem Checklist. *Journal of School Psychology, 23,* 285–289.

Lahey, B. B., McBurnett, K., Loeber, R., & Hart, E. L. (in press). Psychobiology of Conduct Disorder. In G. P. Sholevar (Ed.), *Conduct disorders in children and adolescents: Assessments and interventions.* Washington, DC: American Psychiatric Association.

Leyson, J. E. (1985). Characterization of serotonin receptor binding sites. In A. R. Green (Ed.), *Neuropharmacology of serotonin* (pp. 79–116). Oxford: Oxford University Press.

Lidberg, L., Asberg, M., & Sundquist-Stensman, U. B. (1984). 5-hydroxyindoleacetic acid levels in attempted suicides who have killed their children. *The Lancet, 2,* 928.

Lindgren, T., & Kantak, K. M. (1987). Effects of serotonin receptor agonists and antagonists on offensive aggression in mice. *Aggressive Behavior, 13,* 87–96.

Linnoila, M., Virkhunen, M., Scheinin, M., Nuutila, A., Rimon, R., & Goodwin, F. K. (1983). Low cerebrospinal fluid 5-hydroxyindoleacetic acid concentration differentiates impulsive from nonimpulsive violent behavior. *Life Sciences, 33,* 2609–2614.

McBurnett, K., Lahey, B. B., Frick, P. F., Risch, S. C., Loeber, R., Hart, E. L., Christ, M. A. G., & Hanson, K. S. (1991). Anxiety, inhibition, and Conduct Disorder in children: II. Relation to salivary cortisol. *Journal of the American Academy of Child and Adolescent Psychiatry, 30,* 192–196.

McClure, F. D., & Gordon, M. (1984). Performance of disturbed hyperactive and non-hyperactive children on an objective measure of hyperactivity. *Journal of Abnormal Child Psychology, 12,* 561–571.

Meehl, P. E. (1962). Schizotaxia, schizotypy, schizophrenia. *American Psychologist, 17,* 827–838.

Morris, L. W. (1979). *Extraversion and introversion: An interactional perspective.* Washington, DC: Hemisphere.

Mouret, J. (1982). Biological foundations for the use of sleep deprivation in the treatment of depression. *Encephale, 8,* 229–250.

Muller, E. E., & Nistico, G. (1989). *Brain messengers and the pituitary.* San Diego: Academic Press.

Murphy, D. L. (1976). Clinical, genetic, hormonal, and drug influences on the activity of human platelet monoamine oxidase. In Ciba Foundation Symposium 39, *Monoamine oxidase and its inhibition.* Amsterdam: Elsevier.

Murphy, D. L., Belmaker, R. H., Buchsbaum, M. S., Martin, N. F., Ciarenello, K., & Wyatt, R. J. (1977). Biogenic amine related enzymes and personality variables in normals. *Psychological Medicine, 7,* 149–157.

Neary, R. S., & Zuckerman, M. (1976). Sensation seeking, trait and state anxiety, and the electrodermal orienting reflex. *Psychophysiology, 12,* 205–211.

Nelson, P. B., & Wollen, K. A. (1965). Effects of ethanol and partial reinforcement upon runway acquisition. *Psychonomic Science, 3,* 135–136.

Newman, J. P. (1987). Reaction to punishment in extraverts and psychopaths: Implications for the impulsive behavior of disinhibited individuals. *Journal of Research in Personality, 21,* 464–480.

Newman, J. P., & Kosson, D. S. (1986). Passive avoidance learning in psychopathic and nonpsychopathic offenders. *Journal of Abnormal Psychology, 95,* 257–263.

Newman, J. P., Patterson, C. M., & Kosson, D. S. (1987). Response perseveration in psychopaths. *Journal of Abnormal Psychology, 96,* 145–148.

Newman, J. P., Patterson, C. M., Howland, E. W., & Nichols, S. L. (1990). Passive avoidance in psychopaths: The effects of reward. *Personality and Individual Differences, II,* 1101–1114.

Newman, J. P., Widom, C. S., & Nathan, S. (1985). Passive-avoidance in syndromes of disinhibition: Psychopathy and extroversion. *Journal of Personality and Social Psychology, 48,* 1316–1327.

Nichols, S. L., & Newman, J. P. (1986). Effects of punishment on response latency in extraverts. *Journal of Personality and Social Psychology, 50,* 624–630.

Olds, J., & Milner, P. (1954). Positive reinforcement produced by electrical stimulation of septal area and other regions of rat brain. *Journal of Comparative and Physiological Psychology, 47,* 419–427.

Orlebeke, J. F., & Feij, J. A. (1979). The orienting reflex as a personality correlate. In H. D. Kimmel, E. H. van Olst, & J. F. Orlebeke (Eds.), *The orienting reflex in humans* (pp. 567–585). Hillsdale, NJ: Lawrence Erlbaum.

Patterson, C. M., & Newman, J. P. (1989). *Reflectivity and learning from aversive events: Toward a psychological mechanism for the syndromes of disinhibition.* Unpublished manuscript, University of Wisconsin, Madison.

Paul, S. M., Marangos, P. J., & Skolnick, P. (1981). The benzodiazepine-GABA-chloride receptor complex: Common site of minor tranquilizer action. *Biological Psychiatry, 16,* 213–229.

Pearce-McCall, D., & Newman, J. P. (1986). Expectation of success following noncontingent punishment in introverts and extroverts. *Journal of Personality and Social Psychology, 50,* 439–446.

Perry, E. K., Marshall, E. F., Blessed, B., Tomlinson, B. E., & Perry, R. H. (1983). Decreased imipramine binding sites in the brains of patients with depressive illness. *British Journal of Psychiatry, 142,* 188–192.

Peterson, D. R. (1961). Behavior problems of middle childhood. *Journal of Consulting Psychology, 25,* 205–209.

Pincus, J. P., & Tucker, G. J. (1985). *Behavioral neurology* (3rd ed.). New York: Oxford University Press.

Pliszka, S. R., Rogeness, G. A., Renner, P., Sherman, J., & Broussard, T. (1988). Plasma neurochemistry in juvenile offenders. *Journal of the American Academy of Child and Adolescent Psychiatry, 27,* 588–594.

Posner, M. I. (1988). Structures and function of selective attention. In T. Boll & B. K. Bryant (Eds.), Clinical neuropsychology and brain function: Research, measurement, and practice (pp. 169–202). Washington, DC: American Psychological Association.

Quay, H. C. (1965). Psychopathic personality as pathological stimulation-seeking. *American Journal of Psychiatry, 122,* 180–183.

Quay, H. C. (1986). Classification. In H. C. Quay & J. S. Werry (Eds.), *Psychopathological disorders of childhood* (3rd ed.) (pp. 1–34). New York: John Wiley & Sons.

Quay, H. C. (1987). *Reward, punishment, and aggression.* Paper presented at a conference on assessment, treatment, and treatment evaluation of children who are both emotionally disturbed and aggressive/violent, sponsored by the Antisocial and Violent Behavior Branch of the National Institute of Mental Health and the Child Mental Health Services of the North Carolina Division of Mental Health, Mental Retardation, and Substance Abuse Services, Durham, NC.

Quay, H. C. (1988a). The behavioral reward and inhibition system in childhood behavior disorders. In L. M. Bloomingdale (Ed.), *Attention deficit disorder (Vol. 3): New research in attention, treatment, and psychopharmacology* (pp. 176-186). Oxford: Pergamon Press.

Quay, H. C. (1988b). Attention deficit disorder and the behavioral inhibition system: The relevance of the neuropsychological theory of Jeffrey A. Gray. In L. M. Bloomingdale & J. A. Sergeant (Eds.), *Attention deficit disorder: Criteria: cognition, intervention* (pp. 117–126). Oxford: Pergamon Press.

Quay, H. C. (1990). *Electrodermal responding, inhibition, and reward-seeking in Undersocialized Aggressive Conduct Disorder.* Presented at the annual meeting of the American Academy of Child and Adolescent Psychiatry, Chicago, October.

Quay, H. C., & Peterson, D. R. (1987). Manual for the Revised Behavior Problem Checklist. Coral Gables, FL: Authors.

Rachman, S. (1969). Extraversion and neuroticism in childhood. In H. J. Eysenck & S. B. G. Eysenck (Eds.), *Personality structure and measurement* (pp. 253–264). London: Routledge & Kegan Paul.

Ridgeway, D., & Hare, R. D. (1981). Sensation seeking and psychophysiological responses to auditory stimulation. *Psychophysiology, 18,* 613–618.

Roberts, L. (1974). Comparative physiology of the electrodermal and cardiovascular control systems. In P. A. Obrist, A. H. Black, J. Brener, & L. V. DiCara (Eds.), *Cardiovascular psychophysiology: Current issues in response mechanisms, biofeedback, and methodology* (pp. 163–189). Chicago: Aldine.

Rosenthal, R. H., & Allen, T. W. (1978). An examination of attention, arousal, and learning dysfunctions of hyperkinetic children. *Psychological Bulletin, 85,* 689–715.

Roy, A., DeJong, J., & Linnoila, M. (1989a). Cerebrospinal fluid monoamine metabolites and suicidal behavior in depressed patient: A 5-year follow-up study. *Archives of General Psychiatry, 46,* 609–612.

Roy, A., DeJong, J., & Linnoila, M. (1989b). Extraversion in pathological gamblers: Correlates with indexes of noradrenergic function. *Archives of General Psychiatry, 46,* 679–681.

Russo, M. F., Lahey, B. B., Christ, M. A. G., Frick, P. J., McBurnett, K., Walker, J. L., Loeber, R., Stouthamer-Loeber, M., & Green, S. (1991). Preliminary development of a Sensation Seeking Scale for Children. *Personality and Individual Differences, 12,* 399–405.

Saklofske, D. H. (1977). Personality and the behavior problems of school boys. *Psychological Reports, 41,* 445–446.

Satterfield, J. H. (1976). Central and autonomic nervous system function in the hyperactive child syndrome: Treatment and research implications. In A. Davids (Ed.), *Child personality and psychopathology: Current topics* (pp. 237–258). New York: Wiley.

Scerbo, A. R., Raine, A., O'Brien, M., Chan, C., Rhee, C., & Smiley, N. (1990). Reward dominance in passive-avoidance learning in adolescent psychopaths. *Journal of Abnormal Child Psychology, 18,* 451–463.

Schmauk, F. J. (1970). Punishment, arousal, and avoidance learning in psychopaths. *Journal of Abnormal Psychology, 76,* 325–335.

Schooler, C., Zahn, T. P., Murphy, D. L., & Buchsbaum, M. S. (1978). Psychological correlates of monoamine oxidase activity in normals. *Journal of Nervous and Mental Disease, 166,* 177–186.

Segal, M. (1979). Serotonergic innervation of the locus coeruleus from the dorsal raphe and its action on responses to noxious stimuli. *Journal of Physiology, 286,* 401–415.

Seligman, M. E. P. (1975). *Helplessness.* San Francisco: Freeman.

Shapiro, S. K., Quay, H. C., Hogan, A. E., & Schwartz, K. P. (1989). Response perseveration and delayed responding in undersocialized conduct disorder. *Journal of Abnormal Psychology, 97,* 371–373.

Siegal, R. A. (1978). Probability of punishment and suppression of behavior in psychopathic and nonpsychopathic offenders. *Journal of Abnormal Psychology, 87,* 514–522.

Sigvardsson, S., Bohman, M., & Cloninger, C. R. (1987). Structure and stability of childhood personality: Prediction of later social adjustment. *Journal of Child Psychology and Psychiatry and Allied Disciplines, 28,* 929–946.

Stanley, M., Virgilio, J., & Gershon, S. (1982). Tritiated imipramine binding sites are decreased in frontal cortex of suicides. *Science, 216,* 1337–1339.

Stein, L. (1978). Reward transmitters: Catecholamines and opioid peptides. In M. A. Lipton, A. Dimascio, & K. F. Killam (Eds.), *Psychopharmacology: A generation of progress* (pp. 569–581). New York: Raven Press.

Stein, L. (1983). The chemistry of positive reinforcement. In M. Zuckerman (Ed.), *Biological bases of sensation seeking, impulsivity, and anxiety* (pp. 151–175). Hillsdale, NJ: Lawrence Erlbaum.

Stein, L., Wise, C. D., & Berger, B. D. (1973). Anti-anxiety action of benzodiazepines: Decrease in activity of serotonin neurons in the punishment system. In S. Garattini, E. Mussini, & L. O. Randall (Eds.), *The benzodiazepines* (pp. 299–326). New York: Raven Press.

Stein, L., Belluzzi, J. D., & Wise, C. D. (1977). Benzodiazepines: Behavioral and neurochemical mechanisms. *American Journal of Psychiatry, 134,* 665–669.

Stoff, D. M., Pollock, L., Vitiello, B., Behar, D., & Bridger, W. H. (1987). Reduction of (3H)-imipramine binding sites on platelets of conduct-disordered children. *Neuropsychopharmacology, 1,* 55–62.

Swanson, J. M., Posner, M. I., Potkin, S., Bonforte, S., Youpa, D., Cantwell, D., & Crinella, F. (1991). Activating tasks for the study of visual-spatial attention in ADHD children: A cognitive anatomical approach. *Journal of Child Neurology, 6,* 119–127.

Swanson, J. M., Shea, C., McBurnett, K., Potkin, S. G., Fiore, C., & Crinella, F. (1990). Attention and hyperactivity. In J. T. Enns (Ed.), *The development of attention: Research and theory* (pp. 383–403). Amsterdam: Elsevier/North Holland.

Tarter, R. E., McBride, H., Buonpane, N., & Schneider, D. U. (1977). Differentiation of alcoholics: Childhood history of minimal brain dysfunction, family history, and drinking pattern. *Archives of General Psychiatry, 34,* 761–768.

Thoren, P., Asberg, M., Bertilsson, L., & Traskman, L. (1980). Chlomipramine treatment of obsessive-compulsive disorder: II. Biochemical aspects. *Archives of General Psychiatry, 37,* 1289–1295.

Tucker, D. M., & Williamson, P. A. (1984). Asymmetric neural control systems in human self-regulation. *Psychological Review, 91,* 185–215.

Virkkunen, M., DeJong, J., Bartko, J., Goodwin, F. K., & Linnoila, M. (1989). Relationship of psychobiological variables to recidivism in violent offenders and impulsive fire setters: A follow-up study. *Archives of General Psychiatry, 46,* 600–603.

Virkkunen, M., DeJong, J., Bartko, J., & Linnoila, M. (1989). Psychobiological concomitants of history of suicide attempts among violent offenders and impulsive fire setters. *Archives of General Psychiatry, 46,* 604–606.

von Knorring, L., Oreland, L., & Winblad, B. (1984). Personality traits related to monoamine oxidase activity in platelets. *Psychiatry Research, 12,* 11–26.

Walker, J. L., Lahey, B. B., Russo, M. F., Frick, P. J., Christ, M. A. G., McBurnett, K., Loeber, R., Stouthamer-Loeber, M., & Green, S. (1991). Anxiety, inhibition, and Conduct Disorder in children: I. Relations to social impairment and sensation seeking. *Journal of the American Academy of Child and Adolescent Psychiatry, 30,* 192–196.

Wallbank, J. (1985). Antisocial and prosocial behavior among contemporary Robin Hoods. *Personality and Individual Differences, 6,* 11–19.

Weinshilboum, R. M., Thoa, N. B., Johnson, D. G., Kopin, I. J., & Axelrod, J. (1971). Proportional release of norepinephrine and dopamine-beta-hydroxylase from sympathetic nerves. *Science,* 174, 1349–1351.

Weiss, J. M., Bailey, W. H., Goodman, P. A., Hoffman, L. J., Ambrose, M. J., Salman, S., & Charry, J. M. (1982). A model for neurochemical study of depression. In M. Y. Spiegelstein & A. Levy (Eds.), *Behavioral models and the analysis of drug action* (pp. 195–223). Amsterdam: Elsevier.

West, D. J., & Farrington, D. P. (1973). *Who becomes delinquent?* London: Heineman.

Wilson, C. L., Hirasuna, N., & Lindsley, D. B. (1988). Brainstem-limbic systems and behavior. In G. C. Galbraith, M. L. Kietzman, & E. Donchin (Eds.), *Neurophysiology and psychophysiology: Experimental and clinical applications.* Hillsdale, NJ: Lawrence Erlbaum Associates.

Wilson, C. L., Motter, B. C., & Lindsley, D. B. (1976). Influences of hypothalamic stimulation upon septal and hippocampal electrical activity in the cat. *Brian Research, 107,* 55–68.

Wise, C. D., & Stein, L. (1969). Facilitation of self-stimulation by central administration of norepinephrine. *Science, 163,* 299–301.

Wise, C. D., Belluzi, J. D., & Stein, L. (1977). Possible role of dopamine-beta-hydroxylase in the regulation of norepinephrine biosynthesis in rat brain. *Pharmacology, Biochemistry and Behavior, 7,* 549–553.

Zentall, S. S., & Zentall, T. R. (1983). Optimal stimulation: A model of disordered activity and performance in normal and deviant children. *Psychological Bulletin, 94,* 446–471.

Zuckerman, M. (1971). Dimensions of sensation seeking. *Journal of Consulting and Clinical Psychology, 36,* 45–52.

Zuckerman, M. (1979). *Sensation seeking: Beyond the optimal level of arousal.* Hillsdale, NJ: Lawrence Erlbaum.

Zuckerman, M. (1983a). A biological theory of sensation seeking. In M. Zuckerman (Ed.),

Biological bases of sensation seeking, impulsivity, and anxiety (pp. 37–76). Hillsdale, NJ: Lawrence Erlbaum.

Zuckerman, M. (Ed.). (1983b). *Biological bases of sensation seeking, impulsivity, and anxiety.* Hillsdale, NJ: Lawrence Erlbaum.

Zuckerman, M., & Neeb, M. (1979). Sensation seeking and psychopathology. *Psychiatry Research, 1,* 255–264.

Zuckerman, M., Ballenger, J. C., & Post, R. M. (1984). The neurobiology of some dimensions of personality. In J. R. Smythies & R. J. Bradley (Eds.), *International Review of Neurobiology* (pp. 391–436). Orlando, FL: Academic Press.

Zuckerman, M., Eysenck, S. B. G., & Eysenck, H. J. (1978). Sensation seeking in England and America: Cross-cultural, age, and sex comparisons. *Journal of Consulting and Clinical Psychology, 46,* 139–149.

5 Psychological Aspects of Childhood Cancer

ALICE G. FRIEDMAN AND RAYMOND K. MULHERN

1. Introduction

Eiser (1990) has recently commented that, relative to the number of children affected by different chronic diseases, the psychological adjustment of pediatric cancer patients has received a disproportionate amount of attention by researchers. There are fewer than 10,000 children newly diagnosed with cancer per year, yet there has been a steadily increasing number of psychological studies of these children and their families. Increased interest in pediatric cancer is due, at least in part, to recognition that the medical treatment for cancer is typically more prolonged and aversive than treatment for most other childhood illness. Further, both the disease and its treatment may have potentially damaging and permanent effects on the child's cosmetic, personal–social and neuropsychological functioning. Consequently, perhaps more than most other chronic or potentially life-threatening diseases, the diagnosis of and treatment for cancer places extraordinary demands on the psychological well-being of the child and family (Eiser, 1990). Lastly, rapid and dramatic improvements in the prognosis of children with cancer have resulted in a marked increase in the number of children who survive the disease. Thus interest in childhood cancer is fueled by concerns about the quality of life of long-term survivors (Mulhern *et al.*, 1989).

This chapter will focus on recent psychological research that impacts directly on decisions regarding the medical and supportive care of the pediatric cancer patient. Our emphasis will be on well-controlled

---

ALICE G. FRIEDMAN • Department of Psychology, State University of New York at Binghamton, Binghamton, New York 13902. RAYMOND K. MULHERN • Division of Psychology, St. Jude Children's Research Hospital, 332 North Lauderdale Street, Memphis, Tennessee 38101.

Advances in Clinical Child Psychology, Volume 14, edited by Benjamin B. Lahey and Alan E. Kazdin. Plenum Press, New York, 1992.

empirical studies that address psychological issues that have been the focus of controversy during the past 5 or more years. We focus on leukemia and brain tumors because these two disease groups are the two most common forms of cancer in young children and together account for 50% to 60% of cases of pediatric cancer diagnoses. However, many of the issues discussed will be relevant to other types of cancers as well. Those interested in more general psychological aspects of childhood cancer or in malignancies other than leukemia or brain tumors are referred to Stehbens (1988). Those interested in more global psychological issues related to chronic illness in children are referred to Melamed, Matthews, Routh, Stabler, and Schneiderman (1988).

The first section of the chapter will deal with general information about childhood cancer; the second will cover medical aspects of cancer to acquaint the reader with basic knowledge about the course of illness and side effects of treatment. The third and fourth sections discuss how psychological principles have been valuable in decreasing distress associated with medical treatment and in assessing the long-term impact of cancer. Lastly, we outline important future directions for research in childhood cancer.

1.1. *Epidemiology*

Although childhood cancer is a relatively rare disease, it is the most common cause of disease-related deaths in children below 14 years of age (Silverberg, Boring, & Squires, 1990). In 1987, there were approximately 6,600 cases of newly diagnosed cancer in children under the age of 15 years. There are approximately 36,000 children who are survivors of cancer in the United States. This number exceeds the number of children who have severe retardation, hearing impairment, deafness, and visual handicaps (Peckham, Meadows, Bartel, & Marrero, 1988). The overall incidence of pediatric cancer is 126.3 per 1 million children, which translates to approximately 1 child in every 600 (Silverberg & Lubera, 1986). Thus, in an average elementary school there is typically only one or two children who have been treated for cancer.

The most common forms of childhood cancer are leukemia and brain tumors. Leukemia accounts for approximately 30% of all newly diagnosed cases. Of these, approximately 80% of the children have a variant known as acute lymphoblastic leukemia. Central nervous system tumors, primarily brain tumors, constitute nearly 20% of childhood neoplasms. Leukemia, Wilm's tumor, neuroblastoma, and retinoblastoma are most frequent in children younger than 5 years of age. Brain tumors occur most frequently among children between 5 and 10 years of age. Lymphomas and bone tumors are most prevalent in children older than 10 years (Hockenberry, Coody, & Bennett, 1990).

1.2. *Prognosis*

Major advances in the medical treatment of childhood cancer within the past two decades have resulted in dramatic improvements in the cure rates for many types of malignancy. Seventy percent of children diagnosed with acute lymphocytic leukemia can expect to remain disease free for 5 years or longer. This is in sharp contrast to a 4% five-year survival rate in the early 1960s (Silverberg, Boring, & Squires, 1990). Overall, mortality has declined from 8.3 per 100,000 in 1950 to 3.6 per 100,000 in 1986 (Silverberg *et al.*, 1990). With the improved prognosis associated with contemporary therapies, it is estimated that approximately one in every 1,000 adults now reaching the age of 20 is a survivor of childhood cancer (Meadows & Hobbie, 1986).

The nature of childhood cancer has therefore changed from being an acute, ultimately fatal disease to a chronic illness with an unpredictable course. Improvement in the prognosis of childhood cancer is primarily due to changes in therapeutic medical modalities from single-agent chemotherapies to combinations of multiple agent chemotherapies, radiation therapy, and surgery, and to more aggressive supportive care (Jaffee, 1987). The development and evaluation of new effective chemotherapeutic agents has been facilitated by carefully designed clinical trials using sophisticated experimental designs and involving collaborative efforts across many specialities and institutions (George, 1980). From the first controlled clinical trial in the treatment of childhood cancer conducted in the 1950s to current practices, the medical treatment of childhood cancer has been guided by the coordinated efforts of researchers and practitioners. Medical treatments are typically developed and tested by means of clinical treatment protocols originating from cooperative groups or by studies designed in regional institutions that treat large numbers of pediatric cancer patients (George, 1980).

1.3. *Professional Role of Psychologists*

The consultative role of the psychologist in pediatric oncology settings has been concurrently influenced by medical advances as well as innovations in the field of pediatric psychology. When prognosis was dismal, psychologists provided supportive care to the child and family during the final stages of illness. Their contemporary role encompasses designing and evaluating strategies to alleviate acute and long-term effects of treatment in collaboration with medical colleagues as well as facilitating optimal adjustment for children and their families during and following treatment. Psychologists are now well-integrated members of the Pediatric Oncology Group (POG) and the Children's Cancer Study Group (CCSG), the two major collaborative interinstitutional study groups responsible for developing and evaluating the efficacy of treatments for childhood cancer in this country. Information gathered by psychologists has influenced decisions about the medical treatment of certain cancers. Further, psychologists are now routinely involved in comprehensive care and are usually highly visible members of treatment teams in most pediatric oncology settings.

2. *Medical Aspects*

Despite dramatic medical gains, diagnosis and treatment for cancer continues to place extreme demands on the child and family. Treatment is accompanied by painful medical procedures, disruption of age-appropriate activities, financial burdens that persist for 2 or more years following cessation of therapy, and an unknown ultimate outcome. The disease typically follows an unpredictable course, and there is a continuous fear of relapse or recurrence. Lastly, although still a matter of debate, the neurotoxicity of chemotherapeutic agents and radiation therapy place the child at risk for future neuropsychological deficits. In the following section we discuss medical aspects of acute leukemia and brain tumors because such knowledge is essential to understanding the importance of psychological service and research to oncology settings.

2.1. *Leukemia*

Acute lymphoblastic leukemia (ALL) is a malignancy of the bone marrow characterized by rapid and unregulated proliferation of malignant immature white blood cells (lymphoblasts). Lymphoblasts progressively replace normal bone marrow, infiltrate to other sites, and cause a reduction of normal blood cells and their corresponding functions, resulting in anemia, infection, and hemorrhage. The most common symptoms of leukemia are fatigue, bruising, and fever that may be evident days to weeks preceding diagnosis. Localized or diffuse bone pain, accompanied by limping, irritability, and reluctance to walk, also appears to be a common initial symptom that may result in an initial misdiagnosis of arthritis or musculoskeletal disease (Jonsson, Sartain, Ducore, & Buchanan, 1990). ALL appears to be composed of a group of heterogeneous subtypes, each with differential prognosis linked to certain characteristics present at diagnosis. On the basis of certain "risk factors" such as the child's age, sex, initial white blood count, presence of certain cell markers, children are classified as being at low, medium, or high risk for relapse. Children at greatest risk are given more intensive treatments than those at low risk.

A diagnosis of ALL is confirmed if a bone marrow aspiration reveals lymphoblasts in the bone marrow. A lumbar puncture (spinal tap) is typically conducted to determine if there are leukemic cells in the child's cerebrospinal fluid. If positive, the child also has central nervous system leukemia. Once the diagnosis is made, the child is often referred to a regional cancer center for treatment.

Treatment is typically conducted in three distinct phases. The first, termed remission induction, consists of 4 to 6 weeks of intensive combination chemotherapy, with the goal of destroying all lymphoblasts. A complete remission is achieved in 95% of all children. The second phase, maintenance chemotherapy, which is used to maintain continuous complete remission, consists of continued chemotherapy for approximately 30 months. The third phase, prophylactic central nervous system (CNS) treatment, consists of chemotherapy injected into the spinal canal (intrathecal therapy) sometimes combined with cranial irradiation to obliterate occult leukemic cells in the brain. Prophylactic treatment typically occurs early in the maintenance phase of treatment. Until recently, most children received irradiation. However, because of recent concerns about the long-term neurological effects of cranial irradiation, it is now most commonly used only with children who are at high risk for relapse or who have observable CNS leukemia at diagnosis. Treatment is terminated after successful completion of maintenance therapy, although children continue to return to a clinic at regular intervals for diagnostic procedures to detect recurrence. The majority of children maintain a continuous remission and are considered cured 5 years after diagnosis.

2.2. *Brain Tumors*

In contrast to leukemia, the prognosis for children with the most common types of brain tumors continues to be poor. Prognosis and symptomology depend upon the location and type of brain tumor. The most common type of brain tumors in childhood include astrocytoma, medulloblastoma, brain stem tumors and ependymoma. Brain tumors in children most often originate in the region of the cerebellum. The initial symptoms of brain tumors may be mild, nonspecific, and intermittent, and typically include headaches, nausea, and vomiting. Because these symptoms are similar to those that accompany usual childhood flulike illness, they may be ignored until they have persisted for an extended period of time or worsened. Other symptoms, such as squinting, decreased vision, drowsiness, lethargy, confusion, and distinct personality changes may be more alarming and prompt parents to seek medical attention. In some cases there may be more distinct symptoms such as back pain, seizures, ataxia, loss of balance, difficulty walking, hemiparesis, and endocrine disturbances (Ertel & Boesel, 1979). Diagnositic workup for a child with a suspected brain tumor includes computed tomography (CT) scan, and/or magnetic resonance imaging (MRI), a myelogram and lumbar puncture, along with a thorough neurologic exam. Once a tumor is confirmed, a biopsy may be performed to provide further information about the nature of the tumor. The treatment depends upon the location and extent of the lesion. The most common treatment is a total or partial resection of the tumor followed by radiation therapy. Chemotherapy has proven effective for recurrent brain tumors and is more commonly used prior to irradiation in newly diagnosed children. For some tumors, such as those of the brain stem, excision is not possible.

2.3. *Chemotherapy*

Anticancer chemotherapeutic agents are most often used to interrupt the reproduction of cancer cells, although they may also be used to eradicate malignant cells that are not reproducing (Lilley, 1990). Combinations of agents are typically used because they provide additive and synergistic effects. These agents affect both normal and cancer cells because rapidly proliferating cells are most sensitive to the toxic effects of chemotherapy. These structures include gastrointestinal epithelium, bone marrow, oral mucosa and hair follicles, resulting in adverse side effects. The most common side effects include abdominal pain, diarrhea, nausea and vomiting, anorexia, change in taste perception, alopecia, and fever. Although some of the side effects are temporary, chemotherapy may have long-term adverse affects on all major organ systems.

2.4. *Radiation Therapy*

Radiation therapy plays a major role in the treatment of many types of cancers including ALL and brain tumors. Improved technology has resulted in more effective radiotherapy with a reduction in acute side effects and long-term morbidity. Radiation therapy, used alone or in combination with other treatment modalities, may be given with the intent of curing or to provide symptomatic (palliative) relief. Type and extent of side effects depend upon site of treatment, dose, and interval from treatment. Depending upon site, short-term side effects attributed to radiation therapy include nausea and vomiting, diarrhea, skin and mucosal inflammation, tissue edema, pneumonitism enteritis, myelosuppression, and alopecia (hair loss). Long-term effects may include second malignancy, endocrine and neuropsychological dysfunction, dental problems, cataracts, and infertility. As a group, adult survivors of childhood cancer are significantly shorter than same-sex sibling controls. Growth retardation has previously been attributed to the adverse effects of cranial and craniospinal irradiation on children undergoing treatment for leukemia, although chemotherapy also appears to be an important growth-slowing factor (Holmes, Holmes, Baker, & Hassanein, 1990). Growth deviation among children treated for brain tumors has also been related to irradiation dosage.

3. *Psychological Interventions for Acute Problems*

Despite the dramatic improvements in survival rates for childhood cancer, children undergoing treatment endure medical, psychological, and social stressors that significantly alter their lives. Treatment, consisting of surgery, radiation therapy, and chemotherapy may persist for years. As reviewed earlier, the side effects of treatment are often so serious as to be viewed by the child as more distressing than the disease itself. Two acute side effects of treatment that have been the focus of the bulk of psychological studies on alleviating distress are pain and anticipatory nausea/vomiting. In the following section we present an overview of these two areas with a focus on future needs.

3.1. *Pain Associated with Medical Procedures*

Children endure numerous painful medical procedures for the purpose of differential diagnosis, treatment, assessment of response to treatment, and surveillance following completion of treatment. Children are routinely subjected to laboratory studies requiring "finger sticks" and venipuncture, insertion of intravenous lines for chemotherapy, and bone marrow aspirations and lumbar punctures. Knowledge about pharmacological approaches to pain reduction in children lags behind that for adults. Further, concerns about the toxicity of sedatives, anxiolytics, and hypnotics have limited their use, even for procedures for which adults are routinely premedicated.

There is a large literature on behavioral methods to reduce children's distress during painful medical procedures. However, these studies focus on healthy children undergoing routine dental procedures, venipuncture conducted during routine office visits, and anxiety reduction prior to elective surgery. These situations differ markedly from those experienced by cancer patients both in terms of their intensity, frequency, and context. Fear associated with "finger sticks" conducted during well child visits are not comparable to the anxiety and fears associated with the same procedure in the context of treatment for cancer.

There are surprisingly few well-controlled behavioral intervention studies comparing different strategies of pain control in pediatric cancer patients. Tentative support for the effectiveness of hypnosis has been provided by some investigators who have reported decreased procedural distress following hypnosis (Hilgard & LeBaron, 1984; Zeltzer, 1980). Reports have typically been based on case presentations rather than controlled studies. Studies that have compared hypnosis to other strategies tend to note decreases in self-reports of distress for children receiving any interventions (Katz, Kellerman, & Ellenberg, 1987).

Support for the use of behavioral and cognitive–behavioral strategies to decrease pain has been demonstrated with other populations (Elliott & Olson, 1983) and with children with cancer undergoing bone marrow aspirations and lumbar punctures (Jay, Elliott, Ozolins, Olson, & Pruitt, 1985). These psychological treatments are typically administered in packages consisting of tangible reinforcers to increase motivation and compliance, relaxation training, cognitive self-instruction, and modeling. There have been few attempts to compare strategies, to identify the effective components of these treatments, or to identify the most effective general approach to behavioral and pharmacological treatments.

An exception to this is a study by Jay and colleagues (Jay, Elliott, Katz, & Siegel, 1987). Using a randomized crossover design, Jay *et al.* (1987) compared valium, cognitive–behavior strategies, and attention control groups. The most notable findings of the study were that children receiving cognitive–behavioral interventions (modeling, breathing exercises, emotive imagery, behavioral rehearsal and reinforcement) had lower distress levels as well as lower pain and pulse rates than those in the attention control group. Valium appeared to be beneficial for reducing anticipatory distress but not distress during the procedures. A finding of clinical importance was that children do not appear to be able to benefit from training in cognitive–behavioral strategies unless there is a coach available during the painful procedure. The benefits of the cognitive–behavioral intervention did not generalize to subsequent procedures. This finding has been reported previously (e.g., Elliott & Olson, 1983) and, when considered along with the findings of Katz *et al.* (1987), suggest that the most effective component of behavioral approaches may be the distraction provided by the therapist/coach rather than any specific effects of the treatment components. Because most oncology settings are not equipped with a sufficient number of therapists to provide for all patients, a more realistic strategy may be either to train parents or nurses as therapists or find other methods of distraction. Further, psychologists and medical practitioners should collaborate on developing more effective and less toxic combinations of pharmacological interventions and behavioral strategies.

3.2. *Anticipatory Nausea and Vomiting*

Although nausea and vomiting are inevitable side effects of some chemotherapy treatments, some children develop similar side effects *prior* to receiving treatment. This phenomenon, known as anticipatory nausea and vomiting (ANV), occurs in nearly one-third of children undergoing chemotherapy and is considered a maladaptive learned response. Efforts to prevent and ameliorate the distressing symptoms of ANV represent an area within clinical oncology where psychologists have most closely translated basic psychological principles to actual practice. ANV is thought to be acquired through classical conditioning principles. Infusion of chemotherapy serves as the unconditioned stimulus that signals the onset of nausea and vomiting (unconditioned response). After one or more pairings, stimuli such as the sight, sounds, and smells of the clinic (conditioned stimuli) that are temporally or spatially associated with chemotherapy infusion elicit nausea and vomiting (conditioned response). In a manner consistent with other classically conditioned responses, the severity of ANV appears to increase with repeated pairings (Carey & Burish, 1988), with the aggressiveness of the chemotherapy regimen, and with the severity of posttreatment nausea and vomiting (Dolgin, Katz, McGinty, & Siegel, 1985). Highly anxious children may also be at an increased risk for developing ANV (Carey & Burish, 1988). The conditioning process for ANV is similar to that for acquired taste aversions, which are also prevalent among this population and have been demonstrated experimentally (Bernstein, Webster, & Bernstein, 1982).

Hypnosis, progressive muscle relaxation, and attentional diversion techniques in the form of video games have all showed promise as methods of reducing conditioned side effects of chemotherapy (Carey & Burish, 1988). In one of the most scholarly reviews of the efficacy of these approaches to treating ANV published to date, Carey and Burish (1988) conclude that psychological interventions are clinically effective for reducing these distressing symptoms. They note that a variety of strategies have proven to be effective, although the mechanisms underlying their efficacy remain less clearly understood. We can find no studies that have attempted to identify the essential components of effective treatments used to reduce ANV in children. Further, as with the pain literature discussed earlier, future efforts should focus on integrating the most effective behavioral strategies with the most effective pharmacological approaches.

4. *Neuropsychological Functioning*

A focused interest on the neuropsychological status of children treated for cancer began with the clinical observation that a subset of the first major cohort of survivors of ALL experienced a high frequency of learning problems manifested in school failure. Cross-sectional and, less frequently, longitudinal investigations confirmed that irradiation and/or chemotherapy directed at the CNS could have devastating effects, especially among preschool-aged children. Similarly, psychologists have more recently explored brain–behavior relationships among children treated for malignant brain tumors. The results of psychological studies have had a major influence on the modification of medical treatment protocols to reduce toxicity as well as exposing high risk groups of children to close surveillance and early intervention to avoid or minimize adverse late effects may be arranged.

4.1. *Acute Lymphoblastic Leukemia*

Since the study by Soni and colleagues (Soni, Marten, Pitner, Duenas, & Powazek, 1975) approximately 15 years ago that minimized neuropsychological toxicities secondary to CNS prophylaxis for ALL, more than 50 empirical papers and at least two comprehensive reviews have been published on this issue (Fletcher & Copeland, 1988; Williams & Davis, 1986). Within these reports, the following major questions are addressed: (1) What is the role of cranial irradiation in the development of neuropsychological deficits? (2) Is cranial irradiation toxicity dose-dependent? (3) Are younger children more vulnerable to CNS toxicity than older children? (4) Are deficits measured following CNS treatment progressive, stable, or remit over time?

The findings of relevant studies, restricted to those focused on IQ testing with children 2 or more years following completion of treatment, are summarized in Table 1. The retrospective studies that demonstrated significantly lower mean full-scale IQ in irradiated patients include Moss, Nannis, and Poplack (1981). Schlieper, Esseltine, and Tarshis (1989), Copeland, Fletcher, Pfefferbaum-Levine, Jaffee, Ried, and Maor (1985), and Rowland *et al.* (1984). whereas Ivnik, Colligen, Obetz, and Smithson (1981) and Whitt, Wells, Laurie, and Wilhelm (1984) failed to confirm this finding. Among the prospective studies, only Meadows,

Table 1
Summary of Studies of IQ among Long-Term Survivors of ALL

Study	Observed adverse late effects		
	Treatment with radiation therapy	Younger age at treatment	Increased time since treatment
Moss *et al.* (1981)	Yes	Yes	No
Ivnik *et al.* (1981)	No	No	No
Whitt *et al.* (1984)	No	No	NR*
Schlieper *et al.* (1989)	Yes	No	No
Copeland *et al.* (1985)	Yes	No	NR
Rowland *et al.* (1984)	Yes	No	No
Meadows *et al.* (1981)	Yes	Yes	Yes
Jannoun & Chessells (1987)	NR	Yes	No
Longeway *et al.* (1990)	NR	No	No
Ochs *et al.* (in press)	No	No	Yes

*Not reported.

Massari, Fergusson, Gordon, Littman, and Moss (1981) showed a significant advantage in the nonirradiated group: Jannoun and Chessells (1987) and Longeway *et al.* (1990) lacked nonirradiated patient groups necessary for this comparison.

The effects of the child's age at the time of CNS prophylaxis remain ambiguous. Only the study by Meadows *et al.* (1981) demonstrated declines in IQ over time following CNS prophylaxis. Among the studies previously discussed, Moss *et al.* (1981), Meadows *et al.* (1981) and Jannoun and Chessells (1987) reported increased risk of lowered IQ with younger age, whereas the studies by Ivnik *et al.* (1981), Whitt *et al.* (1984), Schlieper *et al.* (1989), Copeland *et al.* (1985), Rowland *et al.* (1984) and Longeway *et al.* (1990) failed to find age-related differences. The proportion of infants who survive ALL and have been formally studied remains small. However, these very young children may represent an especially high-risk group for neuropsychological deficits, and further investigations are needed.

These divergent, if not contradictory, findings have been variously explained by differences in sample selection criteria that create systematic biases, small sample sizes resulting in unreliable findings and diminished statistical power, differences among neuropsychological tests and assessment intervals, variable inclusion of patients with CNS leukemia at diagnosis and those who have relapses, and methods of assignment to CNS prophylaxis regimens (Fletcher & Copeland, 1988; Williams &

Davis, 1986). An alternative explanation rarely noted by previous investigators is that these discrepancies are secondary to differences in the therapy for ALL beyond the simple inclusion or exclusion of cranial irradiation in CNS prophylaxis. In a recent prospective randomized trial comparing CNS prophylaxis with 18 Gy cranial irradiation and intrathecal methotrexate alone, no increased risk of neuropsychological dysfunction was associated with radiation therapy or younger age at treatment. However, 16 of the 26 children in the chemotherapy group and 14 of the 23 in the irradiation group showed a clinically significant decline in one or more intellectual or academic achievement parameters during the course of their 5-year follow-up (Ochs *et al.*, 1991).

In contrast to the sometimes controversial results of studies of children with ALL who remain in remission and then become long-term survivors, there appears little doubt that children who experience a CNS relapse of leukemia and then require more aggressive and prolonged CNS therapy have a much increased risk of neuropsychological deficits. Approximately 5% to 10% of children treated for ALL will experience a CNS relapse following a period of remission. Only approximately 25% of these children will be cured. Because most centers have only a few such long-term survivors, very few studies have addressed this subgroup of children. Ochs, Rivera, Aur, Hustu, Berg, and Simone (1985) compared 50 children who were long-term survivors of leukemia who remained in complete remission with 23 children who were long-term survivors following one of two CNS relapses. Full Scale IQ as well as scores on standardized measures of spelling, arithmetic, and reading were significantly lower in the children who had relapsed. The survivors of CNS relapse also had a greater incidence of cerebral calcification and neurological deficits including seizures.

In a larger retrospective study, Mulhern, Ochs, Fairclough, Wasserman, Davis, and Williams (1987) studied the psychoeducational status of 40 survivors of CNS relapse. The incidence of reduced intellectual function in this group was quite high with 20% of the survivors functioning below an IQ of 70, approximately 10 times the incidence expected in the general population. Nine of the 40 children required special educational placements. A relative risk analysis indicated that a younger age at diagnosis and relapse, seizures, abnormal CT scan of the head, and more than one course of cranial irradiation (4,200–4,800 cGy total) were highly predictive of lowered IQ.

Only one prospective study of survivors of CNS relapse has been identified. Longeway *et al.* (1990) serially assessed 8 children who experienced a CNS relapse and compared them to 16 children who remained in complete remission. Unlike previous studies, both groups of children had received prophylactic treatment, including 2,400 cGy cranial irradiation, on the same protocol. Annual evaluations began at the time of initial diagnosis and continued for 3 to 6 years. The mean IQ scores of both groups were in the normal range at diagnosis and were not statistically different. The patients who remained in remission maintained or even slightly improved their Full Scale IQ scores with repeated testing 2 to 3 years later. On the other hand, patients who experienced a CNS relapse averaged a 16-point drop in IQ 3 years later and a 25-point drop 5 to 6 years later.

Among children remaining in remission, changes in intellectual performance and academic achievement have also been attributed to factors other than medical treatment, such as school absences (Mulhern *et al.*, 1990), parental education levels (Whitt *et al.*, 1984), social class (Trautman *et al.*, 1988), and gender (Schlieper *et al.*, 1989). We have previously analyzed school absence data from the CNS prophylaxis groups in the study by Ochs *et al.* (1991). Children who missed more than 60 days of school from the diagnosis to the completion of treatment had significantly lower Verbal IQ and reading and mathematics achievement. Both Whitt *et al.* (1984) and Trautman *et al.* (1988) have found family socioeconomic factors to be more important than treatment-related variables in predicting neuropsychological performance of children surviving ALL. Jannoun (1983), Robison, Nesbit, Sather, Meadows, Ortega, and Hammond (1984) and Schlieper *et al.* (1989) have found females to be at greater risk than males for intellectual deficits following treatment for ALL.

4.2. *Brain Tumors*

As shown in Table 2, an analysis of factors that place children with brain tumors at risk for chronic neuropsychological deficits reveals that radiation therapy, age at treatment, and time since treatment are the most frequently investigated variables. The role of other factors such as the presence or absence of hydrocephalus, seizures, and sensorimotor loss has been less well defined.

The deleterious effects of cranial radiation therapy on the intellectual development of children with brain tumors have been demonstrated using a variety of designs, primarily comparing the presence versus absence of irradiation or comparing brain fields/volumes irradiated, but no studies relating dose to IQ toxicity are yet noted. Serial studies of irradiated patients, as well as comparisons between irradiated and nonirradiated patients and between irradiated patients and normal controls have all concluded that radiation therapy has adverse effects on intellectual development (Duffner, Cohen, & Parker, 1988; Ellenberg, McComb, Siegel, & Stowe, 1987; Hirsch, Renier, Czernichow, Ben-

TABLE 2
Summary of Studies of IQ among Long-Term Survivors of Brain Tumors

	Observed adverse late effects		
Study	Treatment with radiation therapy	Younger age at treatment	Increased time since treatment
Chin & Maruyama (1984)	Yes	NR*	NR
Duffner *et al.* (1988)	Yes	Yes	Yes
Ellenberg *et al.* (1987)	Yes	Yes	Yes
Hirsch *et al.* (1979)	Yes	NR	NR
Kun *et al.* (1983)	Yes	No	Yes
Mulhern *et al.* (1989)	Yes	NR	Yes
Mulhern *et al.* (1985)	Yes	Yes	Yes
Packer *et al.* (1989)	Yes	Yes	Yes
Riva *et al.* (1989)	Yes	NR	NR

*Not reported.

veniste, & Pierre-Kah, 1979; Kun, Mulhern, & Crisco, 1983; Mulhern, Horowitz, Kovnar, Langston, & Kun, 1989; Mulhern & Kun, 1985; Packer *et al.*, 1989; Riva, Pantaleoni, Milani, & Belani, 1989). Two studies have also demonstrated greater decrements among children receiving whole brain irradiation compared to those receiving a localized field of treatment. It should be noted that total doses are typically two to three times larger than those given for CNS prophylaxis in ALL (Kun *et al.*, 1983; Chin & Maruyama, 1984).

Investigations that examined the relationship between age at diagnosis and IQ have found that a younger age at diagnosis was related to a lower level of intellectual function (Duffner *et al.*, 1988; Ellenberg *et al.*, 1987; Mulhern *et al.*, 1985; Packer *et al.*, 1989). However, this association is difficult to specify because of variation in the definition of "younger." Some investigators defined young children as those below 3, 6, 7, 7.5, and below 8 years. Of the studies that did not find age at diagnosis to be related to intellectual functioning, Kun *et al.* (1983) found a significant relationship between age at diagnosis and selective attention, with younger children performing more poorly than older children.

The relationship between time since treatment and intellectual level has been evaluated longitudinally. Three investigators found a statistically significant decline in intellectual functioning over time from preirradiation to over 4 years posttreatment (Duffner *et al.*, 1988; Mulhern, Horowitz, Kovnar, *et al.*, 1989; Packer *et al.*, 1989). However, in one investigation this was only true for those patients receiving cranial irradiation and those irradiated at a younger age (Packer *et al.*, 1989). Kun *et al.* (1983) evaluated patients following surgery, before irradiation and again 10 to 26 months later, following irradiation. At the second evaluation, two patients were improved, five stable, and three deteriorated with regard to intellectual status.

Mixed results were found over time within several investigations. Ellenberg *et al.* (1987) reported significant risk in IQ from 1 to 4 months post diagnosis but declined thereafter. This relationship appears to be mediated by tumor location. Finally, Mulhern and Kun (1985) evaluated patients at postsurgery, preirradiation and again 6 months after irradiation. The relationship between time since treatment and intellectual ability varied for older versus younger children with younger children evidencing a greater decline over time in memory functioning than older children. Furthermore, among the older children, females showed more improvement than males over time on Full Scale, Verbal, and Performance IQ.

Fewer studies have examined the relationship between IQ and brain tumor location. Ellenberg *et al.* (1987) examined the IQ scores of patients with brain tumors of the third ventricular region, posterior fossa region, and cerebral hemisphere at four time intervals. Although the IQ scores of patients with hemispheric tumors were lower than those with third ventricular and posterior fossa tumors, over all time intervals, this difference was only significant at the 4-month postdiagnosis evaluation, perhaps due to small sample sizes at the other intervals. Another investigation (Mulhern & Kun, 1985) found a greater increase in IQ scores over time for patients with posterior fossa tumors than for those with third ventricle area and hemispheric tumors, but this relationship was true only for younger children.

Of the studies that have examined the relationship between hydrocephalus and intellectual deficits, most found nonsignificant results. In contrast, Ellenberg *et al.* (1987) reported that patients with hydrocephalus scored significantly lower than those without, both initially and at 4 months. However, an improvement in IQ over the 3-month interval was noted both for patients with and without a history of hydrocephalus. This investigation also examined patients with hydrocephalus who did or did not have shunts. No significant IQ differences existed between these groups initially. At the 4-month interval, a significant increase was noted for those patients with shunts but not for those patients without shunts.

The impact of visual, auditory, and motor impairments secondary to the brain tumor and its treatment has seldom been analyzed with reference to IQ. Cavazzuti, Fischer, Welch, Belli, and Winston (1983) assessed 35 long-term survivors of craniopharyngioma; 18 had received conservative surgical procedures followed by local field radiation therapy, and 17 had received aggressive attempts at gross total resection. Among the 17 patients with aggressive surgery were two subgroups, those whose tumors never recurred and those whose tumor recurred, requiring second surgery and irradiation. Although no permanent visual impairments were noted among irradiated and nonirradiated patients without recurrence, one-third of the patients requiring repeat resection had clinically relevant visual impairments. However, no statistically significant differences between the IQ values of the three groups were noted with all group mean scores falling in the normal range for age. Mulhern and Kun (1985) reported on the sensorimotor status of 26 children with a variety of malignant tumors. Twenty-five percent of the patients had one or more significant visual, auditory, or motor deficits. Although no statistically reliable correlation between these deficits and IQ were found, five of the six patients with IQ < 80 were visually impaired.

Only one investigation has attempted to analyze risk factors in combination, primarily because of the large sample size needed for such an analysis. Ellenberg *et al.* (1987) serially evaluated 43 consecutively diagnosed children with brain tumors at the Children's Hospital of Los Angeles. Multiple regression analysis used IQs at 1 to 4 years of follow-up as the criterion variables. The following factors, listed in descending order of importance, were significant univariate predictors of lower IQ: (a) lower IQ at 1-month postdiagnosis; (b) younger age at diagnosis; (c) cranial (whole brain) radiation therapy field; and (d) cerebral hemisphere tumor site. The authors also found a statistically significant interaction between age at diagnosis and radiation therapy field; younger children receiving local or no cranial irradiation had higher IQs than comparably treated older children, whereas younger children receiving whole brain irradiation had lower IQs than comparably treated older children.

5. *Long-Term Psychological Adjustment*

Questions about the impact of cancer on the psychological adjustment of long-term survivors is a relatively new concern. Until recently, so few children survived that efforts were better spent on decreasing acute distress. Studies that did examine long-term survivors focused on medical problems and intellectual deficits associated with cranial irradiation rather than the child's personal–social adjustment. There are relatively few studies of psychological late effects, and they typically have mixed children with different diagnoses. Study of the psychological adjustment of survivors of childhood cancer began by examining global indices of adjustment among heterogenous groups of survivors. These early studies were largely exploratory, and generalizations were impeded by rapid changes in medical treatments. Thus even children with the same type of cancer treated at different institutions or treated in different years did not receive similar treatments.

Early researchers debated the question of whether survivors of childhood cancer differed significantly from their peers on such global indices of adjustment as employment and marital status, and on more specific indices such as level of depression and self-esteem. These studies were retrospective and used a "horse race" approach, typically pitting cancer patients against healthy, age-matched peers using questionnaires and interviews to detect differences between groups. Examples of these approaches include two classic studies (Holmes & Holmes, 1975; Li & Stone, 1976), both of which used questionnaires and interviews to inquire about important areas of adult functioning, such as marital status and occupation. These early studies described adequate psychosocial adjustment among most of the survivors. However, these studies were conducted on individuals who were treated during an era where survival was less likely. Children who survived may have had treatments that were less aggressive and less toxic than those currently used. Further, children who had serious complications were less apt to survive than with contemporary care.

More recent studies have documented differences between survivors and matched peers on marital status. Byrne and colleagues (Byrne *et al.*, 1989) included 2,170 survivors in a study of marriage and divorce rates of survivors and reported that compared to their siblings, survivors were less likely to ever marry. The average length of their first marriage was shorter than that of the controls. Meadows, McKee, and Kazak (1989) reported similar results of a study of 95 long-term survivors who were interviewed by phone. As a group, the survivors appeared to be making a good adjustment to the demands of young adulthood. However, the survivors in this sample were also less likely to be married than were their siblings.

Studies assessing specific domains of psychological functioning, such as self-esteem, have consistently documented difficulties among selected groups of survivors. In one of the most comprehensive studies of survivors to date, Koocher and O'Malley (1981) included 115 long-term survivors who were 5 or more years postdiagnosis in a project using interviews and inventories to assess various domains of adjustment. The cancer patients compared poorly to a sample of individuals, who had other chronic illnesses. Seventy-five percent of the cancer survivors were viewed as having mild or no adjustment problems. However, some groups of survivors were clearly at an increased risk for problems. Those at highest risk were children who had relapsed, were older at the time of treatment, and who had treatments that were prolonged or resulted in permanent side effects. Children with cancers that appeared in infancy or early childhood had the lowest percentages of psychological symptoms. It is unclear how to interpret these findings because the samples were matched on certain variables, determined by the comparison group and reducing the total sample size, thus greatly increasing the possibility of selection biases.

Subsequent studies of long-term survivors of childhood cancer using univariate analysis have identified gender (Wasserman, Thompson, Wilimas, & Fairclough, 1987), disease severity and treatment toxicity (Fobair, Hoppe, Bloom, Cox, Varghese, & Spiegel, 1986), age at diagnosis (Mulhern *et al.*, 1987), time since completion of treatment (Mulhern *et al.*, 1987), and exposure to cranial irradiation (Rowland *et al.*, 1984) as significant risk factors from univariate analysis. However, preliminary evidence for interactions among these factors, such as age and irradiation (Ellenberg *et al.*, 1987), in selected groups of survivors suggests the need for a large enough series to permit multivariate analyses.

Two studies examined large groups of survivors who were still children at the time of assessment. Consistent with the findings of early studies, Greenberg, Kazak, and Meadows (1989) reported that as a group the survivors were well adjusted and scored within normal limits on measures of self-concept, depression, and locus of control. However, compared to a matched group of children recruited from a well child clinic, the survivors scored significantly more poorly on self-report measures of self-concept and locus of control. Children with significant functional or cosmetic impairments were at highest risk for problems. Mulhern, Wasserman, Friedman, and Fairclough (1989) reported a fourfold increase in school-related problems and somatic complaints of undetermined origin among a sample ($N = 183$) of long-term survivors compared to the rates expected relative to age- and gender-adjusted norms. In contrast to Greenberg *et al.* (1989), who used self-report instruments, this study was based on parental reports of the child's social and academic functioning. Functional impairments increased the risk of academic and adjustment problems. An older age at evaluation, treatment with cranial irradiation, and residence in a single-parent household also significantly increased the survivor's risk of having adjustment problems.

6. *Conclusions*

As the prognosis for many forms of childhood cancer has improved, there has been increasing concern about the quality of life of children during and following treatment (Mulhern, Fairclough, Friedman, & Leigh, 1990). The acute and late deleterious psychological effects of cancer and its treatment are increasingly well-documented. Further, psychologists have been instrumental in generating information to identify children who may be at greatest risk for developing problems, and in developing treatment strategies to alleviate some of the distressing side effects of treatment.

In an earlier volume of this series, Hovanitz and colleagues (Hovanitz, Gerwell, & Russo, 1984) noted that behavioral psychologists, with their emphasis on empiricism and accountability, have the potential to achieve scientifically verifiable successes in treating children in pediatric settings. At that time, there was recognition that empirically derived and well-validated behavioral techniques could be successfully used to prevent and treat disorders in pediatric populations; however, there were few studies that actually documented the utility of these methods (Hovanitz *et al.*, 1984). During the past 8 years, the picture has changed considerably. There has been significant growth in pediatric psychology in general. Empiricism and accountability continue to characterize the field with a growing literature documenting the efficacy of psychological methods in assessing and treating children in medical settings. Psychologists in pediatric oncology settings have been instrumental in demonstrating the utility of these psychological methods.

As noted earlier in this chapter, the role of the psychologist in oncology settings has evolved along with advances in medical treatment from that of providing supportive care during the terminal phases of disease to developing strategies to attenuate the negative side effects of treatment and to facilitate long-term adjustment of children and their families following termination of treatment. This evolution has rendered traditional supportive approaches less important than problem-specific methodologies that are unique to psychology. In fact, in many oncology settings, social workers and other allied health professionals do provide routine psychosocial support to children and their families. Psychologists spend major portions of their time developing and evaluating behavioral interventions to diminish the negative side effects of treatment, coordinating the psychological assessment of children, providing consultation to other health professionals, and conducting research and teaching. This effort is most apparent by the number of studies focusing on the neuropsychological status of children treated for leukemia and brain tumors, and by studies documenting the efficacy of interventions designed to reduce pain and to attenuate conditioned responses associated with chemotherapy. Supportive counseling designed to facilitate adjustment, particularly during the early states of treatment, continues to be an important service for the child and family with an uncomplicated premorbid history. We expect, however, that in the future the providers of these services are even less apt than today to be psychologists.

7. Recommendations

Psychology has had a tremendous impact on the clinical care of children undergoing treatment for cancer. In this chapter, we have attempted to outline the most significant recent advances in the area; however, we recognize that the field is still in a relatively early stage of development. Perhaps the newest and most promising area is the application of behavioral interventions to reduce acute distress associated with medical procedures and treatments. Early successes demonstrating the efficacy of cognitive–behavioral interventions should be followed by studies that identify (a) the essential components of the most effective treatments, (b) factors that predict which children are most likely to benefit from psychological intervention, and (c) which psychological interventions are most effective for particular children. This information would be especially useful for treating children at small cancer centers that often lack the resources to provide routine psychological services to all children. Further, there is also a strong need for interdisciplinary collaborative studies to identify the most effective combinations of pharmacological and psychological treatments.

Studies have been successful in determining that children are at risk for long-term problems in academic and social domains. It is now possible to identify subgroups of children who are at greatest risk for specific difficulties and to concentrate preventive efforts with these children. Whether early intervention will effectively reduce later problems has yet to be determined, but it should be a focus of future research.

The current state of psychological research in childhood cancer is such that the amount of information that can be derived from psychological studies with small sample sizes is diminishing. There is evidence to suggest that interactions among a wide range of factors determine risk for long-term difficulties. Studies designed to identify risk factors or to evaluate the efficacy of interventions must be large enough to permit multivariate analysis. Because most cancer centers treat small numbers of children with different diagnosis, collaborative interinstitutional efforts are needed to accrue a sufficient number of subjects to answer meaningful questions. National consortia, such as the Pediatric Oncology Group and the Children's Cancer Study Group, have been instrumental in acquiring information about large groups of children. Although the focus of this research has been primarily on neuropsychological functioning, future focuses will likely be broadened to include issues such as quality of life, coping, and pain control.

Neuropsychological deficits, particularly those related to CNS treatment for leukemia, may not be evident for 2 or more years following treatment. Clinically, we recommend regular comprehensive evaluations at least to the completion of therapy. For children who demonstrate normal function, we recommend follow-up evaluations at 2 years and 5 years posttherapy. In addition, surveillance of psychological adjustment by brief screening instruments or clinical interviews is warranted. Children who demonstrate neuropsychological deficits may be in need of psychoeducational remediation that may require intensive instruction. Because children with cancer may have already been isolated from peers, it is usually preferable that such instruction be provided in the regular classroom. Public law 94-142 guarantees access to fair and appropriate educational programming to all handicapped children between ages of 3 and 21; however, many parents are unaware of these rights. Likewise, school systems may be reluctant to alter the usual classroom instruction for the special needs of the child. Thus the psychologist may serve as an advocate to ensure that each child's rights are protected and needs met.

Lastly, the bulk of psychological research and clinical practice in childhood cancer has been conducted by psychologists in oncology settings. However, given the growing number of survivors, it is increasingly likely that these patients will require services from psychologists who practice outside the hospital setting. This will require coordination between the hospital and community resources to ensure that the child's potential for academic, emotional, and vocational adjustment is addressed following successful medical therapy.

ACKNOWLEDGMENTS

Preparation of this chapter was supported by the Institute for Research and Training in Clinical Psychology, State University of New York at Binghamton, and by the American Lebanese Syrian Associated Charities (ALSAC).

8. *References*

Bernstein, I. L., Webster, M. M., & Bernstein, I. D. (1982). Food aversions in children receiving chemotherapy for cancer. *Cancer, 50,* 5961–2963.

Byrne, J., Fears, T. R., Steinhorn, S. C., Mulvihill, J. J., Connelly, R. R., Austin, D. F., Holmes, G. F., Holmes, F. F., Latourette, H. B., Teta, J., Strong, L. C., & Meyers, M. H. (1989). Marriage and divorce after childhood and adolescent cancer. *Journal of the American Medical Association, 262,* 2693–2699.

Carey, M. P., & Burish, T. G. (1988). Etiology and treatment of the psychological side effects associated with cancer chemotherapy: A critical review and discussion. *Psychological Bulletin, 104,* 307–325.

Cavazzuti, V., Fischer, E. G., Welch, K., Belli, J. A., & Winston, K. R. (1983). Neurological and psychophysiological sequelae following different treatments of craniopharyngioma in children. *Journal of Neurosurgery, 59,* 409–417.

Chin, H. W., Maruyama, Y. (1984). Age at treatment and long-term performance results in medulloblastome. *Cancer, 53,* 1952–1958.

Copeland, D. R., Fletcher, J. M., Pfefferbaum-Levine, B., Jaffee, N., Ried, H., & Maor, M. (1985). Neuropsychological sequelae of childhood cancer in long-term survivors. *Pediatrics, 75,* 745–753.

Dolgin, M. J., Katz, E. R., McGinty, K., & Siegel, S. E., (1985). Anticipatory nausea and vomiting in pediatric cancer patients. *Pediatrics, 75,* 547–552.

Duffner, P. K., Cohen, M. E., & Parker, M. S. (1988). Prospective intellectual testing in children with brain tumors. *Annals of Neurology, 23,* 575–579.

Eiser, C. (1990). Psychological effects of chronic disease. *Journal of Child Psychology, Psychiatry and Allied Disciplines, 31,* 85–96.

Ellenberg, L., McComb, J. G., Siegel, S. E., & Stowe, S. (1987). Factors affecting intellectual outcome in pediatric brain tumor patients. *Neurosurgery, 21,* 638–644.

Elliott, C. H., & Olson, R. A. (1983). The management of children's behavioral distress in response to painful medical treatments for burn injuries. *Behaviour Research and Therapy, 21,* 675–683.

Ertel, I. J., & Boesel, C. (1979). Brain tumors in children. In C. Pochedly (Ed.), *Pediatric cancer therapy* (pp. 183–197). Baltimore: University Park Press.

Fletcher, J., & Copeland, D. (1988). Neurobehavioral effects of central nervous system prophylactic treatment of cancer in children. *Journal of Clinical and Experimental Neuropsychology, 10,* 495–538.

Fobair, P., Hoppe, R., Bloom, J., Cox, R., Varghese, A., & Spiegel, D. (1986). Psychosocial problems among survivors of Hodgkin's disease. *Journal of Clinical Oncology, 4,* 805–814.

George, S. L. (1980). Statistical design for pediatrics: Past, present, and future. In J. van Eys & M. P. Sullivan (Eds.), *Status of the curability of childhood cancers* (pp. 47–59). New York: Raven Press.

Greenberg, H. S., Kazak, A. E., & Meadows, A. T. (1989). Psychologic functioning in 8- to 16-year-old cancer survivors and their parents. *Journal of Pediatrics, 114,* 488–493.

Hirsch, J. F., Renier, D., Czernichow, P., Benveniste, L., & Pierre-Kahn, A. (1979). Medulloblastoma in childhood: Survival and functional results. *Acta Neurochirugica, 48,* 1–15.

Hilgard, J. R., & LeBaron, S. (1984). *Hypnotherapy of pain in children with cancer.* Los Altos, CA: William Kaufman.

Hockenberry, M. J., Coody, D. K., & Bennett, B. S. (1990). Childhood cancers: Incidence, etiology, diagnosis, and treatment. *Pediatric Nursing, 16,* 239–246.

Holmes, H. A., & Holmes, F. (1975). After 10 years, what are the handicaps and lifestyles of children treated for cancer? *Clinical Pediatrics, 14,* 819–823.

Holmes, G. E., Holmes, F. F., Baker, A. B., & Hassanein, R. S. (1990). Childhood cancer survivors: Attained adult heights compared with sibling controls. *Clinical Pediatrics, 29,* 268–272.

Hovanitz, C. A., Gerwell, E. L., & Russo, D. C. (1984). Behavioral methods in pediatric chronic illness. In B. B. Lahey & A. E. Kazdin (Eds.), *Advances in Clinical Child Psychology (Vol. 7)* (pp. 253–293). New York: Plenum Press.

Ivnik, R. J., Colligen, R. C., Obetz, S. W., & Smithson, W. A. (1981). Neuropsychological performance among children in remission from acute lymphocytic leukemia. *Developmental and Behavioral Pediatrics, 2,* 29–34.

Jaffe, N. (1987). Biological consequences of cancer and its treatment and their relationship to current treatment planning. *The American Journal of Hematology/Oncology, 9,* 62–67.

Jannoun, L. (1983). Are cognitive and educational development affected by age at which prophylactic therapy is given in acute lymphoblastic leukemia? *Archives of Disease in Childhood, 58,* 953–958.

Jannoun, L., & Chessells, J. M. (1987). Long-term psychological effects of childhood leukemia and its treatment. *Pediatric Hemotology Oncology, 4,* 293–308.

Jay, S. M., Elliott, C. H., Ozolins, H., Olson, R., & Pruitt, S. (1985). Behavioral management of children's distress during painful medical procedures. *Behavior Research and Therapy, 23,* 513–520.

Jay, S. M., Elliott, C. H., Katz, E., & Siegel, S. E. (1987). Cognitive behavioral and pharmacologic interventions for children's distress during painful medical procedures. *Journal of Consulting and Clinical Psychology, 55,* 860–865.

Jonsson, O., Sartain, P., Ducore, J. M., & Buchanan, G. R. (1990). Bone pain as an initial symptom of childhood acute lymphoblastic leukemia: Association with nearly normal hematologic indexes. *Journal of Pediatrics, 117,* 233–237.

Katz, E. R., Kellerman, J., & Ellenberg, L. (1987). Hypnosis in the reduction of acute pain and distress in children with cancer. *Journal of Pediatric Psychology, 12,* 132–138.

Koocher, G. P., & O'Malley, J. E. (1981). *The Damocles syndrome: Psychosocial consequences of surviving childhood cancer.* New York: McGraw-Hill.

Kun, L. E., Mulhern, R. K., & Crisco, J. J. (1983). Quality of life in children treated for brain tumors: Intellectual, emotional, and academic function. *Journal of Neurosurgery, 58,* 1–6.

Li, F. P., & Stone, R. (1976). Survivors of cancer in childhood. *Annals of International Medicine, 84,* 551–553.

Lilley, L. L. (1990). Side effects associated with pediatric chemotherapy: Management and patient education issues. *Pediatric Nursing, 16,* 252–272.

Longeway, K. L., Mulhern, R. K., Crisco, J., Kun, L. E., Lauer, S., Casper, J., & Hoffman, R. (1990). Treatment of meningeal relapse in childhood acute lymphoblastic leukemia: II. A prospective study of intellectual loss specific to CNS relapse and therapy. *American Journal of Pediatric Hematology Oncology, 12,* 45–50.

Meadows, A. T., & Hobbie, W. L. (1986). The medical consequences of cure. *Cancer, 58,* 524–528.

Meadows, A. T., McKee, L., & Kazak, A. E. (1989). Psychosocial status of young adult survivors of childhood cancer: A survey. *Medical and Pediatric Oncology, 17,* 466–470.

Meadows, A. T., Massari, D. J., Fergusson, J., Gordon, J., Littman, P., & Moss, K. (1981). Declines in IQ scores and cognitive dysfunctions in children with acute lymphocytic leukemia treated with cranial irradiation. *Lancet, 2,* 1015–1018.

Melamed, B. G., Matthews, K. A., Routh, D. K., Stabler, B., & Schneiderman, N. (1988). *Child Health Psychology.* Hillsdale, NJ: Lawrence Erlbaum Associates.

Moss, H. A., Nannis, E. D., & Poplack, D. G. (1981). The effects of prophylactic treatment of the central nervous system on the intellectual functioning of children with acute lymphocytic leukemia. *American Journal of Medicine, 71,* 47–52.

Mulhern, R. K., & Kun, L. E. (1985). Neuropsychologic function in children with brain tumors: III. Interval changes in the six months following treatment. *Medical Pediatric Oncology, 13,* 318–324.

Mulhern, R. K., Ochs, J., Fairclough, D., Wasserman, A. L., Davis, K. S., & Williams, J. M. (1987). Intellectual and achievement status after CNS relapse: A retrospective analysis of 40 children treated for acute lymphoblastic leukemia. *Journal of Clinical Oncology, 5,* 933–940.

Mulhern, R. K., Horowitz, M. E., Kovnar, E. H., Langston, J., Sanford, R. A., & Kun, L. E. (1989). Neurodevelopmental status of infants and young children treated for brain tumors with preirradiation chemotherapy. *Journal of Clinical Oncology, 7,* 1660–1666.

Mulhern, R. K., Horowitz, M. E., Ochs, J., Friedman, A. G., Armstrong, F. D., Copeland, D., & Kun, L. (1989). Assessment of "quality of life" among pediatric patients with cancer. *Psychological Assessment: A Journal of Consulting and Clinical Psychology, 1,* 130–138.

Mulhern, R. K., Wasserman, A. L., Friedman, A. G., & Fairclough, D. (1989). Social competence and behavioral adjustment of children who are long-term survivors of cancer. *Pediatrics, 83,* 18–25.

Mulhern, R. K., Fairclough, D. L., Friedman, A. G., & Leigh, L. L. (1990). Play performance scale as an index of quality of life of children with cancer. *Psychological Assessment: A Journal of Consulting and Clinical Oncology, 2,* 149–155.

Mulhern, R. K., Fairclough, D., & Ochs, J. (1991). A prospective comparison of neuropsychologic performance of children surviving leukemia who received 18-Gy, 24-Gy, or no cranial irradiation. *Journal of Clinical Oncology, 9*(8), 1348–1356.

Ochs, J., Rivera, G., Aur, R. J. A., Hustu, H. O., Berg, R., & Simone, J. V. (1985). Central nervous system morbidity following an initial central nervous system relapse and its subsequent therapy in childhood acute lymphoblastic leukemia. *Journal of Clinical Oncology, 3,* 622–626.

Ochs, J., Mulhern, R. K., Fairclough, D., Parvey, L., Whitaker, J., Chien, L., Mauer, A., & Simone, J. (1991). Comparison of neuropsychologic functioning and clinical indicators of neurotoxicity in long-term survivors of childhood leukemia given cranial radiation or parenteral methotrexate: A prospective study. *Journal of Clinical Oncology, 9*(1), 145–151.

Packer, R. J., Sutton, L. N., Atkins, T. E., Radcliffe, J., Bunnin, G. R., D'Angio, G., Siegel, K. R., & Schut, L. (1989). A prospective study of cognitive function in children receiving whole brain radiotherapy and chemotherapy: Two year results. *Journal of Neurosurgery, 70,* 707–713.

Peckham, V., Meadows, A., Bartel, N., & Marrero, O. (1988). Educational late effects in long-term survivors of childhood ALL. *Pediatrics, 81,* 127–133.

Riva, D., Pantaleoni, C., Milani, N., & Belani, F. F. (1989). Impairment of neuropsychological functions in children with medulloblastomas and astrocytomas in the posterior fossa. *Children's Nervous System, 5,* 107–110.

Robison, L. L., Nesbit, M. E., Sather, H. N., Meadows, A. T., Ortega, J. A., & Hammond, G. D. (1984). Factors associated with IQ scores in long-term survivors of childhood acute lymphoblastic leukemia. *American Journal of Pediatric Hematology Oncology, 6,* 115–121.

Rowland, J. H., Glidewell, O. J., Sibley, R. F., Holland, J. C., Tull, R., Berman, A., Brecher, M. C., Harris, M., Glicksman, A., Forman, E., Jones, B., Cohen, M., Duffner, P., & Freeman, A. (1984). Effects of different forms of central nervous system prophylaxis on neuropsychologic function in childhood leukemia. *Journal of Clinical Oncology, 2,* 1327–1335.

Schlieper, A. E., Esseltine, D. W., & Tarshis, M. A. (1989). Cognitive function in longterm survivors of childhood acute lymphoblastic leukemia. *Pediatric Hematology Oncology, 6,* 1–9.

Silverberg, E., & Lubera, J. (1986). Cancer statistics 1986. *Ca-A Cancer Journal for Clinicians, 36,* 9–25.

Silverberg, E., Boring, C. C., & Squires, T. S. (1990). Cancer statistics, 1990. *Ca-A Cancer Journal for Clinicians, 40,* 9–28.

Soni, S., Marten, G., Pitner, S. E., Duenas, D. A., & Powazek, M. (1975). Effects of central nervous system irradiation on neuropsychological functioning of children with acute lymphocytic leukemia. *New England Journal of Medicine, 293,* 113–118.

Stehbens, J. A. (1988). Childhood cancer. In D. K. Routh (Ed.), *Handbook of pediatric psychology* (pp. 135–161). New York: Guilford Press.

Trautman, P. D., Erickson, C., Shaffer, D., O'Connor, P. A., Sitarz, A., Correra, A., & Schonfeld, I. S. (1988). Predication of intellectual deficits in children with acute lymphoblastic leukemia. *Developmental and Behavioral Pediatrics, 9,* 122–128.
Wasserman, A., Thompson, E., Wilimas, J., & Fairclough, D. (1987). The psychological status of survivors of childhood/adolescent Hodgkins disease. *American Journal of Diseases of Children, 141,* 626–631.
Whitt, J. K., Wells, R. J., Laurie, M. M., & Wilhelm, C. L. (1984). Cranial radiation in childhood acute lymphocytic leukemia: Neuropsychologic sequelae. *American Journal of Diseases of Childhood, 138,* 730–736.
Williams, J. M., & Davis, K. A. (1986). Central nervous system prophylactic treatments for childhood leukemia: Neuropsychologic outcome studies. *Cancer Treatment Review, 13,* 113–127.
Zeltzer, L. K. (1980). The adolescent with cancer. In J. Kellerman, (Ed.), *Psychological aspects of childhood cancer.* (pp. 70–99) Springfield, IL: Thomas.

6 *Prenatal Nutritional Status and Intellectual Development*

Critical Review and Evaluation

SUSAN LEIGH BAUERFELD AND JULIANA RASIC LACHENMEYER

Malnourished children do not achieve the same levels of intellectual development and ability as adequately nourished children (Barnes, 1976; Birch & Gussow, 1970; Birch, 1972; Cravioto, DeLicardie, & Birch, 1966; Kaplan, 1972; Kelin & Pertz, 1978; Latham & Cobos, 1971; Tizard, 1976; Winick, 1970a; Zeskind & Ramey, 1978, 1981). Many believe that the lowered levels of intellectual development observed in malnourished children are due to structural differences in the brain, such as fewer and smaller brain cells, that are the direct result of inadequate nutrition during critical periods of brain growth (Cravioto *et al.*, 1966; Kaplan, 1972; Kelin & Pertz, 1978; Latham & Cobos, 1971; Winick, 1970b). This line of reasoning suggests that by preventing such structural differences, improved prenatal and childhood nutrition will substantially increase intellectual functioning in prenatally malnourished populations (Barrett, Radke-Yarrow, & Klein, 1982; Dalby, 1978; Graham, 1985; Kaplan, 1972; Kelin & Pertz, 1978). Studies find, however, that structural differences in brain size and cell development, as well as other somatic indexes of development, are not always correlated with intellectual development (Dobbing, 1968; Drillien, 1970; Latham & Cobos, 1971; Saint-Anne Dargassies, 1982) and that nutritional supplementation alone is often not adequate to ameliorate the adverse effects

SUSAN LEIGH BAUERFELD AND JULIANA RASIC LACHENMEYER • Department of Psychology, Fairleigh Dickinson University, Teaneck, New Jersey 07666.

Advances in Clinical Child Psychology, Volume 14, edited by Benjamin B. Lahey and Alan E. Kazdin. Plenum Press, New York, 1992

of prenatal malnutrition on intellectual development (Barnes, 1976; Birch, 1972; Wilson *et al.*, 1986; Zeskind & Ramey, 1978, 1981). Studies of the role of the social environment on a child's cognitive functioning have challenged the causal link between malnutrition and intellectual development (Freeman, Klein, Kagan, & Yarbrough, 1977). Factors such as environmental stimulation and maternal dietary history may influence the level of intellectual development achieved by a prenatally malnourished child. The addition of early environmental stimulation to nutritional supplementation has been shown to ameliorate some of the adverse effects of prenatal malnutrition on later development to a greater extent than nutritional supplementation alone (Barnes, 1976; Birch, 1972; Field *et al.*, 1986; Ramey, Farran, & Campbell, 1979; Read, 1975; Scarr-Salapatek & Williams, 1973; Tizard, 1976; Zeskind & Ramey, 1978, 1981).

The nutritional status of both the mother and her developing child influences the child in indirect, as well as direct, ways. Maternal and fetal dietary intake have direct biological consequences for the developing fetus. Additionally, maternal diet may affect maternal behavior toward offspring, thereby affecting her interaction with the child. The developmental status and needs of the fetus and neonate, in turn, exert physical and emotional demands on the mother.[1] The mother's ability to meet these demands varies according to her developmental history, experience, and environmental circumstances. The mother and child establish patterns of interaction that influence the child's development (Sameroff & Chandler, 1975). The nutritional status of both the mother and child influences these complex interactions but may not be directly and linearly responsible for the outcome of intellectual development. Sameroff and Chandler (1975) suggest that environmental factors may influence and/or cause (a) problems in pregnancy that may lead to malnutrition and (b) later problems in intellectual development often associated with malnutrition. This chapter addresses the implications of findings concerning the relative influence of early (prenatal and neonatal) nutrition on the intellectual development of the young child.

[1] The terms *mother* or *caretaker* are used throughout to refer to the primary caretaker. Although the authors are aware of the increasing prevalence of fathers and other males as primary caretakers and support this trend, they have used the term *mother* throughout the chapter because of their heavy focus on prenatal factors that, by nature, involve the mother more than the father. Most of their comments about environmental influences, including postnatal child/mother interactions, are as pertinent to fathers and other caretakers as they are to mothers.

1. *The Role of Nutrition in Prenatal Development*

1.1. *Physical and Behavioral Characteristics of Malnourished Infants*

When compared to normally nourished full-term and premature neonates, malnourished neonates have the following physical characteristics: large brain weight and body length for size (Naeye, 1970); relatively small spleen, liver, adrenals and thymus, and relatively large heart, lungs, and kidneys for body weight (Naeye, 1970, 1981; Naeye, Blanc, & Paul, 1973; Sinclair, 1970); larger proportion of total weight accounted for by visceral organs, which have higher metabolic rates, and, accordingly, a smaller proportion of total weight accounted for by muscle and supporting structures that have lower metabolic rates (Naeye, 1970); less oxygen consumption for age but more oxygen consumption for weight (Sinclair, 1970); and a dissociation between growth and differentiation, with growth slowing but differentiation continuing (Sinclair, 1970). The brain and skeletal system grow consistently despite deprivation that may affect other parts of the body (Lubchenco, Hansman, & Boyd, 1966).

Fetally malnourished infants are often premature, vulnerable infants with the following behavioral characteristics: poor use of, and responsiveness to, environmental stimuli; inadequate social interactive behaviors; and deviations from the normal infant cry sound. They are often described as apathetic, anxious, withdrawn, and irritable when aroused. (Barnes, 1976; Birch, 1972; Cravioto *et al.*, 1966; Kaplan, 1972; Kelin & Pertz, 1978; Vuori, de Navarro, Christiansen, Mora, & Herrera, 1980; Zeskind & Ramey, 1978, 1981).

1.2. *Nutrition and Brain Growth*

Brain growth *in utero* lays the foundation for intellectual development. The human fetus and its organs grow and develop through a process of cell division, cell differentiation, and increase in cell size (Kaplan, 1972; Kelin & Pertz, 1978; Naeye, *et al.*, 1973; Sinclair, 1970; Villee, 1970; Winick, 1970b). The most rapid period of cell division occurs between 3 months prenatally and 6 months postnatally (Kaplan, 1972). The third trimester is critical to brain development. It is in this period that brain growth is fastest (Dobbing, 1968; Stein, Susser, Saenger, & Marolla, 1972); the nervous system develops through increases in myelination (Kelin & Pertz, 1978; Winick, 1970b); and fetal oxygen consumption increases to meet the demands created by accelerated cell division and metabolic activity (Villee, 1970).

Many nutrients are important at this time to insure normal cell development: The transfer of oxygen to fetal body cells requires B-12, iron and folic acid; DNA formation requires folic acid; and niacin is vital to the development of brain cells. The normal development of the placenta and all the cells in the body depends on an adequate supply of protein (Shapiro, 1983). Prenatal protein deprivation, particularly during the third trimester, can cause growth retardation and a reduction in the number of brain cells. Prenatal deficiencies in these other nutrients can also have an adverse effect on normal brain cell development (Dobbing, Hopewell, & Lynch, 1971). Malnutrition imposed during times of cell division in a rat results in permanent reductions in cell number; however, malnutrition during periods of cell enlargement, rather than division, results in reductions in cell size that are eliminated when the animal is refed. The timing of protein deprivation in relationship to which types of cells are dividing or enlarging influences the effects of malnutrition on brain cell and somatic development (Winick, 1975).

During the third trimester, the fetus is especially vulnerable to the effects of malnutrition (Birch, 1972) because of the rapid increase in brain cell development and other activity described and because of the changing role of the placenta. Throughout the first two trimesters, the placenta is primarily responsible for metabolism. Unless maternal nutritional deprivation is severe, the placenta is capable of developing and providing the fetus with sufficient nutrients (Benirschke & Hoefnagel, 1970; Gruenwald, 1970; Moog, 1970). During the third trimester, however, the fetal liver takes over the responsibility of metabolism, and the activity of the placenta diminishes. The fetus is more active during this period and requires more oxygen (Villee, 1970). This decrease in the activity and resources of the placenta, in combination with the increased demands of the fetus, leaves the fetus relatively unprotected should insufficient maternal nutrition occur during the third trimester. Adequate maternal nutrition during the third trimester and adequate nutrition during the first 6 months postnatally appear, therefore, to be critical to the normal development of a normal number of normal-sized brain cells and to the early stages of myelinization.

Kaplan (1972) reports that, in autopsies of severely malnourished infants, brain weight deficits were found in infants whose greatest period of nutritional deficiency occurred in the last trimester or the first 3 months postnatally. Cravioto *et al.* (1966) reported that the most profound effects of protein deficits were observed in infants below 6 months of age. The major effects of prenatal malnutrition observed after the war in Rotterdam and The Hague occurred only in those fetuses exposed to the famine after the sixth month of gestation (Birch & Gussow, 1970). This evidence further supports the conclusion that the observed effects of malnutrition on the physical development of the fetus are greatest when the malnutrition occurs during the third trimester and first 6 months of postnatal development; conflicting findings exist, however, and may be attributed to, among other things, a lack of control for the duration of the malnutrition (Susser, 1975). For example, Villar, Smeriglio, Martorell, Brown, and Klein (1984) concluded that chronic and/or very early prenatal malnutrition, associated with symmetrical reductions in weight, height, and body measurements had more of an adverse and permanent impact on later development than acute or later prenatal nutritional deprivation, which was associated with asymmetrical (e.g., low weight for length) growth changes. The authors suggest that the former was a manifestation of chronic maternal malnutrition. Susser (1975) suggests that during the *third* trimester a critical period exists for physical growth and mortality, whereas the *first* trimester is critical for central nervous system organogenesis and mortality. The type of malnutrition as well as its severity and chronicity are determinants of its effect on brain development. Caloric restriction and protein deficiencies can, and often do, occur in the same population. Caloric restriction is most important during periods of brain development because it affects replication of DNA as well as rates of mylenization and cell proliferation. When the mother has been deprived of either protein or calories, the infant suffers mild caloric malnutrition; maternal malnutrition affects the quantity, not the quality of lactation. It can be difficult, therefore, to isolate the effects of protein malnutrition on the fetus. Protein deficiency after weaning causes irreversible changes in the brain. Caloric malnutrition, however, does not seem to cause irreversible brain changes if it occurs after cell proliferation and mylenization have ceased (Mizrahi, 1974). When the timing of the malnutrition results in reduced numbers rather than sizes of cells, more permanent deficits ensue (Dobbing *et al.*, 1971; Winick, 1970a).

Studies clearly demonstrate that physical changes in both the brain and bodily structures often accompany prenatal malnourishment. The degree of effect is determined by factors such as the timing of the malnutrition, the chronicity or acuteness of the deprivation, and the nutritional history of the mother. The behavioral consequences of these changes, on the other hand, are affected to a large degree by environmental factors such as stimulation and caretaker responsiveness. It may be, therefore, that the *absolute* potential for intellectual development is determined by genetics and the intactness of CNS structures but that the degree to which the organism meets that potential is affected more by environmental factors (Winick, 1970a). The impact of malnutrition, therefore, varies with the degree of malnutrition and the environment in which it occurs. Severe malnutrition may cause irreversible changes in the structure and the function of the central nervous system; however, as the degree of malnutrition declines, the importance of environmental factors and the child's response to them increases (Read, 1975).

2. *Factors Influencing the Study of the Effects of Prenatal Malnutrition and Brain Growth on Intellectual Development*

Inferences about future intellectual status, as well as prenatal nutritional status, have traditionally been made on the basis of correlations among physical characteristics such as birth weight, height, head circumference, and later IQ (Cravioto *et al.*, 1966; Graham, 1985; Hack & Breslau, 1986; Kaplan, 1972; Wiener, 1970; Wilson *et al.*, 1986). Correlations of early weight gain, intrauterine growth, birth weight and length, and gestational age with behavioral patterns such as irritability, neurobehavioral organization, and sootheability have been found (Dixon *et al.*, 1982). These behavioral factors may be responsible for later advances in cognitive development through their influence on environmental exploration and their effects on caretakers. Genetic, intrauterine, and environmental events are intimately interwoven in their effects on development (Dixon, Tronick, Keefer, & Brazelton, 1982). Conclusions about potential intellectual status based solely on measures of brain maturation such as brain weight and other physical measures such as height may therefore be misleading; for example, increased height at certain ages has been associated with maternal ingestion of neuroleptics during pregnancy (Platt *et al.*, 1988). Additionally, brain size and weight are not always correlated with intellectual status (Dobbing, 1968). Drillien (1970) suggests that neither growth, structure, nor function of the brain are noticeably affected by intrauterine growth retardation, and Saint-Anne Dargassies (1982) states that development of the CNS is relentless and consistent. Clear-cut connections between structural brain changes and behavioral and functional changes remain somewhat hypothetical (Dobbing, 1968) despite advances in neuropsychology that continue to clarify brain–behavior relationships. Studies that focus on the effects of malnutrition on brain and CNS development may be limited in relevance to conclusions about CNS maturity and may not necessarily translate *directly* to conclusions about intellectual development.

Scanlon, Scanlon, and Tronick (1984) state that the increased rate of survival of extremely premature infants provides an opportunity to assess the early development of the CNS, with respect to both postconceptual maturation and neurodevelopmental disruptions. Using the Neonatal Behavioral Assessment Scale for premies, they found that birth factors such as gestational age, birth weight, and 1-minute APGAR scores were poor predictors of early behavior. After 21 days gestational age, however, birth weight, length, and head circumference at birth were more highly correlated with behavior than with factors such as asphyxia. They concluded that behavior past 21 days postnatal reflects both neurological maturation and nutritional status, which has a later and more enduring effect.

Saint-Anne Dargassies (1982) proposes that neurological maturation moves forward despite the existence of circumstances that adversely affect somatic growth; however, Winick (1970b) reports that when deprivation is severe enough, brain cell number may be affected. Both the timing and the duration of the malnutrition are important determinants of the effects of the deprivation on cell number (Winick, 1975). Mild undernutrition in rats during a "brain growth spurt" was found (Dobbing *et al.*, 1971) to result in permanent deficits in brain growth. Although prenatal and early malnutrition have been shown to affect brain weight and size, there is little evidence that such changes always result in functional deficits (Dobbing, 1968).

The study of the effects of prenatal nutritional status on intellectual development is also complicated by factors such as gender of fetus, social environmental factors, and prenatal exposure to drugs, alcohol, nicotine, and caffeine. The complex interactions of these factors raise both methodological and theoretical issues (Freeman *et al.*, 1977). Due to ethical considerations and lack of sophisticated statistics and methodology, early studies were correlational in nature, thereby limiting inferences about causality (Dobbing, 1968). Difficulties in assessing nutritional status and in controlling for variables such as gestational age and Central Nervous System ("CNS") maturity, environmental stimulation and maternal nutritional and social history also make conclusions about the relative contribution of early nutrition to intellectual development difficult (Frankova & Barnes, 1968a; Hack & Breslau, 1986; Lester & Brazelton, 1984; Miller & Hassanein, 1971; Scanlon, 1984).

2.1. *Influence of Teratogens*

Difficulties similar to those encountered in studying the effects of prenatal malnutrition arise in the study of prenatal exposure to teratogens and their later effects on development. The correlation between prenatal lead exposure and cognitive development, for example, is equivocal (Cooney, Bell, McBride, & Carter, 1989). Bellinger, Leviton, Waternaux, Neddleman, and Rabinowitz (1987) found that lead exposure in an otherwise low-risk population resulted in lower development scores even when numerous confounding factors such as social environmental and birth characteristics were controlled. Ernhart, Morrow-Tlucack, Wolf, Super, and Drotar (1989), on the other hand, found the relationship between prenatal lead levels and cognitive development to be dependent on the quality of the caretaking environment: When this was factored out, there was no relationship between cognitive scores and lead levels. They also found that prenatal lead exposure was related to maternal use of alcohol and cigarettes. Social environmental variables such as race, HOME scores, and parental education made a stronger contribution to IQ than lead levels. Similar findings were obtained by Cooney *et al.* (1989).

Maternal use of alcohol, cigarettes, marihuana, and caffeine during pregnancy has behavioral consequences on the neonate. As noted, the use of one of these substances often coexists with other prenatal risk factors such as exposure to lead. Use of nicotine, caffeine, and marihuana are highly correlated. The behavioral consequences of prenatal exposure to these substances may influence parent–infant relationships. In a population low at risk for birth complications, prenatal exposure to marihuana is associated with CNS excitability, jitteriness, and poorer habituation to visual stimulation; prenatal exposure to nicotine through cigarette smoke is associated with reduced birth weight and growth, increased tremors, and poor auditory habituation; and prenatal exposure to alcohol is associated with irritability, lability, and decreased tremors (Fried & Makin, 1987; Fried, Watkinson, Dillon, & Dulberg, 1987). The sequelae of high rates of prenatal alcohol exposure include retardation, learning disabilities, cognitive and language problems, microcephaly, and motor dysfunction, including hyperactivity (Miller & Dow-Edwards, 1988; Risemberg, 1989). In rats, ethanol exposure leads to changes in normal thalamic areas and callosal connections as well as corticospinal projection neurons (Miller & Dow-Edwards, 1988) and to developmental delays, decreased learning ability, hyperactivity, increased reactivity to sensory stimuli, and deficits in response inhibition (Miller & Dow-Edwards, 1988; Potter & Berntson, 1987). Prenatal exposure to caffeine in rats leads to decreased locomotor activity, increased defecation in females, and decreased emergence and increased adrenal weights in males. Maternal behavior in response to caffeine ingestion includes increased ambulation and decreased corner occupancy, that is, hyperactivity (Hughes & Beveridge, 1987).

In addition to effecting physical development, prenatal exposure to each of these substances influences the interactions between the parent and child. When investigating the relationship between prenatal malnutrition and later intellectual development, one should consider these variables, many of which are often associated with retarded intrauterine growth (Risemberg, 1989) and other developmental and behavioral consequences similar in nature to those accompanying malnutrition. Failure to control for the influence of each of these factors may significantly bias conclusions regarding the relationship between prenatal malnutrition and later intellectual development.

2.2. *Measurement of Nutritional Status*

Direct measurements of nutritional status have not yet been used in the study of fetal malnutrition (Miller & Hassanein, 1971; Stein *et al.*, 1972). Identification of *in utero* malnutrition is difficult, particularly at lower gestational ages (Lubchenco *et al.*, 1966). Determination of actual nutritional intake is usually based on assumptions (Susser, 1975). Assessment of nutritional status has historically relied on inferences drawn from physical characteristics such as head circumference, height, weight/length ratios, and weight for age measurements. Birth weight, length, gestational age, and postpartum weight gain have been shown to be related to good neurobehavioral organization (Dixon *et al.*, 1982). Head circumference and height, although associated with nutritional status, do not provide information about the severity, duration, or age at onset of a nutritional insult (Freeman *et al.*, 1977). Furthermore, physical measurements such as length and height vary in different geographical areas. Measurements obtained on a sample of children in Colorado, for example, were significantly smaller than those obtained from similar samples in New York and Baltimore (Lubchenco *et al.*, 1966; Miller & Hassanein, 1971). Infants of the same gestational age and external body dimensions may vary in weight by as much as 30% to 40%, and infants of the same race, sex, weight, and gestational age may have different nutritional statuses (Miller & Hassanein, 1971). Small size at birth may be due to either reductions in cell numbers or in cell size, each of which has different consequences (Winick, 1970a).

2.2.1. *Ponderal Index*

One method commonly used to measure neonatal nutritional status is the Ponderal Index (PI) (Miller & Hassanein, 1971, 1973). The PI is a ratio of weight to body length. Low PIs are often used to identify infants suffering from poor nutrition (Graham, 1985, Miller & Hassanein, 1971; Villar *et al.*, 1984). Als, Tronick, Adamson, and Brazelton (1976), when studying the effects of prenatal malnutrition, use the PI to separate out infants who are low weight and small stature arguing that their low weight is not due to poor nutrition. Despite its common use, the validity of the PI alone as an indicator of nutritional status, as well as the accuracy with which it is generally measured, have been criticized (Lester & Brazleton, 1984; Scanlon, 1984). The PI is differentially affected by variables such as sex, race, and parity prior to and after 38 weeks gestational age (Miller & Hassanein, 1973), as well as by the timing of nutritional deprivation.

2.2.2. *Intrauterine Growth Retardation (IUGR)*

Low birth weight for gestational age, often used as a measure of intrauterine growth retardation (IUGR), has also been used as an indicator of poor nutritional status. Use of this method alone is also problematic. Small-for-date infants do not form a homogenous group (Miller & Hassanien, 1971; Villar *et al.*, 1984). Prenatal ingestion of narcotics, alcohol, caffeine, and nicotine may all lead to IUGR (Risemberg, 1989). Furthermore, both chronic and acute states of prenatal malnutrition may result in IUGR, yet the developmental outcome of each etiology is distinct (Villar *et al.*, 1984). Measurement by low birth weight for gestational age or PI alone is not sensitive to these differences in etiology, which may predict different developmental outcomes (Miller, 1981; Villar *et al.*, 1984). Different measurements of nutritional status reflect different etiologies of IUGR. For instance, low weight for height, as reflected in a low PI, is associated with acute states of prenatal malnutrition and malnutrition during the third trimester. Low height for age, as reflected by an adequate PI and low weight for age measurements, on the other hand, is associated with earlier and/or more chronic states of prenatal malnutrition (Graham, 1985; Villar *et al.*, 1984). Miller and Hassanein (1971) looked at measures of gestational age, body length, head size, and birth weight and identified four distinct patterns of fetal growth impairment: short body length for weight; disproportionate growth of body length and head circumference; excessive soft-tissue mass; and insufficient soft-tissue mass. They argue that consideration of factors other than birth weight improves the precision of descriptions of impaired fetal growth. The exclusive use of any one measure alone as an indicator of poor nutritional status is, therefore, inadequate. However, as a study by Villar *et al.* (1984) demonstrates, the use of both PI and low birth weight for age measurements in combination with head circumference, maternal anthropometric, demographic, and pregnancy intake measurements facilitates the diagnostic discrimination between IUGR attributable to chronic or to acute malnutrition. This discrimination, in turn, facilitates more accurate prediction of different postnatal growth and developmental patterns. The Villar *et al.* study, however, did not assess how the factors measured influenced and correlated with different maternal behaviors such as type and amount of stimulation and interaction with the infant. Such factors may have influenced the results.

2.2.3. *Gestational Age*

Gestational age is relatively difficult to estimate accurately, particularly when single criteria are used (Dubowitz, Dubowitz, & Goldberg, 1970; Miller & Hassanein, 1971). Estimations of gestational age, a critical factor in determining IUGR, have traditionally been based on criteria such as fetal weight and length, behavioral assessment, and maternal reports, all of which are influenced by genetic history, prenatal care, and reporting accuracy (Wiener, 1970). Such difficulties in measuring gestational age have made it difficult to separate "normal" prematurity from poor intrauterine growth (Dubowitz *et al.*, 1970; Scarr-Salapatek & Williams, 1973). Estimation based on scoring systems such as that developed by Dubowitz *et al.* (1970), which use a linear combination of different measurements yielding a total score, are more reliable than estimation based on individual criteria. Some studies of premature infants use a correction for gestational age in order to make equivalent comparisons between full-term and preterm infants (Ment, Scott, Ehrenkrantz & Rothman, 1982; Siegel, 1981; Sigman, Cohen, & Forsythe, 1981). The rationale for this correction is that it allows for the disadvantage of biological immaturity and separates developmental delays associated with prematurity from those caused by central nervous system damage. Palmer, Dubowitz, Levene, and Dubowitz (1982) suggest that this correction factor, if applied to infants 2 or 3 months preterm, results in a distribution that includes abnormal development within the normal range. Miller, Dubowitz, and Palmer (1984) looked at the distribution of developmental quotients ("DQ") in preterm infants with and without abnormal neurological signs. They found the uncorrected DQ for prematurity to be a better predictor of abnormality than the corrected DQ. They explained the conflicting findings by noting that tests of early development were standardized when the survival of a 2 month-old preterm was rare. They also suggest that there is no simple, linear correction for prematurity: For example, the extensor tone of the preterm may lead to overscoring on motor items during the first few months. Additionally, they and others have noted that although infant tests may point to those at risk for developmental delays, these tests are poor predictors of later development (Honzik, 1976; Lewis & McGurk, 1972; Siegal, 1981). Prematurity itself, if not associated with complications, does not necessarily predict later delays (Divitto & Goldberg, 1979; Palmer *et al.*, 1982). Miller *et al.* (1984) suggest using longitudinal normative data from preterms who are relatively free from complications during the neonatal period. Until such data exist, they argue for the use of the uncorrected DQ as a more sensitive index of abnormality, especially after 9 months postnatal.

2.3. *Prematurity*

As noted, a common consequence of prenatal malnutrition, in addition to growth retardation, is prematurity (Birch, 1972; Hack & Breslau, 1986). The CNS of a premature infant is at a different stage of maturity than that of a full-term infant, and functions in qualitatively different ways than that of a full-term infant (Saint-Anne Dargassies, 1986; Scheibel & Scheibel, 1982).

The premature infant may not be ready to function or adapt to the environment in the same way as the full-term infant. The caretaker's response to such an infant may, in turn, be different than his/her response to a full-term infant. Patterns of stimulation and interaction may be established during a time when the infant is not able to respond to, or benefit fully from, the stimulation and interaction. For instance, a caretaker may spend less time stimulating and interacting with a child that does not respond or responds in a negative way than with a child that responds positively to the contact. Or a mother may be overprotective with such a child and restrict his or her contact with the environment. If such a pattern of interaction is established, a deficient environment for development may ensue. This is true for full-term infants as well. Als *et al.* (1976) compared full-term, underweight infants to full-term, full-weight infants. At 10 days postnatal, there were consistent differences between the two groups on motor behavior and interactive processes. By 9 months all infants were within the normal range. Yet 8 of 10 mothers of infants in the initial low weight group described their infant "as difficult to live with." This illustrates the effect that an infant has on the mother and how this continues to affect the mother's perception and the mother–child interaction after the initial weight and concurrent problems have been remedied. Environmental factors may therefore influence whether and how the maturational level of the child is utilized during development. If adequate and appropriate environmental influences are lacking during crucial periods of development, the relevant skills that are optimally attained during these periods may not be acquired. Later attempts to attain these skills will require more effort due to the necessity of neurobehavioral reorganization (Scheibel & Scheibel, 1982).

2.4. *Definition of Intellectual Development*

Scanlon *et al.* (1984) have grouped studies on intellectual development according to how they assess mental functioning: language and concept development; standardized tests and intersensory perception; information processing and learning. The authors point out that the measurement used is determined by the researchers' orientation as well as the expectation as to the area of the brain that is affected by malnutrition. Sensory integration studies, for example, hypothesize a relationship between malnutrition and brain and CNS development. The authors criticize the use of standardized measures of intelligence citing the cultural fairness issue as well as pointing out that the tasks are so complex and so diversified that little information about which specific functions are impaired is available. They suggest that the different areas of cognitive functioning be studied in simplified form.

Read (1975) reports that some of the effects of hunger on classroom behavior in children include apathy, irritability, decreased attention, and increased distractibility, which in turn have adverse effects on learning. The ability to learn may be intact. Much of the research on the effects of malnutrition on learning behavior in various lab animals suggests that performance on learning tasks is affected more by emotional and motivational factors than by associative or cognitive deficits (Levitsky, 1975; Zimmerman, Geist, & Strobel, 1975). Levitsky (1975) points out that performance on learning tasks is influenced by many variables that may have nothing to do with learning and cautions against drawing false conclusions about the effects of variables such as malnutrition and on learning based on data from simple learning paradigms. Food, for example, is often used as reinforcement in animal studies of learning. This creates differential reinforcement effects for malnourished and adequately nourished rats. Aversive stimulation, a frequent alternative to food reinforcements, also results in differential effects due to the exaggerated responses to aversive stimulation observed in malnourished rats. Levitsky, therefore, devised a learning paradigm that did not rely on aversive stimulation and controlled the food motivation of his animals. With these controls he found few differences in learning between the malnourished and adequately nourished rats. He attributed the differences he observed to the hyperemotionality of the malnourished rats rather than to any deficit in the learning mechanisms being studied. In other words, he believed the hyperemotionality of the rats interfered with their ability to perform these tasks.

2.5. *Effects of Supplementation*

Increased levels of physical growth have been observed in children receiving prenatal nutritional supplements. The results of such supplements on cognitive performance appear greater than those of supplementation after weaning (Freeman, Klein, Kagan, & Yarbrough, 1977); however, it is unclear if the gains attributed to the supplement are due solely to the direct physiological effects of the supplement on the fetus or neonate or to some indirect effect of the supplement, such as increased energy and attentiveness in the mother and the child leading to increased amounts of early stimulation and interaction or to differential treatment engendered by the child's size (Freeman *et al.*, 1977; Vuori *et al.*, 1980).

Lifelong nutritional needs and deficiencies as well as dietary habits and beliefs vary widely across individuals and cultures. Although improvements in diet prior to, and during, pregnancy are likely to help insure a more successful pregnancy outcome, blanket dietary statements and prescriptions based on generic criteria regarding general nutritional status can only provide crude estimations of the true nutritional status and needs of any one individual and of the effectiveness of any given form of supplementation (Barker, 1984; Graham, 1985; Olds, Henderson, Tatelbaum, & Chamberlin, 1986). For example, large, vigorous babies were born to Kenyan women despite low weight gains during the third trimester, low protein intake throughout pregnancy, and other adverse conditions that would have designated them as "at risk" by standards from another cultural standpoint (Dixon *et al.*, 1982). There are several large-scale, prospective studies of nutritional supplementation. Low SES Columbian children whose diets were supplemented were taller and heavier than the controls; however, they were smaller than upper-class children of the same age (Mora, Herrera, DeNavarro, Suescun, & Wagner, 1981). In a study of infants born to families at risk for malnutrition, nutritional supplements were introduced at various times from the beginning of the third trimester until 3 years of age. Maternal education was also introduced. The research found that those who received food supplements did better than those who did not, especially on tasks of motor performance. The effects were more pronounced for females. Those who did not get the supplements during the first sixth months but received them later did as well as those who received them earlier. Those whose supplementation was stopped after 6 months did no better than the controls who received no supplementation. Maternal education had a positive effect on language development (Waber *et al.*, 1981).

Studies of the effects of supplementation on physical development are limited by the fact that the effects of maternal intake on fetal growth and disorders of the fetus and placenta are mediated by numerous other social variables (Naeye *et al.*, 1973). Furthermore, in many studies using supplementation, there is little or no control for distribution and actual ingestion of the supplement among the family members (Metcoff *et al.*, 1985; Vuori *et al.*, 1980). It is often unclear in these studies whether growth deficits are due to a caloric or a protein deficit in the maternal diet, or to childbearing problems caused by early childhood malnutrition in the mother or to some other prenatal risk factor such as genetic defect or maternal disease.

For the most part, studies of nutritional rehabilitation show a clear physical change in the infant with few, if any, irreversible effects (depending on the timing, severity, and duration of the malnutrition). Later effects on intellectual development, however, are mediated by factors such as maternal behavior, infant characteristics, and parent–infant interactions.

3. *Environmental Conditions Associated with Malnutrition*

Malnutrition is seldom an isolated problem (Coursin, 1975; Cravioto & DeLicardi, 1975; Susser, 1975). It generally occurs along with impoverished circumstances including low income, poor educational attainment, disorganized family structures, and deficient intellectual stimulation (Birch, 1972; Birch & Gussow, 1970; Hack & Breslau, 1986; Latham & Cobos, 1971; Sameroff & Chandler, 1975; Tizard, 1976). Higher levels of educational attainment across income levels are associated with better diets and higher levels of parental involvement and increased infant stimulation (Barnes, 1976; Birch, 1972). Malnutrition often coexists with other medical conditions, including birth complications, poor postnatal care, and risk of infectious diseases (Scanlon *et al.*, 1984). Inadequate control of factors such as maternal hypertension, smoking, alcohol, caffeine, and other drug consumption during pregnancy, SES, education levels and urban versus rural setting, each of which can lead to malnutrition and affect the measures often used to identify malnutrition, can result in misleading conclusions about nutritional status and its impact on intellectual development (Collis & Janes, 1968; Dalby, 1978; Miller & Hassanein, 1973; Susser, 1975). Many mothers of malnourished children are likely to have lived much of their lives under such adverse environmental conditions, including childhood malnourishment (Birch, 1972; Birch & Gussow, 1970; Naeye, 1970; Tizard, 1976). The nutritional history, growth experiences, and environmental circumstances of the mother significantly affect the prenatal and neonatal experiences of her children (Birch, 1972; Dalby, 1978; Miller, 1981; Sameroff & Chandler, 1975; Tizard, 1976).

As Sameroff and Chandler (1975) suggest, there is not a linear causal relationship between birth complications and intellectual development. Some third factor, or set of factors, may influence birth complications and intellectual development as well as potential CNS maturity. Furthermore, social and environmental factors, in addition to neurological status, influence and predict cognitive ability (Ramey *et al.*, 1979; Ross, Lipper, & Auld, 1985; Saint-Anne Dargassies, 1982).

There appears to be an interaction between fetal malnutrition and the maternal and environmental variables often associated with it that produces negative effects on intellectual development (Kelin & Pertz, 1978). Infants most likely to experience fetal malnutrition and its intellectual disadvantages are those born into poorly educated families living in impoverished environments (Birch, 1972; Birch & Gussow, 1970; Latham & Cobos, 1971; Scarr-Salapatek & Williams, 1973; Tizard, 1976). Mothers in such circumstances are more likely to be young and unmarried, to have had low weight gain during pregnancy, and to have experienced malnutrition throughout their own lives (Kelin & Pertz, 1978; Miller & Hassanein, 1973; Tizard, 1976). A generational cycle seems to exist that contributes to the poor intellectual development of malnourished children in impoverished environments (Goggin, Holmes, Hassanein, & Lansky, 1978; Winick, 1970a). Poverty and ignorance in combination with poor food habits and erroneous beliefs often lead to persistent malnutrition (Birch, 1972; Birch & Gussow, 1970; Scarr-Salapatek & Williams, 1973).

The behaviors and characteristics typical of the malnourished neonate, including irritability, poor responsiveness to stimuli, inadequate social interactive behaviors, and deviant cry sounds, in addition to the physically drained condition of the mother resulting from poor nutrition during pregnancy, may lead to a lack of responsiveness in the child and a decrease in maternal responsiveness to, and involvement with, the child (Vuori *et al.*, 1980). Larger newborns, with better intrauterine growth, are calmer and less irritable, show better neurobehavioral organization, respond more readily to consoling, and are more physiologically stable than smaller newborns (Dixon *et al.*, 1982).

The malnourished child's withdrawn, unresponsive state is thought to be caused by a conservation of energy according to a hierarchy of needs (Kelin & Pertz, 1978; Latham & Cobos, 1971). The child seeks to maintain a steady state of functioning with the energy it has available and to meet needs lower in the hierarchy before expending energy to meet higher needs. When energy levels are low, responding to stimulation is a waste of energy because it uses precious energy to satisfy a "luxury" need while leaving a more primary need unsatisfied. A hypothesized result of this conservative, withdrawn state is a loss of learning time that leads to developmental delays (Barnes, 1976; Birch & Gussow, 1970; Frankova & Barnes, 1968b; Latham & Cobos, 1971; Levitsky & Barnes, 1972; Ramey *et al.*, 1979). Close interaction with a caretaker is important to the early physiological and behavioral organization of the infant (Dixon, *et al.*, 1982).

A common sign of recovery from a malnourished state is an increase in responsiveness (Cravioto *et al.*, 1966). If the environment is unprepared to fulfill the need for stimulation signaled by this readiness to respond (as in the case of poorly established interactive patterns), further delays will follow. In an impoverished environment, the combined effects on the mother of poor nutritional history, lack of education, and economic stress may further increase the likelihood that maternal responsiveness to, and involvement with, the infant will be low. A mother in such an environmental situation is likely to lack the strength, means, support, and knowledge to provide an adequate environment in which the adverse effects of malnutrition can be ameliorated (Birch, 1972). Therefore, unlike the fetally malnourished child born or adopted into an enriched environment, the fetally malnourished child born into an impoverished environment is not provided with the stimulation that would enable him or her to "catch up" to normal infants (Scarr-Salapatek & Williams, 1973). The environmental resources are not available to the infant when he or she is ready to take advantage of them. As a result, poor development ensues, and when the child is grown, his or her offspring are likely to experience the same chain of events.

The long-term environmental conditions affecting the mother and child as well as the reciprocal influence of the mother and child on each other cannot be separated from their nutritional states and needs; however, many studies of the effects of prenatal nutrition lack any control for the nutritional history of the mother and the nutritional content of the maternal diet.

> Recent research emphasizes the inadequacy of considering either genetic or environmental effects during one period of development outside the context of preceding and subsequent influences. It is to long-term consistent influences that importance must be ascribed. (Clarke & Clarke, 1985, p. 50).

Women with poor nutritional histories often have disturbed pregnancies. Their children are more likely to be of low birth weight and to have lower IQs, problems in school, and neurointegrative abnormalities (Birch, 1972; Birch & Gussow, 1970). The nutritional histories of *both* the mother and the child are an integral part of their environmental situation and contribute to determining its nature.

4. *The Importance of Early Stimulation*

The importance of early environmental stimulation for intellectual development has been demonstrated in several studies with "normal" infants who have been hospitalized or institutionalized (Cravioto *et al.*, 1966; Rheingold, 1956; Skeels & Dye, 1939), with fetally malnourished infants (Zeskind & Ramey, 1978, 1981). Zeskind and Ramey (1978, 1981) conducted a longitudinal study with fetally malnourished infants and found that children exposed to a supportive caretaking environment from the age of 3 months to 3 years failed to maintain the behaviors often associated with malnutrition. The children in the supportive condition showed improvements in intellectual and social development, whereas children in the control group did not. Mothers of children in the control group were less involved with their children. Both groups began with similar amounts of observed maternal involvement, and both were given nutritional and medical assistance. Individuals in the supportive condition were also provided with preventive day care 5 days a week, 50 weeks a year. Zeskind and Ramey (1978, 1981) concluded from these findings that the stimulation and support provided by the day care changed the behaviors of the infants and led to increased maternal involvement and stimulation. These combined effects resulted in improved intellectual and social development, whereas improved postnatal nutrition alone had no such effect.

An important conclusion drawn by Zeskind and Ramey (1978, 1981) is that much of the observed increased in intellectual development was attributable to the maternal support provided by the day care. The importance of maternal social support to pregnancy outcome and mother–infant interactions among low SES populations has been demonstrated in other studies (Crnic, Greenberg, Ragozin, Robinson, & Basham, 1983; Olds *et al.*, 1986). Social support enables the mothers to become more involved with, and responsive to, their children and to encourage responsiveness in the children. This points to the importance of the environmental conditions that surround pregnancy and early childhood to *both* the mother and child. Early stimulation facilitates rewarding infant–parent interactions and increased caretaker confidence and establishes a positive pattern of parent–infant interactions. Correlations between parental acceptance of a nurturing role and a positive attitude toward increased responsiveness in the child have been observed (Heinicke, Diskin, Ramsey-Klee, & Given, 1983). Early stimulation may directly benefit the caretaker as much as it directly or indirectly affects the child's intellectual development. The child's benefits also increase later from the increased caretaker confidence and involvement with the child.

When adopting such a view, caution must be exercised in order not to place all responsibility on the caretaker for the success of early interactions. Both the child and its caretaker play a role in determining the nature of their environment and interactive patterns (Clarke & Clarke, 1985; Heinicke *et al.*, 1983; Ramey *et al.*, 1979; Tizard, 1976). Infant, as well as maternal characteristics and behavior, influence interactive patterns (Heinicke *et al.*, 1983; Thomas & Chess, 1957; Tizard, 1976). Heinicke *et al.* (1983), for example, found that infant alertness covaried with parental stimulation and that infant soothability was related to parental responsiveness. Winberg and De Chateau (1982) report a relationship between the alertness and eye contact of the infant with the arousal of caretaking behaviors in the mother. They suggest that early contact between a mother and her child increases the likelihood that synchronous interactions will be established. They further suggest that such contact is more important for the mother than it is for the child because it fosters more self-confidence in the mother. One of the maternal behaviors they found to be associated with early contact and stimulation is a larger number of verbalizations (Latham & Cobos, 1971), containing fewer commands than the verbalizations of control mothers. In contrast, one of the behaviors often observed among mothers of low PI infants is increased negative feedback to their infants (Goggin *et al.*, 1978). The mother's motivation and ability to provide effective feedback is therefore influenced not only by her environment and developmental history but by the characteristics of her infant.

A number of studies indicate that the reciprocal stimulation of the infant and mother is important to development and has both psychological and physiological effects. Tactile stimulation facilitates somatic growth and behavioral organization (Field *et al.*, 1986). The mother's early contact with her infant after birth helps to stimulate such physiological processes as contraction of the uterus and improved circulation (Montagu, 1978). As mentioned, if the child is unable to respond in ways that encourage positive interaction, inadequate interactive patterns may be established. If the child is not adequately stimulated she or he may, in turn, not develop behaviors necessary to foster and encourage the maternal stimulation and interaction she or he needs. Malnutrition may, therefore, affect intellectual development by restricting a child's opportunity to accumulate environmental information early in life rather than by directly affecting his or her ability to learn (Levitsky, 1975).

Early stimulation and supportive caretaking have been shown to improve intellectual functioning and increase maternal involvement with premature, low birth weight, disadvantaged infants. In a study of infants' tactile and visual stimulation Scarr-Salapatek and Williams (1973) provided infants' mothers with toys and instructional visits to the home upon discharge from the hospital. The results of the study indicated that the early stimulation had a significant positive effect on the subsequent intellectual and physical development of the children as well as on the involvement of the mothers with the children.

Further compelling evidence for the influence of early stimulation and maternal social and educational history on intellectual development is provided by Scarr and Weinberg (1976). They found that black children adopted by advantaged white families before the age of 6 months showed dramatic increases in IQ (similar to those shown by white adoptees) over comparable black youngsters in black families and black infants adopted after the first year of life. Although the IQs were higher than those of comparable black children and higher than the average white population, the adopted children's IQs were not as high as those of the natural offspring of the adoptive parents. Fetal nutrition, other fetal risk factors, lack of very early infant–caretaker contact, and poor temperamental match may have contributed to this difference.

Related evidence for the influence of environmental deprivation on intellectual development in malnourished children is provided by Barrett *et al.* (1982). They investigated the effects of early caloric supplementation on the social and emotional functioning of school-age children in chronically malnourished villages in Guatemala. Their findings indicate that supplemental caloric intake increased performance only on tasks that demanded attentional processes; however, the quality of the home environment and stimulation provided was often a good predictor of performance on cognitive tasks.

Cravioto and Delicardie (1975) found a lag in language development in severely malnourished children from a rural community in Mexico that persisted after clinical recovery took place. They collected descriptive statistics on numerous features of the community environment. The only feature of the environment they found to be significantly associated with the presence or absence of malnourishment in the children was regular maternal contact with the outside world through radio. No other familial circumstance or parental characteristic measured, including biological, social, or cultural, was associated with the presence or absence of malnourishment in the children. They then went on to measure the amount of home stimulation present at age 6 months and age 48 months and found that control children (adequately nourished) had a significantly greater amount of stimulation at home than did the malnourished children. When they calculated correlations among the effects of body height, home stimulation, and number of bipolar concepts present at 46 months of age and partialed out their relative effects on each correlation, they obtained results suggesting the following: Body height mediates the relationship between home stimulation and number of bipolar concepts; home stimulation contributes relatively more to the variance of body height than to the variance of number of bipolar concepts; and body height contributes more to the variance of bipolar concepts than to home stimulation. In other words, physical development and environmental factors interact to influence measures of intellectual development such as the achievement of bipolar concepts. Cravioto and Delicardie (1975) conclude from this study that features of the microenvironment contribute to the lag in language development observed in malnourished children but do not contribute sufficiently to the relationship to be totally responsible for it; however failures of the microenvironment seem to lead to the most severe cases of malnutrition. They further argue that intervention at the microenvironmental level may prevent severe cases of malnutrition without requiring more difficult changes in the macroenvironment.

In summary, the environmental features characteristic of low SES, where fetal malnourishment due to poor prenatal and general health care is most likely (Miller, 1981; Olds *et al.*, 1986), affect the mother as well as the child, and contribute to the adverse effects of fetal malnutrition on intellectual development (Sameroff & Chandler, 1975). Regardless of infant nutritional status, Ramey *et al.* (1979) found that mothers in a low SES group were less verbal, less interactive, less warm, and less involved at home than those in a high SES group. In the low SES group, day care intervention from the age of 3 months on was found to be a significant predictor of intellectual development, whereas the mother's IQ was not. Scarr-Salapatek and Williams (1973) and Scarr and Weinberg (1976) also found that, although maternal IQ was associated with the developmental status of low SES children, it was *not* associated with the environmental stimulation of such children. Furthermore, Heinicke *et al.* (1983) found that maternal variables such as confidence in the role of mother, active emotional expression, IQ, and capacity for forming relationships were better predictors of developmental outcome in normal infants from mid- to high-SES groups than were variables relating to SES.

The results of these studies indicate that when adequate environmental conditions exist, as in higher SES families, mothers are more likely to have the personal, social, and financial resources necessary to provide adequate early nutrition and stimulation (Miller, 1981), both of which provide a necessary basis for any advantage in intellectual development. When a child is malnourished and/or a victim of poverty, gains in intellectual development are highly dependent on adequate early stimulation, which assumes caretaker interest and solicitude toward the infant (Cravioto *et al.*, 1966). This stimulation may be more important than optimal nutrition, although certainly not more important than adequate nutrition (Barnes, 1976). In cases of moderate malnutrition, there is no evidence for retarded growth leading to retarded brain functioning, although severe cases of malnutrition may have more far-reaching consequences (Dobbing, 1968; Dobbing *et al.*, 1971; Latham & Cobos, 1971). The presence of environmental conditions such as adequate nutrition and stimulation appear necessary in order for positive factors such as parental IQ and any associated genetic component to express themselves.

Thus the adverse effects of malnutrition on intellectual development may be ameliorated by providing both the mother and the child with adequate nutrition, support, and environmental and social stimulation (Barnes, 1976). Likewise, the advantages to intellectual development that a malnourished child born or adopted into a higher SES family can potentially expect to receive are ultimately influenced by prenatal and genetic factors, once stimulation and adequate nutrition are provided.

5. *Generalizations from Animal Literature*

Many studies of the influence of prenatal malnutrition on intellectual development have been conducted using animals and, indeed, much of the experimental literature on the effects of malnutrition on the brain cited earlier comes from animal studies. These studies clearly demonstrate that physical changes in both brain and bodily structures often accompany prenatal malnourishment. The degree of effect is determined by factors such as the timing of the malnutrition, the chronicity or acuteness of the deprivation, and the nutritional history of the mother. The behavioral consequences of these changes, on the other hand, are affected to a large degree by environmental factors such as stimulation and caretaker responsiveness.

Stewart (1975) found that pups born to dogs that were fed a marginally deficient diet from birth had birth weights that were 20% below those of a well-fed group. The pups were usually small with short legs, were often more active than their well-fed mates, and showed less motor control and coordination. Abnormal EEGs were recorded for the malnourished group. Their brain sizes were reduced but were large when considered relative to their body weight. Histological studies revealed increases in numbers of neuroglial cells and in the number and caliber of astroglial fibers. Some reduction in neurons and Nissl granules was observed. No degeneration of the myelin was observed. Autopsies performed on some of the mother dogs suggested that supporting tissues such as the placenta were insufficient in the marginally deficient group.

The animal literature also confirms that the timing and duration of malnutrition is important. Chow and Rider (1973) found that the effects of malnourishment were more severe when they occurred during gestation and lactation periods rather than simply during gestation. Teodosio *et al.* (1979) compared early malnutrition to chronic malnutrition and found the effects of the later to be more severe. Bresler, Ellison, and Zamenhof (1975) found that rats whose grandmothers were protein-deprived showed lower neonatal body and cerebral weight, cerebral

DNA, and cerebral protein. When the animals matured, these differences were no longer apparent because of general brain and body growth. The authors suggest that malnutrition may result in "inheritable learning deficits that are due to a variety of abnormal biochemical changes that are not genetically transmitted" (p. 321). They suggest, for example, that protein restriction may lead to abnormalities in kidney development and functioning, reduced feeding efficiency, low nitrogen balance, and excessive amino acid excretion.

Marginally deficient diets in rats over several generations lead to significant reductions in litter size, total litter weight, and individual birth weights, as well as small brain weight for age but heavy relative to body weight. Slow growth rates, increased activity levels, and increased sensitivity and reactivity to noise were also observed. Reductions in brain cell number were observed, but there was no evidence of cell or fiber degeneration. Dendritic development was delayed but did achieve normal levels (Stewart, 1975). Turkewitz (1975) demonstrated that learning curves for discrimination tasks in generationally malnourished rats were significantly lower than in adequately malnourished rats for complex discrimination tasks but not for simple discrimination tasks. He attributes this discrepancy to the malnutrition across generations and attributes the failure of other studies to show this difference to a failure to include generationally malnourished rats. He concludes that intergenerational malnutrition can affect both the ability to learn and the rate of learning when motivation and motor ability are held constant. Stewart (1975) instituted three conditions of rehabilitation after the tenth generation of malnourishment in rats. A high-protein diet provided from the time of weaning led to some improvement in size but no improvement in behavior or sensitivity to noise. Transfer at birth to well-fed dams greatly improved growth rates, weights, and behavior, and eliminated or reduced noise sensitivity. Although this result is attributed to the improved nutrition provided through suckling by the well-nourished mother, it is also noted that the marginally nourished mothers were less responsive to their pups despite the increased levels of activity in the pups. Providing the mother with a better diet during pregnancy provided the most dramatic improvements in birth weight and growth rate, particularly after weaning; however, excessive sensitivity to noise and other behavioral deficits remained (Stewart, 1975). It appears that the well-fed dams were best able to provide environmental conditions optimal to "normal" development, although improved maternal diet during pregnancy led to better physical recovery.

Frankova (1971) found that protein-deprived mother rats retrieved their young less efficiently and attended to them less. Malnourished rat dams spend more time with their pups and delay their dispersal from the nest area, thereby isolating them from their environment (Levitsky,

1975). Eckert, Levitsky, and Barnes (1975) found that choline acetyltransferase was decreased in malnourished animals; in those who were handled after being malnourished, this was prevented. These findings suggest that malnutrition leads to patterns of interaction that, in turn, affect the offspring. Leathwood, Bush, Berent, and Mauron (1974), in a study on the learning of avoidance behavior, found that malnourished rats learned avoidance behavior more slowly and did not improve after nutritional rehabilitation. The authors suggest that it is difficult to separate the effects of the environment from the effects of malnutrition. In this study, the larger litter size was related to the avoidance learning.

There are several studies that look at the interaction of the environment and malnutrition in animals. Some report that rats born to and nursed by malnourished mothers showed deficits in learning (Barnes *et al.*, 1966; Cowley & Griesel, 1964). Zamenhoff, van Marthens, and Margolis (1968) found that rats placed on a low-protein diet 1 month prior to mating and during gestation have offspring with lower levels of DNA.

One-year-old monkeys on a low-protein diet showed alterations in curiosity, manipulation, and social behavior, although discrimination, learning, and operant conditioning were not affected. Similar observations were obtained with monkeys malnourished at earlier ages. No differences in learning were observed on tasks involving delayed response, learning set, long- or short-term memory, object discrimination, object-quality discrimination, or simple reversal learning. Differences were observed, with the malnourished monkeys demonstrating impaired performance, on responses to new and novel sources of stimulation and in tasks requiring production of a stimulus–response, stimulus–reinforcement, or response–reinforcement discontinuity. The authors posit that this constellation of observations suggests impairment of subcortical structures. Significant behavioral differences between well-nourished and malnourished monkeys were observed. Malnourished monkeys had highly emotional, avoidant reactions to new objects or sudden changes in the environment and had maladaptive responses to stress such as defecation, screaming, and a rigid, fetallike position. The well-nourished monkeys in the same situations were curious and developed different strategies for avoiding stress (Zimmerman *et al.*, 1975). These behaviors are similar to those of the tactically deprived monkeys in the Harlow studies (Montagu, 1978).

Several authors have noted the similarity in the behavior and performance of children and animals suffering from deficient nourishment and from deficient stimulation (Coursin, 1975; Levitsky, 1975). Levitsky (1975) investigated whether a common mechanism might be responsible for the similar behavioral effects of the two different etiologies. He used a 3 × 2 factorial design to look at the effects of three different environments on malnourished rats (fed a low-casein diet) and well-nourished rats (fed an adequate, control diet). Control rats were weighed once a week and had food and bedding changed three to four times a week. They were weaned to individual cages. Stimulated rats were held daily, weaned to two animals per cage, and were exposed to a large playground with toys and five other animals of the same group for 1 hour daily. Isolated rats were reared in soundproof, lightproof chambers. Rats were placed in the experimental conditions for 7 weeks (3 weeks of lactation and 4 weeks of weaning) and were then placed in the control environment where they received 12 weeks of the control diet. Results indicate that the locomotor deficits often observed in malnourished rats were completely eradicated by the stimulation condition and exacerbated by the isolation condition. Other behaviors showed similar exacerbation in the isolation condition but not complete obliteration in the stimulation condition. Levitsky concludes that the long-term effects of malnutrition on behavior may occur by contributing to reductions in environmental exploratory behaviors that functionally isolate the animal from its environment. Environments with a paucity of stimulation exacerbate these effects, whereas those rich in stimulation may override these effects.

Strupp and Levitsky (1983) have criticized traditional animal learning tasks as insensitive to metabolic insults, such as neonatal hypothyroidism, that are known to lead to cognitive deficits in humans. They distinguished between advantageous learning and essential learning. The former is similar to incidental learning in humans and consists of acquisition of information not motivated by direct reinforcement or biological need. They compared learning in previously malnourished rats with learning in rats with hypothyroidism. The previously malnourished rats who were given nutritional rehabilitation did not maintain any permanent deficits in "observational learning," although those with hypothyroidism did sustain permanent cognitive deficits. Stewart, Sheppard, Preece, and Waterlow (1980) found that nutritional rehabilitation led to a full physical recovery in rats after 10 generations of malnourishment. Those whose rehabilitation started *in utero* were no different than those whose rehabilitation started at birth, although full rehabilitation may require more than one generation. They also found that maternal behavior affects the behavior of the offspring: Rats raised by the malnourished mother had more bizarre behavior than rats who were cross-fostered at birth. Pettus, Geist, Schultz, and Zimmerman (1974) also found that the effects of early malnutrition, motivation for food, and responsiveness to novel stimuli became normal after 6 months of nutritional rehabilitation.

The degree to which animals provide a good model for human brain and nervous system development has been questioned. Both animal and human behavior is extremely complex; control for all relevant variables is difficult (Collis & Janes, 1968; Frankova & Barnes, 1968a). Additionally, the timing of brain-growth spurts varies with different species (Dobbing, 1968). More highly cephalized animals have relatively shorter gestation periods and longer postnatal learning and development periods (Tolaas, 1983). Human brain cell development and myelination, although most rapid around the time of birth, continue into adolescence (Saint-Anne Dargassies, 1982; Winick, 1970b). Brain cell and nervous system development in typical laboratory animals such as mice and dogs is usually complete *in utero* or very soon after birth. The effects of prenatal malnutrition on these systems in laboratory animals may be more severe and permanent than they are in humans (Birch, 1972). Postnatal environmental factors may, therefore, be more important in human brain and CNS development than in animal brain and CNS development. Nevertheless, animal studies provide a unique opportunity to investigate prenatal developmental under controlled circumstances that are difficult to achieve in human studies due to both practical and ethical considerations.

Despite these cautions, it is interesting to note that many of the findings on early malnutrition in the animal literature parallel those in the human literature. Early malnutrition does appear to affect learning and emotional behavior. When, how severe, and for how long the malnutrition occurs, as well as environmental issues, are also important influences. Additionally, in both the animal literature and the human literature, it is difficult to determine what are the effects of the malnutrition *per se*, the ways the malnutrition affects parental behavior, and what additional environmental factors affect the offspring. Studies of nutritional rehabilitation also indicate that intellectual functioning is often not permanently affected by early malnutrition.

6. *A Synergistic Approach to the Effects of Fetal Malnutrition on Intellectual Development*

It is clear that there is not a simple, linear, causal relationship between prenatal malnutrition and intellectual development (Latham & Cobos, 1971). The timing, chronicity, duration, and severity of the malnutrition influence the degree and permanence of its effects on intellectual development. Poor environmental characteristics interact with malnutrition to produce a synergistic effect on intellectual development (Zeskind & Ramey, 1981). Long-range predictions about the effects of birth complications and pregnancy are successful only when the nature of the subsequent caretaking environment is taken into account (Sameroff & Chandler, 1975). Weakened physical states in both mother and child, impoverished environmental circumstances, and inadequate neonatal stimulation often accompany poor prenatal nutritional status and interact with it in a synergistic manner. The respective contribution to intellectual development of each of these factors, as well as their interactions, cannot be easily determined. The influence of social or genetic factors does not occur in a constant way, and their interactions are complex (Clarke & Clarke, 1985).

7. References

Als, H., Tronick, E., Adamson, L., & Brazelton, T. B. (1976). The behavior of the full-term but underweight newborn infant. *Developmental Medicine and Child Neurology, 18,* 590–602.

Barker, W. (1984). Nutritional factors: Can they reduce the incidence of mental handicap? *Health Visitor, 57,* 73–77.

Barnes, R. H. (1976). Dual role of environmental deprivation and malnutrition in retarding intellectual development. *The American Journal of Clinical Nutrition, 29,* 912–917.

Barnes, R. H., Cunnild, S. R., Zimmerman, R. R., Simmons, H., MacLeod, R. B., & Krook, C. (1966). Influence of nutritional deprivation in early life on learning behavior of rats as measured by performance on a water maze. *Journal of Nutrition, 89,* 399–410.

Barrett, D. E., Radke-Yarrow, M., & Klein, R. E. (1982). Chronic malnutrition and child behavior: Effects of early caloric supplementation on social and emotional functioning at school age. *Developmental Psychology, 18*(4), 541–556.

Bellinger, D., Leviton, A., Waternaux, C., Needleman, H., & Rabinowitz, M. (1987). Longitudinal analyses of prenatal and postnatal lead exposure and early cognitive development. *The New England Journal of Medicine, 316,* 1037–1043.

Benirschke, K., & Hoefnagel, D. (1970). In H. A. Waisman, & G. R. Kerr (Eds.), *Fetal growth and development* (pp. 1–11). New York: McGraw-Hill.

Bresler, D. E., Ellison, G., & Zamenhof, S. (1975). Learning deficits in rats with malnourished grandmothers. *Developmental Psychobiology, 8*(4), 315–323.

Birch, H. G. (1972). Malnutrition, learning and intelligence. *American Journal of Public Health, 62*(6), 773–784.

Birch, H. G., & Gussow, J. D. (1970). *Disadvantaged children: Health, nutrition and school failure.* New York: Harcourt, Brace & World, Inc.

Chow, B. F., & Rider, A. A. (1973). Implications of the effects of maternal diets in various species. *Journal of Animal Science, 36*(1), 167–173.

Clarke, A. D. B., & Clarke, A. M. (1985). Constancy and change in the growth of human characteristics, In S. Chess & A. Thomas (Eds.), *Annual progress in child psychiatry and development* (pp. 27–52). New York: Brunner/Mazel.

Collis, W., & Janes, M. (1968). Multifactorial causation of malnutrition and retarded growth and development. In N. S. Scrimshaw & J. E. Gordon (Eds.), *Malnutrition, learning and behavior* (pp. 55–71). Cambridge: The Massachusetts Institute of Technology.

Cooney, G. H., Bell, A., McBridge, W., & Carter, C. (1989). Neurobehavioral consequences of prenatal low level exposures to lead. *Neurotoxicology and Teratology, 11*(2), 95–104.

Coursin, D. B. (1975). Some comments on the effects of malnutrition on brain function. In G. Serban (Ed.), *Nutrition and mental functions* (pp. 231–234). New York: Plenum Press.

Cowley, J. R., & Griesel, R. D. (1964). Low protein diet and emotionality in the albino rat. *Journal of Genetic Psychology, 104,* 89–98.

Cravioto, J., & DeLicardie, E. (1975). Longitudinal study of language development in severely malnourished children. In G. Serban (Ed.), *Nutrition and mental functions* (pp. 143–192). New York: Plenum Press.

Cravioto, J., DeLicardie, E. R., & Birch, H. G. (1966). Nutrition, growth and neurointegrative development: An experimental and ecologic study. *Pediatrics, 38*(2), 319–365.

Crnic, K. A., Greenberg, M. T., Ragozin, A. S., Robinson, N. M., & Basham, R. B. (1983). Effects of stress and social support on mothers and premature and full-term infants. *Child Development, 54,* 209–217.

Dalby, J. T. (1978). Environmental effects on prenatal development. *Journal of Pediatric Psychology, 3*(3), 105–109.

DiVitto, B., & Goldberg, S. (1979). The effects of newborn medical status on early parent-infant interaction. In T. M. Field (Ed.), *Infants born at risk: Behavior and development* (pp. 311–333). New York: SP Medical and Scientific Books.

Dixon, S., Tronick, E., Keefer, C., & Brazelton, T. B. (1982). Perinatal circumstances and newborn outcome among the Gusii of Kenya: Assessment of risk. *Infant Behavior and Development, 5,* 11–32.

Dobbing, J. (1968). Effects of experimental undernutrition on development of the nervous system. In N. S. Scrimshaw & J. E. Gordon (Eds.), *Malnutrition, learning and behavior* (pp. 181–204). Cambridge: The Massachusetts Institute of Technology.

Dobbing, J., Hopewell, J. W., & Lynch, A. (1971). Vulnerability of developing brain: VII. Permanent deficit of neurons in cerebral and cerebellar cortex following early mild undernutrition. *Experimental Neurology, 32,* 439–447.

Drillien, C. M. (1970). Intellectual sequelae of "fetal malnutrition." In H. A. Waisman & G. R. Kerr (Eds.), *Fetal growth and development* (pp. 271–284). New York: McGraw-Hill.

Dubowitz, L. M. S., Dubowitz, V., & Goldberg, C. (1970). Clinical assessment of gestational age in the newborn infant. *The Journal of Pediatrics, 77*(1), 1–10.

Eckert, C. D., Levitsky, D. A., & Barnes, R. H. (1975). Postnatal stimulation: the affects on cholinergic enzyme activity in undernourished rats. *Proceedings of the Society for Experimental Biological Medicine, 149,* 860–863.

Ernhart, C. B., Morrow-Tlucak, M., Wolf, A. W., Super, D., & Drotar, D. (1989). Low level lead exposure in the prenatal and early preschool periods: Intelligence prior to school entry. *Neurotoxicology and Teratology, 11,* 161–170.

Field, T. M., Schanberg, S. M., Scafidi, F., Bauer, C. R., Vega-Lahr, N., Garcia, R., Nystrom, J., & Kuhn, C. M. (1986). Tactile/kinesthetic stimulation effects on preterm neonates. *Pediatrics, 77*(5), 654–658.

Frankova, S. (1971). Relationship between nutrition during lactation and maternal behaviour of rats. *Activitas Nervosa Superior, 13,* 1–8.

Frankova, S., & Barnes, R. H. (1968a). Influence of malnutrition in early life on exploratory behavior of rats. *Journal of Nutrition, 96,* 477–484.

Frankova, S., & Barnes, R. H. (1968b). Effect of malnutrition in early life on avoidance conditioning and behavior of adult rats. *Journal of Nutrition, 96,* 485–593.

Freeman, H. E., Klein, R. E., Kagan, J., & Yarbrough, C. (1977). Relations between nutrition and cognition in rural Guatemala. *American Journal of Public Health, 67*(3), 233–239.

Fried, P. A., & Makin, J. E. (1987). Neonatal behavioural correlates of prenatal exposure to marihuana, cigarettes and alcohol in a low-risk population. *Neurotoxicology and Teratology, 9,* 1–7.

Fried, P. A., Watkinson, B., Dillon, R. F., & Dulberg, C. S. (1987). Neonatal neurological status in a low-risk population after prenatal exposure to cigarettes, marijuana, and alcohol. *Developmental and Behavioral Pediatrics, 8,* 318–326.

Goggin, J. E., Holmes, G. E., Hassanein, K., & Lansky, S. B. (1978). Observations of postnatal developmental activity in infants with fetal malnutrition. *Journal of Genetic Psychology, 132,* 247–253.

Graham, G. G. (1985). Poverty, hunger, malnutrition, prematurity, and infant mortality in the United States. *Pediatrics, 75*(1), 117–125.

Gruenwald, P. (1970). Fetal malnutrition. In H. A. Waisman & G. R. Kerr (Eds.), *Fetal growth and development* (pp. 235–240). New York: McGraw-Hill.

Hack, M., & Breslau, N. (1986). Very low birth weight infants: Effects of brain growth during infancy on intelligence quotient at 3 years of age. *Pediatrics, 77*(2), 196–202.

Heinicke, C. M., Diskin, S. D., Ramsey-Klee, D. M., & Given, K. (1983). Pre-birth parent characteristics and family development in the first year of life. *Child Development, 54,* 194–208.

Honzik, M. P. (1976). Value and limitations of infant tasks: An overview. In M. Lewis (Ed.), *Origins of intelligence: Infancy and early childhood* (pp. 59–95). New York: Plenum Press.

Hughes, R. N., & Beveridge, I. J. (1987). Effects of prenatal exposure to chronic caffeine on locomotor and emotional behavior. *Psychobiology, 15*(2), 179–185.

Kaplan, B. J. (1972). Malnutrition and mental deficiency. *Psychological Bulletin, 78*(5), 321–334.

Kelin, R. H., & Pertz, D. L. (1978). Nutrition and learning. *Academic Therapy, 13*(5), 527–534.

Latham, M. C., & Cobos, F. (1971). The effects of malnutrition on intellectual development and learning. *American Journal of Public Health, 61*(7), 1307–1324.

Leathwood, P., Bush, M., Berent, C., & Mauron, J. (1974). Effects of early malnutrition on Swiss white mice: Avoidance learning after rearing in large litters. *Life Sciences, 14,* 157–162.

Lester, B. M., & Brazleton, T. B. (1984). A lean argument: Reply to Scanlon. *Child Development, 55*(2), 672–674.

Levitsky, D. A. (1975). Malnutrition and animal models of cognitive development. In G. Serban (Ed.), *Nutrition and mental functions* (pp. 75–90). New York: Plenum Press.

Levitsky, D., & Barnes, R. (1972). Nutritional and environmental interactions in the behavioral development of the rat: Long-term effects. *Science, 176,* 68–71.

Lewis, M., & McGurk, H. (1972). Evaluation of infant intelligence. *Science, 178,* 1174–1177.

Lubchenco, L. O., Hansman, C., & Boyd, E. (1966). Intrauterine growth in length and head circumference as estimated from live births at gestational ages from 26 to 42 weeks. *Pediatrics, 37*(3), 403–408.

Ment, L. R., Scott, D. T., Ehrenkrantz, R. A., & Rothman, S. G. (1982). Neonates of < 1,250 g. birthweight: Prospective neurodevelopmental evaluation during the first year postterm. *Pediatrics, 70,* 292–296.

Metcoff, J., Costiloe, P., Crosby, W. M., Dutta, S., Sandstead, H. H., Milne, D., Bodwell, C. E., & Majors, S. H. (1985). Effect of food supplementation (WIC) during pregnancy on birth weight. *The American Journal of Clinical Nutrition, 41,* 933–947.

Miller, G., Dubowitz, L. M. S., & Palmer, P. (1984). Follow-up of pre-term infants: Is correction of the developmental quotient for prematurity helpful? *Early Human Development, 9,* 137–144.

Miller, H. C. (1981). Intrauterine growth retardation: An unmet challenge. *American Journal of Diseases in Childhood, 135,* 944–948.

Miller, H. C., & Hassanein, K. (1971). Diagnosis of impaired fetal growth in newborn infants. *Pediatrics, 48,* 511–522.

Miller, H. C., & Hassanein, K. (1973). Fetal malnutrition in white new-born infants: Maternal factors. *Pediatrics, 52,* 504–512.

Miller, M. W., & Dow-Edwards, D. L. (1988). Structural and metabolic alterations in rat cerebral cortex induced by prenatal exposure to ethanol. *Brain Research, 474,* 316–326.

Mizrahi, G. K. (1974). Some methodological problems in studies of cognitive development in relation to malnutrition. *Danish Medical Bulletin, 21,* 183–189.
Montagu, A. (1978). *Touching: The human significance of the skin* (2nd ed.). New York: Harper & Row.
Moog, F. (1970). Enzyme development and functional differentiation in the fetus. In H. A. Waisman, & G. R. Kerr (Eds.), *Fetal growth and development.* New York: McGraw-Hill.
Mora, J. O., Herrera, M. G., De Navarro, L., Suescun, J., & Wagner, M. (1981). The effects of nutritional supplementation on physical growth of children at risk of malnutrition. *American Journal of Clinical Nutrition, 12,* 810–814.
Naeye, R. L. (1970). Structural correlates of fetal undernutrition. In H. A. Waisman & G. R. Kerr (Eds.), *Fetal growth and development* (pp. 241–252). New York: McGraw-Hill.
Naeye, R. L. (1981). Common environmental influences on the fetus. In R. L. Naeye, J. M. Kissane, & N. Kaufman (Eds.), *International Academy of Pathology Monograph: Perinatal disease.* Baltimore: Williams & Wilkins.
Naeye, R. L., Blanc, W., & Paul, C. (1973). Effects of maternal nutrition on the human fetus. *Pediatrics, 52,* 494–503.
Olds, D. L., Henderson, C. R., Jr., Tatelbaum, R., & Chamberlin, R. (1986). Improving the delivery of prenatal care and outcomes of pregnancy: A randomized trial of nurse home visitation. *Pediatrics, 77*(1), 16–28.
Palmer, P., Dubowitz, L. M. S., Levene, M. I., & Dubowitz, V. (1982). Developmental and neurological progress of preterm infants with intraventricular hemorrhage and ventricular dilation. *Archives of Diseases of Childhood, 57,* 748–753.
Pettus, J. P., Geist, C. R., Schultz, G. E., & Zimmerman, R. R. (1974). Recovery from malnutrition: Food preference and neophobia. *Perceptual and Motor Skills, 38,* 767–773.
Platt, J. E., Friedhoff, A. J., Broman, S. H., Bond, R. N., Laska, E., & Lin, S. P. (1988). Effects of prenatal exposure to neuroleptic drugs on children's growth. *Neuropsychopharmacology, 1*(3), 205–212.
Potter, B. M., & Berntson, G. G. (1987). Prenatal alcohol exposure: Effects on acoustic startle and prepulse inhibition. *Neurotoxicology and Teratology, 9,* 17–21.
Ramey, C. T., Farran, D. C., & Campbell, F. A. (1979). Predicting IQ from mother-infant interactions. *Child Development, 50,* 804–814.
Read, M. S. (1975). Nutrition, environment, and child behavior. In G. Serban (Ed.), *Nutrition and mental functions* (pp. 193–200). New York: Plenum Press.
Rheingold, H. L. (1956). The modification of social responsiveness in institutional babies. *Monographs of the Society for Research in Child Development, 21*(2).
Risemberg, H. M. (1989). Fetal neglect and abuse. *New York State Journal of Medicine, 89*(3), 148–151.
Ross, G., Lipper, E. G., & Auld, P. A. (1985). Consistency and change in the development of premature infants weighing less than 1,501 grams at birth. *Pediatrics, 76*(6), 885–891.
Saint-Anne Dargassies, S. (1982). Developmental neurology from the fetus to the infant: Some French works. In W. W. Hartup (Ed.), *Review of child development research* (Vol. 6, pp. 45–72). Chicago: University of Chicago Press.
Sameroff, A. J., & Chandler, M. J. (1975). Reproductive risk and the continuum of caretaking casualty. In F. Horowitz (Ed.), *Review of child development research* (Vol. 4, pp. 187–243). Chicago: University of Chicago Press.
Scanlon, J. W. (1984). To ponder ponderal's length: A question to Lester *et al. Child Development, 55*(2), 669–671.
Scanlon, K. B., Scanlon, J. W., & Tronick, E. (1984). The impact of perinatal and neonatal events on the early behavior of the extremely premature human. *Developmental and Behavioral Pediatrics, 5*(2), 65–73.
Scarr, S., & Weinberg, R. A. (1976). IQ test performance of black children adopted by white families. *American Psychologist, 31*(10), 726–739.

Scarr-Salapatek, S., & Williams, M. L. (1973). The effects of early stimulation on low-birth-weight infants. *Child Development, 44,* 94–101.

Scheibel, M. E., & Scheibel, A. B. (1982). Some neural substrates of postnatal development. In W. W. Hartup (Ed.), *Review of child development research* (Vol. 6, pp. 481–519). Chicago: University of Chicago Press.

Shapiro, H. I. (1983). *The pregnancy book for today's woman.* New York: Harper & Row.

Siegel, L. S. (1981). Infant tests as predictors of cognitive and language development at two years. *Child Development, 52,* 545–557.

Sigman, M., Cohen, S. E., & Forsythe, A. B. (1981). The relation of early infant measures to later development. In S. L. Friedman & M. Sigman (Eds.), *Preterm birth and psychological development* (pp. 313–328). New York: Academic Press.

Sinclair, J. C. (1970). Energy metabolism and fetal development. In H. A. Waisman & G. R. Kerr (Eds.), *Fetal growth and development* (pp. 201–220). New York: McGraw-Hill.

Skeels, H. M., & Dye, M. H. (1939). A study of the effects of differential stimulation in mentally retarded children. *Proceedings of the American Association of Mental Deficiencies, 44,* 114–136.

Stein, Z., Susser, M., Saenger, G., & Marolla, F. (1972). Nutrition and mental performance. *Science, 178,* 708–712.

Stewart, R. J. C. (1975). Long continued marginal protein-energy deficiency. In G. Serban (Ed.), *Nutrition and mental functions* (pp. 13–32). New York: Plenum Press.

Stewart, R. J. C., Sheppard, H., Preece, R., & Waterlow, J. C. (1980). The effect of rehabilitation at different stages of development of rats marginally malnourished for 10 to 12 generations. *British Journal of Nutrition, 43,* 403–412.

Strupp, B. J., & Levitsky, D. A. (1983). Early brain insult and cognition: A comparison of malnutrition and hypothyroidism. *Developmental Psychobiology, 16*(6), 535–549.

Susser, M. (1975). Introductory remarks to workshop on nutrition. In G. Serban (Ed.), *Nutrition and mental functions* (pp. 227–230). New York: Plenum Press.

Teodosio, N. R., Filho, J. E. C., Guedes, R. C. A., Costa, J. A., Costa, F. B. R., & Da Silva, A. T. (1979). Learned and emotional behavior in chronically malnourished rats. *Acta Physiologica Latinoamericana, 29,* 255–262.

Thomas, A., & Chess, S. (1957). An approach to the study of individual differences in child behavior. *Journal of Clinical and Experimental Psychopathology: Quarterly Review of Psychiatry and Neurology, 18,* 347–357.

Tizard, J. (1976). Nutrition, growth and development. *Psychological Medicine, 6,* 1–5.

Tolaas, J. (1983). Encephalization and gestation in placental mammals. *Perspectives in Biology and Medicine, 27*(1), 39–47. (From *Psychological Abstracts,* 1984, Vol. 71, Abstract No. 19737.)

Turkewitz, G. (1975). Learning in chronically protein-deprived rats. In G. Serban (Ed.), *Nutrition and mental functions* (pp. 113–120). New York: Plenum Press.

Villar, J., Smeriglio, V., Martorell, R., Brown, C. H., & Klein, R. E. (1984). Heterogeneous growth and mental development of intrauterine growth-retarded infants during the first 3 years of life. *Pediatrics, 74*(5), 783–791.

Villee, C. A. (1970). Enzymic development of the placenta in relation to fetal growth. In H. A. Waisman & G. R. Kerr (Eds.), *Fetal growth and development* (pp. 11–18). New York: McGraw-Hill.

Vuori, L., de Navarro, L., Christiansen, N., Mora, J. O., & Herrera, M. G. (1980). Food supplementation of pregnant women at risk of malnutrition and their newborns' responsiveness to stimulation. *Developmental Medicine and Child Neurology, 22,* 61–71.

Waber, D. P., Vuori-Christiansen, L., Ortiz, N., Clement, J. R., Christiansen, N. E., Mora, J. O., Reed, R. B., & Herrera, M. G. (1981). Nutritional supplementation, maternal education, and cognitive development of infants at risk of malnutrition. *American Journal of Clinical Nutrition, 34,* 807–813.

Wiener, G. (1970). The relationship of birth weight and length of gestation to intellectual development at ages 8 to 10 years. *The Journal of Pediatrics, 76*(5), 694–699.

Wilson, D. M., Lawrence, D. H., Duncan, P. M., Dornbusch, S. M., Ritter, P. L., Hintz, R. L., Gross, R. T., & Rosenfeld, R. G. (1986). Growth and intellectual development. *Pediatrics, 78*, 646–650.

Winberg, J., & De Chateau, P. (1982). Early social development: Studies of infant-mother interaction and relationships. In W. W. Hartup (Ed.), *Review of child development research* (Vol. 6, pp. 1–44). Chicago: University of Chicago Press.

Winick, M. (1970a). Nutrition and mental development. *Medical Clinics of North America, 54*(6), 1413–1429.

Winick, M. (1970b). Cellular growth of the fetus and placenta. In H. A. Waisman & G. R. Kerr (Eds.), *Fetal growth and development* (pp. 19–28). New York: McGraw-Hill.

Winick, M. (1975). Nutrition and brain development. In G. Serban (Ed.), *Nutrition and mental functions* (pp. 65–74). New York: Plenum Press.

Zamenhoff, S., van Marthens, E., & Margolis, F. L. (1968). DNA (cell number) and protein in neonatal brain: Alteration by maternal dietary protein restriction. *Science, 160*, 322–323.

Zeskind, P. S., & Ramey, G. T. (1978). Fetal malnutrition: An experimental study of its consequences on infant development in two caregiving environments. *Child Development, 49*(4), 1155–1162.

Zeskind, P. S., & Ramey, G. T. (1981). Preventing intellectual and interactional sequelae of fetal malnutrition: A longitudinal, transactional, and synergistic approach to development. *Child Development, 52*(1), 213–218.

Zimmerman, R. R., Geist, C. R., & Strobel, D. A. (1975). Behavioral deficiencies in protein-deprived monkeys. In G. Serban (Ed.), *Nutrition and mental functions* (pp. 33–64). New York: Plenum Press.

7 Rumination Disorder

Diagnosis, Complications, Mediating Variables, and Treatment

SUSAN DICKERSON MAYES

Rumination is the voluntary and pleasurable repeated regurgitation of stomach contents in the absence of organic cause. Foods or fluids are brought up into the mouth and reswallowed or expelled. Although some ruminators may strain and noticeably contract their gastroesophageal muscles or use their fingers to induce rumination, the act of rumination for many ruminators appears almost effortless (Humphrey, Mayes, Bixler, & Good, 1989; Mayes, 1988, 1992; Mayes, Humphrey, Handford, & Mitchell, 1988).

Based on a comprehensive review of the rumination literature (63 publications involving 123 cases of rumination disorder), two distinct types of rumination disorder are evident: rumination in mentally retarded individuals of any age and rumination in infants, the majority of whom are developmentally normal (Mayes, 1992; Mayes *et al.*, 1988). For mentally retarded ruminators, rumination occurs almost exclusively in severely and profoundly retarded individuals and is construed as a form of self-stimulation commonly present in persons functioning at these levels of retardation. According to the literature, rumination in infants is felt to be secondary to a disturbance in the caretaker–child relationship, with reports of emotional and physical neglect, psychosocial stress, separation from the parent, and parent psychiatric disorders. Prevalence data for the two types of rumination disorder in the general population have not been determined, and it is unknown which subtype is more common. However, more cases (62% of the total) of rumination in mentally retarded individuals are described in the literature than rumination in infants.

SUSAN DICKERSON MAYES • Department of Psychiatry, Pennsylvania State University College of Medicine, Milton S. Hershey Medical Center, Hershey, Pennsylvania 17033.

Advances in Clinical Child Psychology, Volume 14, edited by Benjamin B. Lahey and Alan E. Kazdin. Plenum Press, New York, 1992

Although the two rumination disorder subtypes differ on essential dimensions, they share important features. For both, the disorder is significantly more prevalent in males than in females; the act of rumination is purposeful, self-induced, and pleasurable; and the ruminator turns inward for gratification, as opposed to externally deriving satisfaction from the environment and others.

1. Rumination in Mentally Retarded Individuals

The literature includes 76 cases of rumination in mentally retarded persons (Azrin & Wesolowski, 1975; Ball, Hendricksen, & Clayton, 1974; Barmann, 1980; Barton & Barton, 1985; Becker, Turner, & Sajwaj, 1978; Borreson & Anderson, 1982; Bright & Whaley, 1968; Conrin, Pennypacker, Johnston, & Rast, 1982; Daniel, 1982; Davis, Wieseler, & Hanzel, 1980; Duker & Seys, 1977; Foxx, Snyder, & Schroeder, 1979; Galbraith, Byrick, & Rutledge, 1970; Hogg, 1982; Humphrey *et al.*, 1989; Jackson, Johnson, Ackron, & Crowley, 1975; Kohlenberg, 1970; Libby & Phillips, 1979; Lobato, Carlson, & Barrera, 1986; Luckey, Watson, & Musick, 1968; Marholin, Luiselli, Robinson, & Lott, 1980; Mayes, 1988, 1992; Mayes *et al.*, 1988; McKeegan, Estill, & Campbell, 1987; Minness, 1980; Mulick, Schroeder, & Rojahn, 1980; O'Neil, White, King, & Carek, 1979; Rast, Ellinger-Allen, & Johnston, 1985; Rast & Johnston, 1986; Rast, Johnston, Allen, & Drum, 1985; Rast, Johnston, & Drum, 1984; Rast, Johnston, Drum, & Conrin, 1981; Rast, Johnston, Lubin, & Ellinger-Allen, 1988a; Simpson & Sasso, 1978; Singh, Manning, & Angell, 1982; Smith & Lyon, 1976; Watkins, 1972; White & Taylor, 1967; Whitehead, Drescher, Morrill-Corbin, & Cataldo, 1985; Wright & Menolascino, 1970; Wright & Thalassinos, 1973). Across these cases, the male to female ratio is 57 to 19, suggesting that rumination in mentally retarded persons is three times more common in males than in females.

For the 76 cases, the mean age at onset of rumination ranges from 3 months to 21 years, with a mean of 5.7 years. The mean age at the time of treatment also varies extensively, from 11 months to 36 years, with a mean of 14.9 years. These data indicate that rumination is a potentially chronic disorder in mentally retarded individuals, given the difference of 9.2 years between mean age at onset and at treatment.

Based on the literature review, rumination disorder is not reported in borderline or mildly retarded individuals, and the incidence increases with greater degrees of mental retardation. Of the 76 cases reviewed, 7% are functioning in the moderate range of retardation, 20% in the severe range, and 73% in the profound range. In order to estimate the mental age at onset of rumination, each individual's IQ was multiplied by his or her chronological age at onset and divided by 100. Where specific IQs were not reported, IQs were approximated using the mean IQ for the person's level of retardation, as defined by the American Association on Mental Retardation. These calculations indicate a mean mental age at onset of rumination of 9.5 months, with a range of 7 days to 4.3 years.

Rumination in mentally retarded individuals may occur in a nurturing environment, and it is not typically considered to be precipitated by a disturbance in the relationship with the caretaker. It is speculated that the mentally retarded person's organic cognitive impairment impedes the normal utilization of external sources of gratification and predisposes the person to engage in atypical, self-stimulating behaviors as a source of satisfaction.

The prevalence of rumination in the general population of mentally retarded individuals is not known. However, for mentally retarded persons in residential care settings, reported incidence rates range from 6% to 10% (Rast, Ellinger-Allen, & Johnston, 1985; Rast *et al.*, 1981; Rojahn, 1984; Singh *et al.*, 1982). For the 76 cases in the literature, 31% are living at home and 69% in residential care. It remains to be determined if the incidence of rumination varies disproportionately as a function of type of care setting.

2. *Rumination in Infants*

A total of 47 cases of infant rumination are reported in the literature (Arensberg, 1956; Chatoor, Dickson, & Einhorn, 1984; Cunningham & Linscheid, 1976; Ferholt & Provence, 1976; Flanagan, 1977; Fleisher, 1979; Fullerton, 1963; Hollowell & Gardner, 1965; Lang & Melamed, 1969; Linscheid & Cunningham, 1977; Madison & Adubato, 1984; Menking, Wagnitz, Burton, Coddington, & Sotos, 1969; Mestre, Resnick, & Berman, 1983; Murray, Keele, & McCarver, 1976; Richmond, Eddy, & Green, 1958; Sajwaj, Libet, & Agras, 1974; Sauvage, Leddet, Hameury, & Barthelemy, 1985; Sheagren, Mangurten, Brea, & Lutostanski, 1980; Sheinbein, 1975; Stein, Rausen, & Blau, 1959; Toister, Condron, Worley, & Arthur, 1975; Wright, Brown, & Andrews, 1978). The male to female ratio across these cases is 37 to 10, suggesting that rumination in infants is 3.7 times greater in males than in females.

The reported age at onset of rumination in infants ranges from the neonatal period to 17 months, with a mean of 5.7 months. At the time of treatment, the infants ranged in age from 1 to 20 months, with a mean of 9 months. Thus rumination in infants occurs at a significantly younger mean age (5.7 months) than does rumination in mentally retarded persons (5.7 years). However, the mean mental age at onset for mentally retarded ruminators (9.5 months) is close to the age at onset for infants.

Only 8 of the 47 published cases of infant ruminators are described as developmentally delayed. In 13 cases, developmental functioning is not addressed and for 26, development is noted as normal. A longitudinal study of 20 infant ruminators by Sauvage *et al.* (1985) indicates that 5 years after diagnosis, all but 4 ruminators earned developmental quotients at least within the normal range (i.e., $\geq$ 80). The 4 who did not achieve normal developmental status have diagnoses suggesting an organic basis for the presence of mental retardation (i.e., congenital hyperammonemia with other significant neonatal complications, trisomy 13, autism, and atypical pervasive developmental disorder).

Family pathology or psychosocial stress are suggested in all of the 45 published cases of infant rumination that address environmental and caretaker issues. Reports include emotional deprivation, physical neglect, psychosocial stress, marital problems, separation from the mother, and maternal disorders, the most common of which is depression followed by anxiety disorder and then single instances of schizophrenia, antisocial disorder, personality disorder, substance abuse, and traumatic brain injury. Sauvage *et al.* (1985) note in their study of 20 infant ruminators that rumination "occurred in the context of disturbed relationships (chronic tensions and/or deprivation)" (p. 202). The literature also discloses 3 cases of rumination in a neonatal intensive care unit (Sheagren *et al.*, 1980). Two infants were diagnosed with necrotizing enterocolitis and 1 with bronchopulmonary dysplasia. Thus they experienced atypical care involving medical interventions and a potentially stressful environment, and they were deprived of a normal parent–child relationship.

Published hypotheses regarding the etiology of infant rumination focus on a disturbance in the mother–infant relationship and lack of the mother's ability to fulfill a warm, loving, and nurturing role (Bakwin & Bakwin, 1972; Chatoor *et al.*, 1984; Flanagan, 1977; Fleisher, 1979; Fullerton, 1963; Menking *et al.*, 1969; Richmond *et al.*, 1958; Sheinbein, 1975; Stein *et al.*, 1959; Wright *et al.*, 1978). In the majority of these publications, infant rumination is viewed from a psychodynamic perspective. Rumination is interpreted as the infant turning inward for gratification through the regurgitation of food to replace the loss of external gratification normally derived from the mother–infant relationship. Some authors speculate further that rumination reflects infant depression or anxiety or that it is a tension-reducing mechanism in response to stress.

Holvoet (1982) reports familial stress in all 19 cases of infant rumination in her review. Although an association between rumination and inadequate mothering and stress is suggested, Holvoet emphasizes that such findings are uncovered primarily by therapists attempting to identify psychopathology. Therefore, research is needed to empirically establish the etiological factors in infant rumination and to investigate the possible role of the infant in the development of this disorder. At this point, it is not known to what extent infant temperament or preexisting infant pathology may interfere with the development of a nurturing and mutually fulfilling relationship with the caretaker and contribute to the onset of rumination.

With the exception of the presence of rumination, infant ruminators appear to be a diverse group in terms of behavioral, social, and emotional functioning. Some case reports describe infant ruminators as responsive and alert (e.g., Richmond *et al.*, 1958; Sheinbein, 1975), and others report lethargy (e.g., Sajwaj *et al.*, 1974; Sheagren *et al.*, 1980). Of 14 infant ruminators earning developmental quotients greater than 80 (normal range or higher) at diagnosis, only 4 were described as unhappy and apathetic in the study by Sauvage *et al.* (1985). The remainder were considered to be normal in terms of temperament, behavior, and communication. For the three ruminators in the Sauvage *et al.* study (1985) with development quotients of 70 to 80, two were portrayed as irritable and one as depressed and withdrawn. Some of the infant ruminators in this study exhibited other self-stimulating behaviors, including excessive mouthing (60%) and head or body rocking (30%). Although infant ruminators do not present as a homogeneous group in terms of social and behavioral features, the treatment literature suggests preintervention deficits in these areas because improvements in social responsiveness, mood, and development are usually reported when rumination is reduced or eliminated.

According to the description of "Rumination Disorder of Infancy" found in the *Diagnostic and Statistical Manual of Mental Disorders*—Third Edition—Revised (DSM-III-R), "spontaneous remissions are thought to be common" (American Psychiatric Association, 1987, p. 70). Although no empirical studies have been conducted determining spontaneous recovery rates, rumination in infants may be a time-limited disorder given the finding that the oldest case in the literature is a 20-month-old. This is in contrast to rumination in mentally retarded individuals, which is a potentially chronic disorder and which has been reported in older adults with mental ages through 4.3 years.

3. *Diagnosis*

3.1. *Diagnostic and Statistical Manual of Mental Disorders*

According to the DSM-III-R, the diagnostic criteria for "Rumination Disorder of Infancy" are twofold: (1) "repeated regurgitation, without nausea or associated gastrointestinal illness, for at least one month following a period of normal functioning" and (2) "weight loss or failure to make expected weight gain" (American Psychiatric Association, 1987, p. 70). The DSM-III-R diagnostic criteria and description of rumination disorder have been critically analyzed (based on the literature and current knowledge regarding rumination disorder), and several modifications have been recommended (Mayes, 1992).

First, the DSM-III-R offers only one diagnostic category (rumination disorder of infancy), instead of subdividing the disorder into the two apparent types: rumination in infants and rumination in mentally retarded individuals. It is evident that diagnoses of rumination in the literature are based merely on the presence of rumination, without considering weight as a diagnostic factor. Although weight loss or failure to gain expected weight is associated with approximately 84% of the cases of rumination in the literature, such problems do not always accompany rumination, especially if regurgitated food is reswallowed. Therefore, decreased weight might more accurately be considered a complication of rumination rather than a diagnostic criterion.

The DSM-III-R stipulation that rumination must occur "following a period of normal functioning" is also not supported by the literature. Rumination has been reported as early as the neonatal period, and rumination in mentally retarded individuals is preceded by retarded development and often other forms of self-stimulation. The DSM-III-R criterion for rumination to have occurred "for at least one month" may be arbitrary and impede the prompt diagnosis and treatment of this potentially life-threatening disorder.

In summary, the essential diagnostic features of rumination disorder consistent with the general consensus in the literature are summarized by the following definition: purposeful and pleasurable repeated regurgitation of stomach contents in the absence of organic cause. Other suggested revisions for the DSM-III-R section on rumination disorder involve the DSM-III-R description of the act of rumination, associated features, age at onset, course, impairment, complications, predisposing factors, familial pattern, sex ratio, and differential diagnosis (Mayes, 1992).

3.2. *Differential Diagnosis*

Rumination is a voluntary behavior and must be differentiated from organic medical or physiological conditions with involuntary regurgitation as a symptom. Organic conditions described in the literature that may produce involuntary regurgitation include hiatal hernia, lower esophageal stenosis, pyloric stenosis, intestinal obstruction, gastrointestinal infection, and diaphragmatic hernia. An involuntary gastroesophageal influx (GER) as a result of esophogeal sphincter incompetence or other pathology is frequently misdiagnosed as rumination (Mayes, 1988, 1992). An involuntary GER is common in infants. Literature reviews also reveal that gastroesophageal reflux is present in approximately 12% of severely disabled individuals in residential care (Farrell, in press) and even more prevalent (up to 27%) in children with severe cerebral palsy (Kozlowski, 1990).

The first step in the diagnosis of rumination is to obtain appropriate medical evaluations, such as an upper gastrointestinal (GI) study (barium swallor or esophagram), milk scan, or pH probe (esophageal pH monitoring), in an attempt to rule out anatomical–medical problems. Sometimes organic etiologies are readily apparent through medical examinations and radiographic studies. However, the determination of whether regurgitation is voluntary or involuntary may be complex, and the distinction between rumination and an involuntary GER may require more than a milk scan, upper GI study, or pH probe. Radiographic and other studies may indicate reflux (i.e., the backward flowing of stomach contents into the esophagus) but, in the absence of obvious pathology, such studies cannot determine whether the reflux is voluntary (rumination) or involuntary secondary to, for example, lower esophageal sphincter dysfunction. In other words, rumination and involuntary GER may appear identical on a milk scan, upper GI study, or pH probe.

Clinical observations over an extended period of time and a careful history must form the basis for a differential diagnosis between rumination disorder and involuntary GER in cases where medical studies do not yield a definitive diagnosis. The following seven descriptors may assist in clinically distinguishing between the two disorders: (a) an involuntary GER is, as stated, involuntary, versus rumination disorder, which is purposeful; (b) an involuntary GER can be triggered by an environmental stimulus, such as movement, versus rumination disorder, which is completely self-induced; (c) an involuntary GER is unexpected, whereas rumination is planned; (d) regurgitation secondary to an involuntary GER is not experienced as pleasant and instead, the individual may show discomfort or distress, whereas rumination is a form of enjoyable self-stimulation, and the ruminator often retains and savors the regurgitated matter in his or her mouth; (e) in an involuntary GER, large amounts may be regurgitated, whereas smaller quantities (usually only a mouthful) are typically ruminated; (f) in general, ruminators thoroughly enjoy eating, but individuals with an involuntary GER may not, and there may be associated feeding problems; and (g) features usually found in conjunction with rumination disorder include other self-stimulating behaviors and severe to profound mental retardation or a disturbance in the infant–caretaker relationship, which are not necessarily associated features with an involuntary GER. However, involuntary GER is quite prevalent in persons of all ages who have developmental disabilities or cerebral palsy (Farrell, in press; Kozlowski, 1990), in addition to being common in infants.

Retrospectively, response to treatment may either support or fail to support a diagnosis. According to published reports, infants who are hospitalized for chronic regurgitation and are provided with warm and nurturing care in a stimulating environment but not given specific medical intervention usually stop regurgitating if the disorder is rumination. Similarly, if regurgitation in an infant or mentally retarded individual is responsive to behavioral approaches (which involve modifying the antecedents or consequences of the behavior), the regurgitation is likely to be under voluntary control and, therefore, rumination. However, both rumination and an involuntary gastroesophageal reflux can be affected by medical intervention. Medical treatments might include antireflux positioning following meals (prone at a 30- to 40-degree angle with head up); medication, such as an antacid with metoclopramide or bethanechol, to accelerate gastric emptying and increase lower esophageal sphincter pressure; or surgery, such as a Nissen fundoplication, enabling the lower esophageal sphincter to close more tightly above the stomach. These measures all impede the backward flowing of stomach contents into the esophagus, thus, reducing the likelihood of an involuntary GER as well as making it more difficult (although not impossible) for a ruminator to purposefully regurgitate.

Another important diagnostic distinction involves differentiating between regurgitation (i.e., the reflux or backward flowing of undigested foods or fluids into the esophagus or mouth) and vomiting (the forcible expulsion of stomach contents through the mouth). Rumination involves regurgitation and should not be confused with conditions that have vomiting as a symptom. Vomiting may be caused by food allergies, gastrointestinal disorders (such as GI infections), or feeding disorders. Vomiting may occur during the feeding process in individuals with hyperreactive oral–esophageal–gastric mechanisms. It may also occur following feeding in individuals who have an aversion to oral intake, which may develop in developmentally or medically disabled children who have been sustained at or near birth on gastrostomy tube feedings for a prolonged period of time.

Vomiting may also be a symptom of a variety of psychiatric disorders (Leibovich, 1973), the most prevalent being self-induced vomiting associated with anorexia or bulemia nervosa. The literature also contains several references to psychogenic vomiting in individuals, for example, with diagnoses of anxiety disorder, depression, conversion disorder, and schizophrenia (Alford, Blanchard, & Buckley, 1972; Leibovich, 1973; Spergel, 1975; Wright & Thalassinos, 1973). In addition to the essential physiological distinction between vomiting versus regurgitation, vomiting associated with psychiatric disorders differs in many other ways from regurgitation in rumination disorder. Psychogenic vomiting is more common in females than in males, the age at onset is considerably later than that for rumination, and mental retardation or a disturbed infant–caretaker relationship are not associated features.

Finally, regurgitation related to anxiety and stress must be differentiated from rumination. The literature describes two cases of male children presenting with the symptom of regurgitation at approximately 2 years of age and coinciding with psychosocial stress (Griffin, 1977; Mayes, 1992). At the time of treatment (7 and 4 years of age, respectively), both children showed anxiety and other symptomatology, including enuresis, bruxism, severe nail biting, or psychosomatic leg pain. The anxiety-related regurgitation in these two cases differs from rumination in that it is not a voluntary, pleasurable, and self-stimulatory act. In fact, both children complained of gastric discomfort.

The differential diagnosis between rumination and involuntary, organically or anxiety-based regurgitation and medical or psychiatric conditions with vomiting as a symptom is important because the etiologic implications and treatments vary considerably among these disorders. The behavioral and social interventions most frequently used to intervene with rumination are based on the assumption that the regurgitation is voluntary and under the individual's control, and in the case of infant rumination, that the family and home situation need to be addressed.

4. *Complications*

For both mentally retarded individuals and infants, complications associated with rumination disorder include weight loss, growth retardation, malnutrition, dehydration, aspiration, aspiration pneumonia, gastric disorders, esophagitis, tooth decay and tooth erosion, anemia, electrolyte imbalance, lowered resistance to disease, and in some cases, death. However, because of medical advances such as parenteral hyperalimentation, mortality is a relatively rare consequence today. Mortality rates for mentally retarded ruminators are not known, and what little data are available are quite old. However, Rast *et al.* (1981) report that over a 3-year period in the late 1970s, rumination was a "primary contributing factor" in three deaths at one institution for mentally retarded individuals (p. 121). Data for infant ruminators suggest that mortality may be declining with time. In a review by Sajwaj *et al.* (1974), the authors report a mortality estimate of 12.5%, in contrast to 17% in a 1959 publication and 21% in 1957. The DSM-III-R states that as many as 25% of infant ruminators die from the disorder (American Psychiatric Association, 1987). However, based on a longitudinal study of 20 infant ruminators, Sauvage *et al.* (1985) feel that the rate reported in the DSM-III-R is inflated. Clearly, current data are needed to replace the older mortality rates quoted in the literature that predate medical advances and interventions affecting the outcome for rumination in infants.

For the 47 cases of infant rumination reviewed in the literature, 41 (87%) of the infants were losing weight or had not achieved expected weight. For 6 (13%), weight was within normal limits. Similarly, for the 58 cases of rumination in mentally retarded individuals for which weight data are provided, 47 (81%) showed weight loss, failure to thrive, or body weight less than the ideal for age or height. The remaining 11 (19%) did not exhibit weight problems, with the exception of 2 described as obese. According to a survey by Rast, Ellinger-Allen, and Johnston (1985) in a large institution, 96% of adult ruminators were more than 10% below their estimated ideal body weight. However, independent of rumination, growth failure is associated with mental retardation (Crump, 1987). Therefore, the degree to which weight problems are attributed specifically to rumination in mentally retarded individuals needs to be investigated further.

In addition to the aforementioned complications, rumination may preclude the development of functional behaviors and its continuation serves to strengthen the individual's drive for internal stimulation, thus interfering with more normal social and emotional functioning. Rumination is a very unpleasant and noxious disorder, and it can have an extremely negative impact on families and staff. Because of the odor and sight of regurgitated material and the increased demands to clean the ruminator, clothing, and surroundings, others may avoid or interact negatively with the ruminator, which serves to further impair social relatedness and reduce the amount of positive contact with others.

5. *Mediating Variables*

5.1. *Social and Environmental Factors*

Rumination may occur anywhere any time given the availability of stomach contents to ruminate. However, research suggests that an increase in social attention and stimulation are associated with a decline in rumination. The provision of nurturing and warm care within a stimulating environment has been effective in treating infant rumination (Arensberg, 1956; Ferholt & Province, 1976; Flanagan, 1977; Fleisher, 1979; Fullerton, 1963; Hollowell & Gardner, 1965; Mayes, 1992; Menking *et al.*, 1969; Richmond *et al.*, 1958; Sheagren *et al.*, 1980; Sheinbein, 1975; Stein *et al.*, 1959), and a few cases of rumination in mentally retarded persons (Whitehead *et al.*, 1985; Wright & Menolascino, 1970).

Additional support for mediating social and environmental variables is derived from research on self-injurious behaviors, under the heading of which rumination falls (Demchak & Halle, 1985). In a study of self-injurious behaviors in mentally retarded children, Iwata, Dorsey, Slifer, Bauman, and Richman (1982) found that, overall, a decrease in self-injurious behaviors was related to opportunity to play with toys, minimal demands, and reinforcement of behaviors incompatible with the self-injurious ones. Favell, McGimsey, and Schell (1982) found a similar relationship and report that frequency of self-injurious behaviors was highest when individuals were unoccupied and alone and lowest when opportunities for play with toys were available.

A naturalistic study of a profoundly retarded, 12-year-old ruminator in residential care was conducted by Humphrey *et al.* (1989) by collecting data at 15-minute intervals during all waking hours for 4 weeks. In addition to a significant association between rumination frequency and intake of food (i.e., rumination rates were highest during meals and declined steadily thereafter), the following variables were related to a decrease in rumination: participation in the school program, increased individual attention, and assignment to caretakers who like the child more than do other caretakers. The results show that rumination rates were highest during activities coinciding with the ingestion of foods and fluids. Middle rates occurred during nonschool activities, and the lowest rates were during school activities. The favorable impact of the school program on rumination was also supported by the day of the week analysis. For each of the 4 weeks of the study, rumination frequency increased dramatically to its highest level on Saturdays, decreased to its second highest level on Sunday, decreased markedly on Monday to its lowest level, and increased on Tuesdays. This pattern suggests that the child was reacting to the loss of the school program on Saturdays, accommodating to this loss on Sundays, responding to the reinstatement of school on Mondays, and adjusting to this change on Tuesdays. Degree of individual attention was also related to frequency of rumination. Excluding activities confounded by the ingestion of food, rumination rates were highest during independent play, lower during group activities, and lowest when the child was receiving one-to-one attention. This was true even within the classroom setting, with rumination rates greater during group activities than during individual instruction. Finally, staff were requested to complete a scale indicating the degree to which they liked the child. A significant correlation was found between increasing likability and decreasing rumination (i.e., the child ruminated less with caretakers who liked him more and vice versa).

A study by Rast and Johnston (1986) suggests that the mere presence of others does not necessarily affect rumination frequency. With four severely to profoundly retarded adolescent and young adult ruminators in residential care, no differences in rumination rates were found as a function of whether each subject was alone in a dayroom versus with other residents and staff in the same location (in the latter case, interactions were minimal). Thus the added social stimulation of the group situation did not decrease or substitute for rumination. Conversely, the finding does not support the hypothesis that rumination is maintained by social attention because the withdrawal of attention when the ruminator was alone was not associated with a decline in rumination frequency. Thus in order for social variables to have an impact on rumination, they may need to be rather intrusive and to actively involve the ruminator.

5.2. Factors Related to Intake

5.2.1. Mealtime

Numerous researchers report that rumination frequency is greatest during and immediately following meals. This is the case for both rumination in mentally retarded individuals (Ball *et al.*, 1974; Borreson & Anderson, 1982; Humphrey *et al.*, 1989; Kohlenberg, 1970; Marholin *et al.*, 1980; Rast, Ellinger-Allen, & Johnston, 1985; Singh *et al.*, 1982; White & Taylor, 1967; Wright & Thalassinos, 1973) and for rumination in infants (Murray *et al.*, 1976; Sajwaj *et al.*, 1974; Sheinbein, 1975). Based on rumination data for a profoundly retarded 12-year-old, a highly significant correlation coefficient of .91 was obtained between decreasing rumination frequency and each 15-minute period following meals (Humphrey *et al.*, 1989). However, rumination never reached zero frequency, even immediately preceding the next meal or snack. The relationship between rumination and mealtime is, of course, logical and may be a function of both gastric emptying (i.e., the decreasing availability of food or fluids in the stomach to ruminate) and the increasingly unpleasant taste of regurgitated stomach contents over time (Ekvall, Ekvall, & Mayes, in press). Even so, some ruminators do ruminate during all waking hours (Mayes, 1988).

5.2.2. Rate of Food Consumption

Two studies with individual severely to profoundly retarded adults address the influence of pace of food consumption on rumination and report conflicting results. In one study by McKeegan *et al.* (1987), postmeal rumination decreased when the ruminator was forced to eat his food at a rate slower than his normal rapid pace. Rate of consumption was controlled by slowly giving the individual bite-size portions of food and small sips of fluid. In contrast, Rast *et al.* (1981) found no difference between baseline and intervention rumination rates when a similar program was implemented with their subject. This approach was also unsuccessful for the author with a 16-year-old profoundly retarded ruminator who actually became agitated and ruminated at a higher frequency when his rapid pace of food consumption was modified by the slow introduction of single bite-size amounts.

5.2.3. Quantity

Decreasing food quantity does not reduce rumination, and in fact, if ruminators are given smaller and more frequent meals, rumination often increases. In contrast, several published studies show that postmeal rumination immediately and significantly decreases or ceases entirely when severely to profoundly mentally retarded adult ruminators in residential care are permitted to eat to satiation (Borreson & Anderson, 1982; Foxx *et al.*, 1979; Jackson *et al.*, 1975; Johnston & Greene, in press; Libby & Phillips, 1979; Lobato *et al.*, 1986; Rast, Ellinger-Allen, & Johnston, 1985; Rast & Johnston 1986; Rast, Johnston, Allen, & Drum, 1985; Rast, Johnston, Lubin, & Ellinger-Allen, 1988b; Rast *et al.*, 1981, 1984). When a ruminator is "satiated" and refuses to consume more food, rumination often loses its reinforcing property and consequently subsides. This outcome is maintained as long as satiation conditions are in effect.

In order to achieve satiation, large quantities of food must be consumed. Although individuals satiate at different levels, a ruminator generally must eat between 3 and 6 times normal meal portions in order for rumination rates to be affected. Some research shows that if mentally retarded ruminators are given only double servings, rumination rates actually increase (Johnston & Greene, in press; Rast *et al.*, 1981). Beyond this point, as quantity of food increases in 10-ounce increments, rumination rates decrease (Rast *et al.*, 1984). Conversely, as amount of food ingested decreases, rumination increases (Rast *et al.*, 1984). Rast *et al.* (1988b) have also found rumination to decrease when ruminators are given supplemental quantities of fluid before and during meals. However, the impact of food satiation is considerably greater than the effect of providing additional fluids.

5.2.4. *Calories, Volume, Weight, Stomach Distention, and Oropharyngeal Stimulation*

Johnston and his colleagues have conducted several well-controlled and systematic investigations attempting to partial out the relative effectiveness of various factors that may influence the impact of satiation on rumination. It is clear that there are multiple contributing variables; however, caloric density appears to be the most important single variable. Rast, Johnston, Allen, and Drum (1985) have shown if the volume, weight, and chewing requirements of a starch satiation diet are maintained but calories are reduced by substituting lower calorie for higher calorie foods, rumination significantly increases. Conversely, rumination decreases with an increase in calories while the other variables are held constant. Similarly, if the volume of food consumed is increased to match the volume of a starch satiation diet but calories are not increased and, instead, kept at the baseline level, rumination decreases only slightly (versus significantly when calories are increased). Likewise, if the weight of this high-volume low-calorie diet is increased to the weight of the high-calorie satiation diet, a slight further decrease in rumination is noted. Thus, volume and weight have some impact on rumination, but not as great an impact as caloric density.

The influence of stomach distention on rumination was investigated by giving ruminators one to three tablespoons of wheat bran per meal plus 64 ounces of noncaloric liquids a day (Rast, Johnston, Allen, & Drum, 1985). Thus, stomach distention increased, whereas caloric intake was only minimally affected. The result was only a slight decrease in rumination frequency. The effect of oropharyngeal stimulation relative to satiation was also investigated by Rast *et al.* (1988a). This study showed that premeal gum chewing produced a moderate decrease in postmeal rumination, although again, not as significant as with a satiation diet.

Overall, the research of Johnston and his colleagues indicates if calories are increased or decreased while other parameters (volume, weight, and chewing) are held constant, rumination significantly decreases or increases, respectively. In contrast, when calories are maintained at a baseline level and the other parameters (including degree of stomach distention) are modified, the impact on rumination is only slight. However, an increase in calories alone is not enough to achieve the effect of a satiation diet. If the number of calories in a starch satiation diet are matched with high-calorie foods but the ruminator does not eat to satiation, rumination decreases but not to the extent as it does following a satiation diet (Rast, Johnston, Allen, & Drum, 1985). Similarly, Johnston, Greene, Rawal, Vazin, and Winston (1991) demonstrated with three severely to profoundly mentally retarded adult ruminators in residential care that when meal portions were maintained at their normal size but calories were increased by adding oil, sugar, and Polycose, postmeal rumination decreased 15% to 43%. This represents a significant reduction, although not as much as following food satiation.

Most satiation research has been conducted with high-calorie starch diets using rice, potatoes, grits, cereal, and bread. Overall, starch satiation diets appear to be more effective than low-calorie satiation diets (J. M. Johnston, personal communication, April 30, 1990). However, low-calorie satiation has been at least moderately successful with some mentally retarded adult ruminators (Lobato *et al.*, 1986; Rast, Johnston, Allen, & Drum, 1985). In the study by Rast, Johnston, Allen, and Drum (1985) with two mentally retarded adult ruminators, low-calorie satiation with vegetables (approximately 3,600 calories per day) decreased rumination to a level comparable to that obtained with a high-calorie starch satiation diet (4,980 calories per day). However, the two ruminators had to consume more low-calorie than high-calorie food to achieve satiation. Thus the low-calorie satiation diet involved greater volume, weight, and degree of oropharyngeal stimulation than the starch satiation diet, factors that may have compensated for the reduction in calories.

5.2.5. Consistency and Texture

The impact of consistency or texture on rumination has been studied only to a limited extent. Johnston, Greene, Vazin, Winston, Rawal, and Chuang (1990) showed that rumination rates following a pureed diet were somewhat higher than following a diet of normal consistency in three profoundly retarded adult males in an institutional setting. The authors hypothesize that this modest effect on rumination may have been the result of a decrease in oropharyngeal stimulation because pureed food requires less chewing than food of normal consistency. Thus ruminators may seek additional oropharyngeal stimulation through rumination following pureed diets.

It may also be speculated that, from a mechanical perspective, pureed food is easier to ruminate than thicker food. However, the impact of food density was investigated by Greene, Johnston, Rossi, Rawal, Winston, and Barron (1991) in a study of effects of peanut butter on rumination in five severely to profoundly mentally retarded adults in residential care. The researchers found a nonsignificant difference between rumination rates when, after each meal, the subjects were given three-fourths of a cup of unaltered creamy peanut butter versus a thinner preparation created by blending the peanut butter with milk. These results support previous reports that thickened feedings are not successful in reducing rumination.

The peanut butter investigation by Greene *et al.* (1991) was undertaken following a study by Barton and Barton (1985) in which four severely to profoundly retarded children were given three tablespoons of peanut butter every 2 to 3 hours and their fluid intake was restricted during meals. This resulted in zero to near-zero rumination frequencies. Greene *et al.* (1991) confirmed the effectiveness of peanut butter with mentally retarded adult ruminators and found that optimal results were obtained with three-fourths of a cup of peanut butter (versus smaller amounts) following meals. Greene *et al.* systematically varied the calories (using regular peanut butter versus a low-calorie peanut butter preparation) and the consistency (regular peanut butter versus peanut butter blended with milk) and demonstrated that caloric density (versus thickness) appeared to be the main factor accounting for the success of treatment with peanut butter. The subjects received approximately 3,600 additional calories per day when three-fourths of a cup of peanut butter was given after each of their three meals. Both the regular (high calorie) and low-calorie peanut butter, which were equivalent to each other in consistency, reduced rumination, but the high-calorie peanut butter was considerably more effective than the low-calorie peanut butter. Regular peanut butter and a thinner, though calorically equivalent, peanut butter mixture (created by blending peanut butter with milk) both decreased rumination, without a significant difference between the two. Therefore, the higher calorie thinner peanut butter had a substantially greater impact on rumination than did the lower calorie thicker peanut butter.

5.2.6. *Content and Taste*

Knowledge regarding the impact of food content and taste on rumination is sparse. It is known that some substances (e.g., chocolate or fatty foods) may decrease lower esophageal sphincter pressure and that tomatoes and citrus products (e.g., orange juice) may irritate the esophagus. Therefore, ingestion of these substances is not recommended for individuals with gastroesophageal reflux (Kozlowski, 1990). However, Rast *et al.* (1981) found no differences between rumination rates in severely to profoundly retarded adult ruminators following a standard institutional diet versus a diet without tomatoes and with minimal fat. In contrast, anecdotal reports from clinical cases suggest that some ruminators do ruminate specific foods more so than others. For example, a severely to profoundly retarded adult ruminator treated by this author was considerably more likely to ruminate orange juice and food prepared with tomatoes than other foods or fluids. In this instance, the increase in rumination related to intake may reflect a physiological response to the substances ingested, with lower esophageal sphincter pressure affected. However, systematic research is needed in this area.

Controlled research studies are also necessary to determine if taste influences rumination and if ruminators are more likely to regurgitate preferred than nonpreferred foods. Administering a taste-aversive substance (e.g., vanilla extract, lemon juice, or Tabasco sauce) following each episode of rumination is an effective treatment approach and significantly reduces or eliminates rumination (Becker *et al.*, 1978; Bright & Whaley, 1968; Hogg, 1982; Marholin *et al.*, 1980; Mayes, 1992; O'Neil *et al.*, 1979). This indicates that rumination can be affected by taste. However, it is not known the extent to which the taste of various foods normally consumed impacts on rumination rates.

6. *Treatment of Rumination Disorder in Mentally Retarded Individuals*

6.1. *Overview*

Successful intervention techniques found in the literature for reducing or eliminating rumination in mentally retarded individuals are summarized in Table 1. Positive developmental, social, emotional, and nutritional gains following treatment are also reported in many of these studies. Only treatments with demonstrated individual effectiveness in controlling rumination (i.e., alone or when added to another intervention) are included in the table. Cases from studies combining treatment approaches without partialing out the effectiveness of the separate components are omitted. As shown in Table 1, the most common published interventions are satiation and aversive techniques, accounting for 37.5% and 27.3% of the cases, respectively.

6.2. *Satiation Diet*

Much of the existing knowledge on satiation is credited to the work of Johnston and his associates, whose research accounts for 75.8% of published cases treated with satiation (Johnston & Greene, in press; Rast, Ellinger-Allen, & Johnston, 1985; Rast & Johnston, 1986; Rast,

TABLE 1
Published Effective Treatments for Rumination in Mentally Retarded Individuals

Number of cases	Treatment
33	Satiation diet
24	Aversive techniques
9	Presentation/withdrawal of reinforcement
9	Peanut butter
4	Noncontingent attention and stimulation
3	Modified feeding
3	Medication
2	Holding around mealtime
1	Contingent exercise

Johnston, Allen, & Drum, 1985; Rast, Johnston, & Drum, 1984; Rast, Johnston, Drum, & Conrin, 1981). The remaining cases are reported in studies by Borreson and Anderson (1982), Foxx *et al.* (1979), Jackson *et al.* (1975), Libby and Phillips (1979), and Lobato *et al.* (1986). All of the published research on satiation to date involves severely to profoundly mentally retarded adults in residential care.

In the satiation procedure used by Johnston and his colleagues, the ruminator is presented with a full tray of food, which is refilled as food is consumed. If the ruminator slows his or her pace of consumption or stops eating, staff encourage him or her to eat more. After three refusals without intervening eating, the meal is discontinued (Johnston & Greene, in press). This procedure has significantly reduced or eliminated rumination in approximately 25 ruminators treated by Johnston *et al.*

To reach satiation (which varies from individual to individual and meal to meal), usually three to six times normal meal quantities are consumed. As noted previously, double portions may result in an increase in postmeal rumination. According to Johnston and Greene (in press), none of the subjects in their studies ruminated after eating meals larger than 2,000 grams, although not all ruminators consumed this much. Some stopped ruminating after meals as small as 1,000 grams. Johnston and Greene (in press) report that the effect of satiation is marked and rapid, with all subjects responding at least within a few days and some after the initial satiation meal. However, there is individual variation in overall effectiveness, and not all ruminators achieve zero rumination frequency.

The research of Johnston and his associates also demonstrates that when satiation conditions are removed and individuals again consume normal meal quantities, rumination rates increase, often returning to baseline levels (Rast, Ellinger-Allen, & Johnston, 1985; Rast & Johnston, 1986; Rast, Johnston, Allen, & Drum, 1985; Rast *et al.*, 1981, 1984). Therefore, in order to maintain suppression of rumination, a satiation diet must remain in effect indefinitely. The longest a ruminator has been maintained on satiation in studies by Johnston *et al.* is 6.4 months. However, there are potential limitations to long-term use of satiation, such as excessive weight gain.

The satiation procedures used in other studies with severely to profoundly mentally retarded adults in residential care vary somewhat from the approach of Johnston and his colleagues. In an investigation by Foxx *et al.* (1979), two adults were offered double meal portions at lunch, which resulted in mean rumination decreases of 45.9% and 84.2% during the 30-minute periods following lunch. In another study (Borreson & Anderson, 1982), satiation to refusal at lunch yielded a 63.3% mean decrease in rumination during 1-hour postlunch intervals. Two ruminators in a study by Jackson *et al.* (1975) ate until food refusal during all meals and received milkshakes throughout the day. During 1-hour postmeal periods, rumination decreased by averages of 50% and 94%. Libby and Phillips (1979) eliminated rumination in one individual who ate to satiation at breakfast, was given four meal portions plus four cups of cereal at lunch and dinner, and consumed three bananas before bed. When the diet was modified to include only a large breakfast, double portions at lunch and dinner, and snacks, rumination remained at zero frequency.

Lobato *et al.* (1986) investigated the effectiveness of a low-calorie satiation diet. The two subjects in their study consumed regular meal portions plus unlimited quantities of low-calorie foods and fluids, comprising vegetables, fruits, toast, low-calorie pudding, and water. These were offered at hourly intervals during all waking hours. Data were collected for 45 minutes beginning 30 minutes after the end of breakfast three times a week. Results showed approximate 60% and 63% decreases in rumination. Although caloric intake increased by about 67% and 24%, the subjects maintained their weights within the ideal range at 10 months follow-up.

A mealtime interaction effect is reported with satiation. Rast *et al.* (1984) demonstrated that as breakfast meal quantity increases, postlunch rumination decreases. Similarly, Johnston and Greene (in press) found diminishing postdinner rumination rates when lunch quantities increased. A cumulative effect may also be present. For example, Greene *et al.* (1991) gave their subjects three-fourths of a cup of peanut butter following meals and found that the reduction in rumination was greater after the second experimental meal of the day (dinner) than after the first (lunch). These findings support the earlier research of Foxx *et al.* (1979) who report that lunchtime satiation affected other meals, with concomitant, though smaller, decreases in rumination following breakfast and dinner. Therefore, if satiation conditions cannot be implemented at all meals, some effects may be achieved by allowing ruminators to eat to satiation at only some meals.

6.3. *Aversive Techniques*

Twenty-four cases involving the successful use of aversive procedures to treat rumination disorder in mentally retarded persons are found in the literature. The most frequently reported technique (nine cases) is the use of a taste-aversive substance (lemon juice, Tabasco sauce, or vanilla extract) immediately following each episode of rumination. This has been effective with 2- to 16-year-old severely to profoundly retarded individuals, some of whom were residing at home and others in residential care (Becker *et al.*, 1978; Bright & Whaley, 1968; Hogg, 1982; Marholin *et al.*, 1980; Mayes, 1992; O'Neil *et al.*, 1979). The next most common aversive procedure in the literature (seven cases) is contingent electric shock used to treat rumination in 4- to 23-year-old moderately to profoundly retarded individuals living at home and in residential settings (Galbraith *et al.*, 1970; Kohlenberg, 1970; Luckey *et al.*, 1968; Watkins, 1972; White & Taylor, 1967).

In five cases, a combination of taste-aversive procedures and overcorrection was used to significantly decrease rumination in 10- to 25-year-old severely to profoundly retarded ruminators living at home and in residential care. The program for four of these individuals involved 2 minutes of cleansing the teeth and/or gums with Listerine in response to each instance of rumination (Foxx *et al.*, 1979; Singh *et al.*, 1982). The remaining ruminator was successfully treated by contingent oral administration of lemon juice, followed by washing of lips with soap and water for 30 seconds (Simpson & Sasso, 1978).

Overcorrection procedures for two other severely to profoundly retarded ruminators in residential care (19 and 36 years of age) involved restitution and/or positive practice. One was required to clean up the regurgitated matter and bend over the toilet bowl with open mouth for several seconds and then flush the toilet whenever rumination occurred (Azrin & Wesolowski, 1975). For the other, a 20-minute procedure was enforced contingent on rumination that involved washing the individual's face with cold water and then requiring her to clean the floor (or wherever she ruminated) and additional areas, such as the window sills and walls (Duker & Seys, 1977). Another published case of a ruminator treated with aversive procedures is a 13-year-old profoundly retarded female in residential care who was pinched on the back of her hand each time she ruminated (Minness, 1980).

This author has successfully treated several ruminators using a taste-aversive contingency, as shown by the following multiply replicated AB design (Figures 1 and 2). Whenever using substances to be ingested, a physician's supervision is necessary. However, to date, no ill effects have been associated with this procedure in this author's experience.

Two ruminators undergoing taste-aversive treatment by this author were a 13-year-old male and a 10-year-old female, both severely to profoundly retarded and living at home. They ruminated at relatively low frequencies, with mean baseline preintervention rates of 44.3 and 22.5 ruminations per day, respectively. The former individual had been ruminating for 8 months and the latter, for 5 years. Because the individuals reswallowed the regurgitated material and their rates of rumination were comparatively low, the health of neither was significantly jeopardized. Therefore, both were treated on an outpatient basis. Intervention involved the immediate administration of two to three drops of vanilla extract (from a bottle with a squeeze dropper) in response to each episode of rumination, during all waking hours. Care was taken to administer the vanilla extract immediately after the ruminated material was reswallowed or expelled from the mouth. Otherwise, the vanilla extract had the reverse effect, mixing with the regurgitated matter and creating a pleasant taste. As shown in Figure 1, this treatment approach was highly successful. By Day 5 of intervention, both individuals achieved almost total elimination of rumination. Follow-up for both 1-year later disclosed only rare episodes of rumination, not exceeding one per week.

For other individuals treated by this author, rumination occurs at extremely high levels and/or is a life-threatening disorder. Data for two such ruminators are presented in Figure 2. Both were malnourished and required hospitalization to treat their rumination-associated medical complications and to implement an intervention program. One individual ruminated an average of 56.0 times per day. He was functioning in the severe range of mental retardation and was 3 years of age at the time of treatment. He had had several acute care admissions in the past for malnutrition and dehydration, secondary to rumination disorder. This individual derived immense pleasure from rumination, and the mildly aversive effect of vanilla extract was not enough to render rumination unpleasant for him. Therefore, two to three drops of Tabasco sauce were substituted, which had the desired impact. Follow-up over

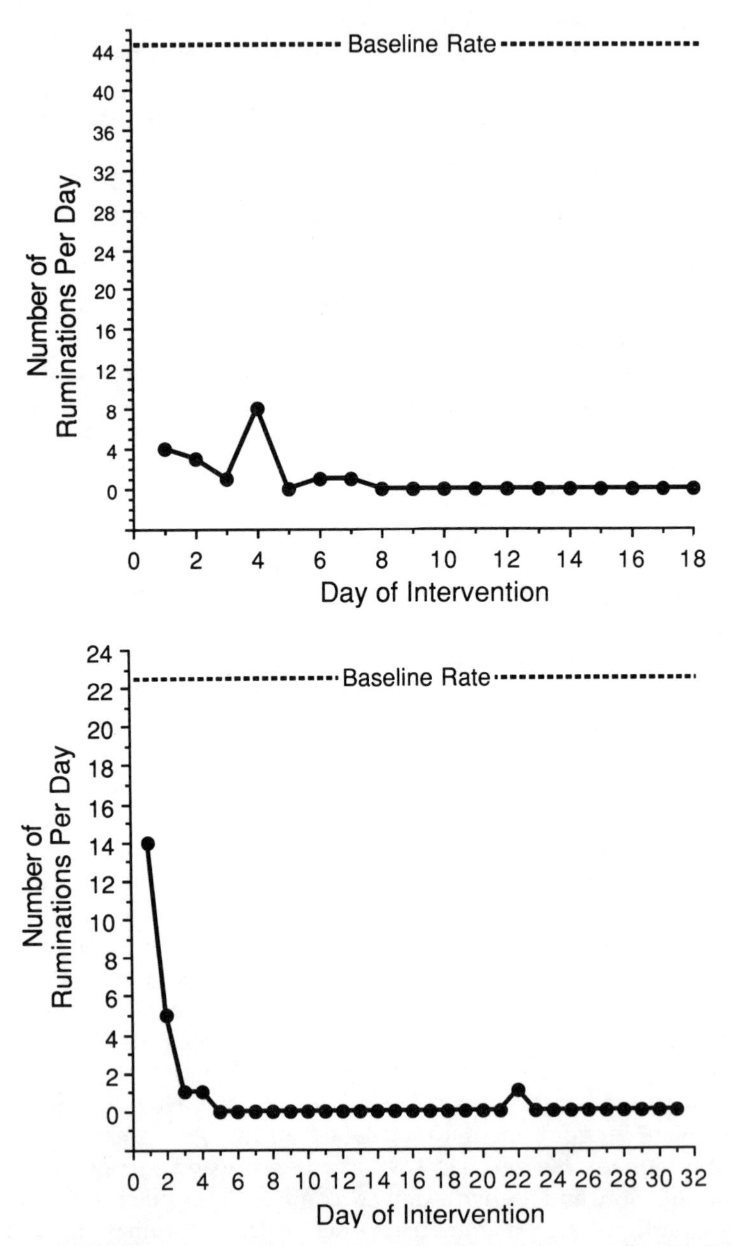

FIGURE 1. Outpatient treatment of rumination disorder in two mentally retarded individuals using a taste-aversive substance (vanilla extract).

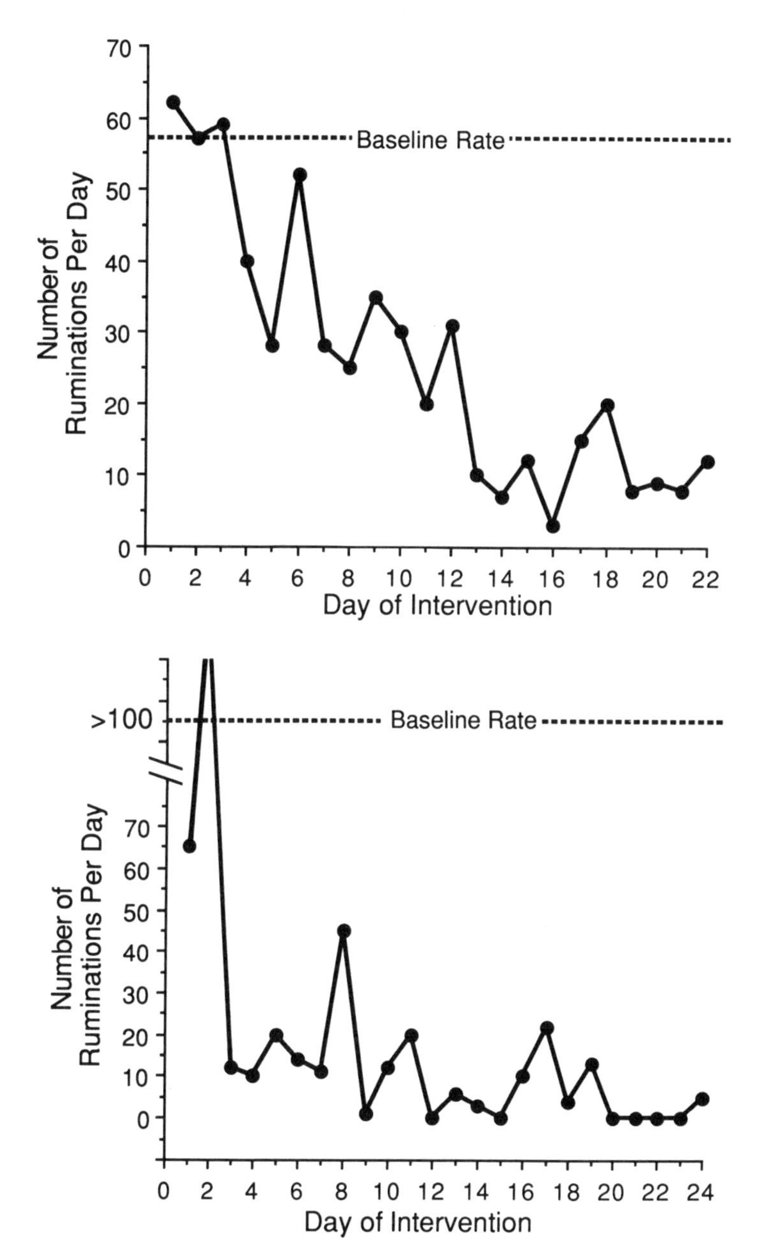

FIGURE 2. Inpatient treatment of rumination disorder in two mentally retarded individuals using taste-aversive substances.

the past 5 years indicates that the child only occasionally ruminates, at most a few times a week. When rumination occurs, it is again curtailed by the reintroduction of Tabasco sauce.

The remaining case is of a 4-year-old profoundly retarded male who was ruminating several hundred times per day and was severely malnourished and dehydrated on admission. As shown in Figure 2, significant results were obtained using two to three drops of vanilla extract in response to each episode of rumination. Follow-up 3 months after discharge from the hospital revealed rumination in the range of 0 to 5 times per day.

6.4. *Presentation/Withdrawal of Reinforcement*

As shown in Table 1, the manipulation of reinforcing contingencies was used to treat rumination in nine cases. Intervention for four of these ruminators involved providing positive reinforcement (e.g., differential reinforcement of other behavior or reinforcement of incompatible behavior) during nonruminating periods (Barmann, 1980; Conrin *et al.*, 1982; McKeegan *et al.*, 1987). These ruminators were 6 to 23 years of age, functioning in the severe to profound range of mental retardation, and living both at home or in residential care. Conversely, two other severely to profoundly mentally retarded ruminators (21 and 26 years of age and living in an institution) were treated using time-out or the withdrawal of reinforcement contingent on rumination (Borreson & Anderson, 1982; Davis *et al.*, 1980). The remaining three ruminators were treated combining contingent time-out from reinforcement with reinforcement during nonruminating periods (Mulick *et al.*, 1980; Smith & Lyon, 1976; Whitehead *et al.*, 1985). The latter ruminators were severely to profoundly retarded, 2 to 25 years of age, and lived at home or in residential care settings.

6.5. *Peanut Butter Therapy*

The addition of peanut butter to the diet of ruminating individuals has proven effective in reducing rumination in two research studies (Barton & Barton, 1985; Greene *et al.*, 1991). In the study by Barton and Barton (1985), four 5- to 10-year-old severely to profoundly retarded students were given three tablespoons of creamy peanut butter every 2 to 3 hours, and their fluid intake was restricted during meals. This resulted in a substantial decrease in rumination frequency, which at baseline ranged from 15.5 to 26.0 ruminations per day (mean = 17.0). According to the authors, when peanut butter therapy was discontinued, rumination frequency for the four subjects remained at zero or near-zero levels.

Greene *et al.* (1991) also report a significant reduction in rumination in five severely to profoundly mentally retarded 22- to 53-year-olds in residential care when peanut butter therapy was initiated. The authors found that three-fourths of a cup of peanut butter following meals significantly suppressed rumination. As indicated in a previous section, the authors demonstrated that this result was primarily due to increased calories and not the thickness of the peanut butter. The investigators demonstrated that regular peanut butter blended with milk was considerably more effective in reducing rumination than a thicker but lower calorie peanut butter preparation. In contrast to the results of Barton and Barton (1985), discontinuation of peanut butter therapy in the study by Greene *et al.* (1991) resulted in a significant increase in rumination frequency. Greene *et al.* hypothesize that the discrepancy in findings may be a function of the older ages and higher baseline rumination rates of the subjects in their study versus those in the investigation by Barton and Barton (1985).

6.6. *Noncontingent Attention and Stimulation*

In a study by Wright and Menolascino (1970), four severely to profoundly retarded 6- to 10-year-old ruminators living in residential care were provided with special attention and stimulation not contingent on the absence of rumination. According to the authors, this led to the eventual elimination of rumination.

6.7. *Modified Feeding*

Three severely to profoundly retarded ruminators, 6 to 23 years of age in residential and home settings were successfully treated by modifying their feeding. Two were provided with increased stimulation during feeding, and they were encouraged to participate more actively in the feeding process (Ball *et al.*, 1974). The other's rapid rate of food consumption was decreased when he was given bite-size portions of food and small sips of fluid one at a time at a slow pace (McKeegan *et al.*, 1987).

6.8. *Medication*

Consistent, though moderate, decreases in rumination frequency have been achieved with metoclopramide or bethanechol, medications that quicken gastric emptying and increase lower esophageal sphincter pressure. This was shown with three 3- to 16-year-old severely to profoundly retarded individuals residing at home and in residential settings (Mayes, 1992).

6.9. *Holding around Mealtime*

In a study by Whitehead *et al.* (1985), an 11-month-old and a 4-year-old severely to profoundly retarded ruminator (one living at home and the other in residential care) were simply held for 10 to 15 minutes before, during, and after meals. According to the authors, this resulted in a significant decrease in rumination.

6.10. *Contingent Exercise*

Lastly, a 10-year-old profoundly retarded ruminator living at home was required to walk once around a 5-foot square each time he ruminated in school (Daniel, 1982). Daniel describes the exercise contingency as "functionally incompatible" with rumination and "mildly punitive," one or both of which may have served to eliminate rumination.

6.11. *Dietary Management*

Johnston and his colleagues have conducted extensive research to understand the aspects of satiation that are responsible for its effectiveness. As a result of these investigations, several dietary factors have been identified that affect rumination rates. Although a combination of these factors may serve to reduce rumination somewhat, the effects are modest in comparison to the impact of a satiation diet. Johnston and his colleagues have determined that, generally, as caloric intake increases in severely to profoundly mentally retarded adult ruminators in residential care, rumination decreases. Therefore, if it is not possible to implement a full satiation diet to control rumination, one could allow ruminators to satiate at some meals, or one could substitute high-calorie for low-calorie foods and supplement diets with peanut butter, Polycose, oil, sugar, and so forth.

Other dietary manipulations that have some impact on rumination, though not as great an effect as increasing calories, include increasing the weight and volume of food consumed, stomach distention (e.g., by giving bran with fluids), and oropharyngeal stimulation (e.g., encouraging premeal gum chewing and increasing the chewing requirements of food by, for example, limiting pureed foods). Johnston and his colleagues found that providing supplementary fluids also serves to decrease rumination. Although, again, this has far less of an impact than a satiation diet.

6.12. *Social and Environmental Management*

Research on treatment of rumination and variables associated with frequency of rumination suggests that environmental management may reduce rumination, although not generally to the same degree as a rigorous treatment program using behavioral techniques or satiation. Some authors found that, with severely to profoundly retarded children, simply increasing attention, stimulation, or holding reduces rumination frequency (Whitehead *et al.*, 1985; Wright & Menolascino, 1970). Similarly, a study investigating variables associated with rumination in a 12-year-old profoundly retarded ruminator (Humphrey *et al.*, 1989) suggests that rumination rates could be positively affected by providing the individual with structured programming and individual attention following meals and by pairing the child with caretakers who like the child most (because a significant correlation was found between increasing likability and decreasing rumination).

6.13. *Comparative Analysis of Treatment Strategies*

Research on the treatment of rumination clearly indicates that response to intervention is highly individual. What works with one ruminator may not with another. Although the treatment strategies reviewed in the preceding sections have proven successful with some ruminators, published studies demonstrate that most of these strategies have been ineffective with other ruminators. Unsuccessful treatment regimens reported in the literature include food satiation, decreasing the pace of feeding, various dietary intake changes, thickened feedings, noncontingent special attention, reinforcement or punishment procedures contingent on rumination (i.e., reinforcement of incompatible behavior, differential reinforcement of other behavior, time-out from reinforcement, verbal reprimand, and presentation of an aversive smell), and use of hand restraints. Additionally, when evaluating the comparative effectiveness of treatment approaches, it is important to consider the varying degrees of rumination. A moderate reduction in rumination for a severe ruminator may be equivalent in terms of treatment success to the total elimination of rumination in a mild ruminator.

The two most well-substantiated and commonly used interventions reported in the literature are satiation and aversive procedures. Satiation is a very appealing treatment modality because it is nonaversive and it has a high success rate. However, the use of satiation has some potential limitations. In order for the suppression of rumination to be maintained, satiation conditions must be in effect indefinitely. Research demonstrates that when satiation is discontinued, rumination usually resumes (Rast, Ellinger-Allen, & Johnston, 1985; Rast & Johnston, 1986; Rast, Johnston, Allen, & Drum, 1985; Rast *et al.*, 1981, 1984). However, the long-term implementation of satiation may not be advisable.

Another limitation involves the nature of published satiation research to date. All investigations are with severely to profoundly retarded adults in residential care, and the effects of satiation with infants and children have not yet been studied. Additionally, no long-term research involving the use of satiation beyond 6.4 months is available. Thus it is not known how long satiation conditions can be effectively and safely maintained. Finally, rumination data in all published satiation studies were collected during half- to 1-hour intervals following meals. Although this is reasonable given the fact that rumination is greatest after meals, the impact of satiation on rumination at more distant time intervals following meals has not yet been empirically studied. Because quantity of food consumed increases under satiation conditions, the amount of time that food is available in the stomach to ruminate also increases. However, J. M. Johnston (personal communication, April 30, 1990) has not found any cases of delayed ruminating following satiation in his subjects.

In many instances, satiation results in zero or near-zero levels of rumination. However, as with any treatment strategy used to intervene with rumination disorder, satiation may not always yield clinically acceptable levels of rumination and may not alone be sufficient to control rumination. For example, Borreson and Anderson (1982) found a mean 63.3% decrease in rumination during the 1-hour period following satiation at lunch. When satiation was coupled with time-out each time the individual ruminated, rumination was eliminated. Similarly, Foxx *et al.* (1979) found mean 45.9% and an 84.2% drops in rumination following satiation with their two subjects. When an oral hygiene overcorrection procedure (i.e., cleansing each ruminator's teeth or gums for 2 minutes with Listerine following each episode of rumination) was added to satiation, rumination declined by 96.6% and 97.2%, in comparison to baseline rates. When the program was modified so that oral hygiene overcorrection was used after each instance of rumination and satiation at only one meal a day Monday through Friday, rumination for both subjects remained near zero at follow-up 4 months later.

Another potential difficulty with satiation involves inducing the ruminating individual to consume sufficiently large quantities of food. The amount of food needed to attain satiation and favorable results varies from individual to individual. Johnston and his associates showed that when meal portions were increased only twofold, postmeal rumination increased. In contrast, Foxx *et al.* (1979) reported a significant drop in rumination frequency following double meal portions. This author found yet a different pattern with a 16-year-old profoundly retarded male. The ruminator resides in a small group home and was on a satiation diet three meals a day for 1 month. For 20% of the meals, the individual refused to consume large quantities, and in fact, ate only a normal single portion or less. However, in these instances, postmeal rumination rates were also relatively low, with rumination occurring during a mean of 58.3% of the postmeal periods. In this case, it appeared that rumination was linked to motivation to eat, which is logical and supports satiation theory (i.e., when not hungry, the individual was also comparatively not motivated to ruminate). For 54.9% of the meals, the individual consumed two to four times normal meal quantities. However, rumination increased following these meals, occurring during 81.8% of the postmeal intervals. In contrast, when the individual consumed five to seven times the normal number of meal servings, rumination decreased to 46.7% of the postmeal periods. However, the individual consumed five to seven servings at only 25% of his meals. Thus slightly more than half of the time, the satiation program was actually associated with an increase in rumination.

The final disadvantage of satiation concerns possible negative repercussions for health, the most obvious of which is undesired weight gain. For example, the two 16-year-old severely to profoundly retarded ruminators treated with satiation by this author both gained significant weight (2.1 kg during a 29-day satiation program and 2.3 kg after 52 days of satiation). One individual also experienced considerable abdominal discomfort and became lethargic whenever he ate to satiation.

Johnston (who has been involved in satiation programs with approximately 25 severely to profoundly retarded adult ruminators) states that, with the exception of weight gain, he has found no adverse health effects related to satiation (Johnston & Greene, in press). However, Johnston and Greene caution that satiation

> should not be used for clients who are at or above their normal weight, and all clients considered for this procedure should receive medical and dietary clearances. In fact, it is inadvisable to view satiation feeding using normal caloric densities as any more than an initial and temporary treatment procedure for severe cases of rumination. However, a variation of this procedure using low calorie foods can be used chronically without producing weight gain, although it may not yield as great a decrease in ruminating as normal calorie satiation. (in press, p. 8)

Considering the aforementioned limitations, satiation may not always be the optimal treatment choice, and aversive procedures may be necessary if less aversive techniques fail to reduce rumination to clinically acceptable levels. The most obvious criticism of using an aversive contingency is that it is unpleasant for the individual because the process involves rendering the inappropriate target behavior unpleasant by the aversive consequence. Furthermore, the effects of using an aversive contingency may generalize to other behaviors or become associated with the implementors. Ethical and legal issues are also involved, and the use of aversive techniques may be prohibited in some settings.

However, in view of the considerable risks associated with rumination disorder and the limitations of satiation, justification may exist for using an aversive approach, especially with a severe ruminator whose health is jeopardized and who has not responded to less aversive strategies.

In this author's clinical experience, taste-aversive treatment has had greater relative effectiveness in controlling rumination in severely to profoundly mentally retarded children and adults than other techniques, including satiation, decreasing feeding pace, peanut butter therapy, overcorrection (prolonged and vigorous face washing), medication (metoclopramide and bethanechol), time-out from reinforcement, contingent reinforcement, and noncontingent increased stimulation and attention. Support for the effectiveness of aversive procedures compared to other strategies for treating self-injurious and self-stimulating behaviors is also found in the literature. For example, Iwata *et al.* (1982) state that "the only treatments that have been consistently effective in treating self-injury are those based on punishment in the form of aversive stimulation" (p. 4). Similarly, LaGrow and Repp (1984) reviewed more than 60 studies using aversive contingencies, positive reinforcement procedures, or the manipulation of settings or antecedent events to treat self-stimulating behaviors in handicapped individuals. The authors conclude that "aversive procedures proved to be the most effective of the three broad categories of intervention" (p. 606). A review of 382 studies from 1967 to 1987 in which severe behavior problems in individuals with mental retardation were treated (Matson & Taras, 1989) indicated that most studies employed an aversive component, that the results using aversive procedures were usually rapidly obtained, that no significant differences in negative side effects were found between studies using aversive techniques versus positive reinforcement, and that more studies using aversive contingencies had follow-up data than studies using positive reinforcement and the follow-up data indicated significant maintenance of intervention gains. Matson and Taras conclude that recent criticisms of the use of aversive procedures are not substantiated by empirical research.

Another rationale for the aggressive treatment of rumination involves the multitude of adverse side effects associated with the disorder. Rumination is often chronic in severely to profoundly mentally retarded individuals, and it may lead to weight loss, growth retardation, malnutrition, dehydration, aspiration, aspiration pneumonia, gastric disorders, esophagitis, tooth decay and tooth erosion, anemia, electrolyte imbalance, lowered resistance to disease, and in a few cases, death. Rumination is also a very noxious behavior that can have a disruptive and negative effect on family, staff, and others. It also affects whether or not the individual is liked or even tolerated by others. Because of the sight and smell of the regurgitated material and increased demands to clean the ruminator and affected environment, others may react by avoiding or interacting negatively with the ruminator. This then deprives the individual of positive social interchanges and further impairs social relatedness. It can be argued that allowing a ruminator to continue to ruminate (and thus, placing the individual at risk for numerous medical complications, as well as negative psychosocial repercussions) is far more aversive and involves greater risks than implementing a short-term taste-aversive behavior program. Using a taste-aversive substance like vanilla extract over the short term is certainly less dangerous than ruminating gastric digestive acids over the long term.

A taste-aversive contingency provides a potentially quick, effective, and enduring treatment for rumination, and it is also nonpainful. In this author's experience, it has not been necessary to resort to more extreme consequences, such as electric shock. A distinct advantage of using a taste-aversive approach is the likelihood of permanently reducing rumination to clinically acceptable low levels without requiring continued ongoing intervention. In other words, effects are often maintained after the aversive contingency is no longer needed, and the contingency is reintroduced only if the behavior recurs. This is in contrast to an approach such as satiation, which requires indefinite implementation in order to maintain suppression of rumination.

Finally, it could be argued that it is unethical and not in the best interest of the ruminator to withhold a potentially safe, effective, and enduring treatment and, instead, to permit rumination to continue or to implement a less effective program. It is hoped that nonaversive strategies will be developed that yield equally rapid, effective, and permanent results without requiring long-term or indefinite program implementation to control rumination. Until then, it may be necessary to use a taste-aversive approach, especially in severe cases that do not respond to less aversive techniques.

7. *Treatment of Infant Rumination*

Table 2 presents a summary of intervention strategies from the literature reported to be effective in controlling rumination in infants. The treatment literature for rumination disorder in infants is far less rigorous than that for treatment of rumination in mentally retarded individuals. Methodological limitations render it difficult to determine the degree to which specific intervention components are responsible for reductions in rumination. Many infant treatment programs employ a combination of procedures, without attempting to empirically partial out the relative

TABLE 2
Published Treatments for Rumination in Infants

Number of cases	Treatment
23	Noncontingent attention with psychotherapy for parent(s)
14	Noncontingent attention alone
3	Contingent electric shock
2	Contingent taste-aversive substance
1	Contingent taste-aversive substance and social reinforcement
1	Contingent time-out with reprimand[a]
1	Noncontingent attention plus contingent time-out with reprimand
1	Contingent hand restraint and social reinforcement

[a]This is the only ruminator not hospitalized for treatment.

impact of each (e.g., coupling noncontingent special attention and care with psychotherapy for the parents). Most problematic is the fact that all but one of the infant ruminators were hospitalized for treatment, thus adding confounding variables coinciding with the treatment programs. In the majority of cases, treatment success was attributed to noncontingent special attention, stimulation, and care. In a smaller proportion of cases, declines in rumination were viewed as a consequence of specific behavioral intervention. However, all but one of these infants were hospitalized and, therefore, they may also have received increased attention and stimulation during treatment relative to that provided before hospitalization.

As noted in Table 2, the treatment most frequently used (82.6% of the cases) included providing the hospitalized infant with noncontingent stimulation, attention, and care. This approach was used alone in 14 cases (Arensberg, 1956; Fleisher, 1979; Fullerton, 1963; Hollowell & Gardner, 1965; Mayes, 1992; Menking *et al.*, 1969; Richmond *et al.*, 1958; Sheagren *et al.*, 1980; Stein *et al.*, 1959) and combined with psychotherapy for the natural mother or parents in 23 cases (Ferholt & Provence, 1976; Flanagan, 1977; Sauvage *et al.*, 1985). For 1 other, noncontingent special attention was used in conjunction with a verbal reprimand and time-out from reinforcement whenever the infant ruminated (Chatoor *et al.*, 1984). Treatment for the remaining 8 cases entailed contingent behavioral techniques. Punishment was used alone with 6 infants. This included electric shock in 3 cases (Lang & Melamed, 1969; Linscheid & Cunningham, 1977; Toister *et al.*, 1975), taste-aversive lemon juice or Tabasco sauce in 2 cases (Mestre *et al.*, 1983; Sajwaj *et al.*,

1974), and time-out paired with a verbal reprimand in 1 case (Madison & Adubato, 1984). In another case, social reinforcement during non-ruminating periods was coupled with the administration of a taste-aversive substance (Murray *et al.*, 1976), and in the remaining case, it was coupled with hand restraints contingent on rumination (Sheinbein, 1975). In all published reports, rumination significantly decreased or was eliminated, and the infants gained weight. In 57.7% of the cases, improvements in the areas of affect, developmental functioning, and responsiveness to people and the environment were also noted.

The case study literature also contains reports of treatments that were ineffective in reducing infant rumination. These include various dietary changes, thickened feedings, small amounts at meals, hand restraints, taste-aversive conditioning using lemon juice, parent psychotherapy, and hospitalization with special attention. As is true with rumination in mentally retarded individuals, successful treatment with one infant ruminator may be unsuccessful with another.

Noncontingent special attention in a hospital setting alone or in conjunction with psychotherapy for the parent(s) was used to treat 80.4% of the infant ruminators in the literature. In contrast, only 4.5% of published cases of mentally retarded ruminators were treated with noncontingent attention, stimulation, and care. This marked difference in approach to intervention with the two subgroups of rumination disorder is most likely a reflection of the perceived etiological distinctions between the two groups. Although many of the published cases involving treatment of infant ruminators are not empirically rigorous and do not control possible contributing variables, extensive anecdotal case reports support the effectiveness of providing special attention, stimulation, and care in a hospital environment to eliminate or significantly reduce infant rumination. This is similar to other disorders, such as psychosocial dwarfism and some cases of nonorganic failure to thrive that are allegedly associated with a disturbance in the caretaker–child relationship or the home environment and that respond with symptom remission when adequate care is provided outside the home.

8. *Summary*

Rumination is the voluntary and pleasurable repeated regurgitation of stomach contents in the absence of organic cause. Rumination disorder comprises two subtypes: rumination in mentally retarded individuals of any age and rumination in infants, the majority of whom are developmentally normal. Based on a comprehensive literature review, the mean age at onset for mentally retarded ruminators is 5.7 years, in contrast to a mean of 5.7 months for infant ruminators. Rumination in mentally retarded individuals is a form of self-stimulation and occurs almost solely in severely and profoundly retarded persons. In contrast, rumination in infants is felt to be a consequence of a disturbance in the caretaker–child relationship, with the infant turning inward for gratification as opposed to deriving pleasure externally from the environment and others. For both subgroups, rumination is three to four times more common in males than in females.

Rumination is a voluntary behavior that must be distinguished from organic medical or physiological conditions that have involuntary regurgitation as a symptom. Rumination may be confused with an involuntary gastroesophageal reflux, which is common in both infants and developmentally disabled individuals. Appropriate medical evaluations, radiographic studies, and clinical observations are needed to make a differential diagnosis. Complications associated with rumination in both infants and mentally retarded persons include weight loss, growth retardation, malnutrition, dehydration, aspiration, aspiration pneumonia, gastric disorders, esophagitis, tooth decay and tooth erosion, anemia, electrolyte imbalance, lowered resistance to disease, and in rare cases, death.

A review of the rumination treatment literature reveals extensive individual variation in response to intervention. An effective technique with one ruminator may be ineffective with another. Table 1 summarizes nine strategies reported in the literature to be successful in curtailing rumination in mentally retarded individuals. The most commonly used interventions, accounting for a total of 64.8% of published cases, are a satiation diet and aversive contingencies (e.g., administering a taste-aversive substance, such as vanilla extract, in response to each episode of rumination). Both techniques have a high success rate. However, there are advantages and disadvantages unique to these two types of intervention. In contrast to rumination in mentally retarded individuals, 80.4% of infant ruminators in published reports were hospitalized and effectively treated with noncontingent stimulation, attention, and care, provided alone or in conjunction with parent psychotherapy. The difference in treatment approach between the two rumination subtypes corresponds with the etiologic distinctions between the two groups.

9. *References*

Alford, G. S., Blanchard, E. B., & Buckley, T. M. (1972). Treatment of hysterical vomiting by modification of social contingencies: A case study. *Journal of Behavior Therapy and Experimental Psychiatry, 3*, 209–212.

American Psychiatric Association. (1987). *Diagnostic and Statistical Manual of Mental Disorders* (3rd ed., revised). Washington, DC: Author.

Arensberg, B. (1956). Loving care does the trick. *American Journal of Nursing, 56,* 622–623.

Azrin, N. H., & Wesolowski, M. D. (1975). Eliminating habitual vomiting in a retarded adult by positive practice and self-correction. *Journal of Behavior Therapy and Experimental Psychiatry, 6,* 145–148.

Bakwin, H., & Bakwin, R. M. (1972). *Behavior disorders in children* (4th ed.). Philadelphia: W. B. Saunders.

Ball, T. S., Hendricksen, H., & Clayton, J. (1974). A special feeding technique for chronic regurgitation. *American Journal of Mental Deficiency, 78,* 486–493.

Barmann, B. C. (1980). Use of contingent vibration in the treatment of self-stimulatory hand-mouthing and ruminative vomiting behavior. *Journal of Behavior Therapy and Experimental Psychiatry, 11,* 307–311.

Barton, L. E., & Barton, C. L. (1985). An effective and benign treatment of rumination. *Journal of the Association for Persons with Severe Handicaps, 10,* 168–171.

Becker, J. V., Turner, S. M., & Sajwaj, T. E. (1978). Multiple behavioral effects of the use of lemon juice with a ruminating toddler-age child. *Behavior Modification, 2,* 267–278.

Borreson, P. M., & Anderson, J. L. (1982). The elimination of chronic rumination through a combination of procedures. *Mental Retardation, 20,* 34–38.

Bright, G. O., & Whaley, D. L. (1968). Suppression of regurgitation and rumination with aversive events. *Michigan Mental Health Research Bulletin, 11,* 17–20.

Chatoor, I., Dickson, L., & Einhorn, A. (1984). Rumination: Etiology and treatment. *Pediatric Annals, 13,* 924–929.

Conrin, J., Pennypacker, H. S., Johnston, J., & Rast, J. (1982). Differential reinforcement of other behaviors to treat chronic rumination of mental retardates. *Journal of Behavior Therapy and Experimental Psychiatry, 13,* 325–329.

Crump, I. M. (1987). Evaluation of the nutritional status of the handicapped child. In I. M. Crump (Ed.), *Nutrition and feeding of the handicapped child* (pp. 29–39). Boston, MA: College-Hill Press.

Cunningham, C. E., & Linscheid, T. R. (1976). Elimination of chronic infant ruminating by electric shock. *Behavior Therapy, 7,* 231–234.

Daniel, W. H. (1982). Management of chronic rumination with a contingent exercise procedure employing topographically dissimilar behavior. *Journal of Behavior Therapy and Experimental Psychiatry, 13,* 149–152.

Davis, P. K., & Cuvo, A. J. (1980). Chronic vomiting and rumination in intellectually normal and retarded individuals: Review and evaluation of behavioral research. *Behavior Research of Severe Developmental Disabilities, 1,* 31–59.

Davis, W. B., Wieseler, N. A., & Hanzel, T. E. (1980). Contingent music in management of rumination and out-of-seat behavior in a profoundly mentally retarded institutionalized male. *Mental Retardation, 18,* 43–45.

Demchak, M. A., & Halle, J. W. (1985). Motivational assessment: A potential means of enhancing treatment success of self-injurious individuals. *Education and Training of the Mentally Retarded, 20,* 25–38.

Duker, P. C., & Seys, D. M. (1977). Elimination of vomiting in a retarded female using restitutional overcorrection. *Behavior Therapy, 8,* 255–257.

Ekvall, S. W., Ekvall, V., & Mayes, S. D. (in press). Rumination. In S. W. Ekvall (Ed.), *Pediatric nutrition in chronic diseases and developmental disorders.*

Farrell, M. (in press). Nutrition in gastrointestinal disorders of infancy and childhood. In S. W. Ekvall (Ed.), *Pediatric nutrition in chronic diseases and developmental disorders.*

Favell, J. E., McGimsey, J. F., & Schell, R. M. (1982). Treatment of self-injury by providing alternate sensory activities. *Analysis and Intervention in Developmental Disabilities, 2,* 83–104.

Ferholt, J., & Provence, S. (1976). Diagnosis and treatment of an infant with psychophysiological vomiting. *Psychoanalytic Study of the Child, 31,* 439–459.

Flanagan, C. H. (1977). Rumination in infancy—Past and present. *Journal of the American Academy of Child Psychiatry, 16,* 140–149.
Fleisher, D. R. (1979). Infant rumination syndrome: Report of a case and review of the literature. *American Journal of Diseases of Children, 133,* 266–269.
Foxx, R. M., Snyder, M. S., & Schroeder, F. (1979). A food satiation and oral hygiene punishment program to suppress chronic rumination by retarded persons. *Journal of Autism and Developmental Disorders, 9,* 399–412.
Fullerton, D. T. (1963). Infantile rumination: A case report. *Archives of General Psychiatry, 9,* 593–600.
Galbraith, D. A., Byrick, R. J., & Rutledge, J. T. (1970). An aversive conditioning approach to the inhibition of chronic vomiting. *Canadian Psychiatric Association Journal, 15,* 311–313.
Greene, K. S., Johnston, J. M., Rossi, M., Rawal, A., Winston, M., & Barron, S. (1991). The effects of peanut butter on ruminating. *American Journal on Mental Retardation, 95,* 631–645.
Griffin, J. B., Jr. (1977). Rumination in a 7-year-old child. *Southern Medical Journal, 70,* 243–245.
Hogg, J. (1982). Reduction of self-induced vomiting in a multiply handicapped girl by "lemon juice therapy" and concomitant changes in social behaviour. *British Journal of Clinical Psychology, 21,* 227–228.
Hollowell, J. G., & Gardner, L. I. (1965). Rumination and growth failure in male fraternal twin: Association with disturbed family environment. *Pediatrics, 36,* 565–571.
Halvoet, J. F. (1982). The etiology and management of rumination and psychogenic vomiting: A review. In J. H. Hollis & C. E. Meyers (Eds.), *Life threatening behavior: Analysis and intervention* (pp. 29–77). Washington, DC: American Association on Mental Deficiency.
Humphrey, F. J., II, Mayes, S. D., Bixler, E. O., & Good, C. (1989). Variables associated with frequency of rumination in a boy with profound mental retardation. *Journal of Autism and Developmental Disorders, 19,* 435–447.
Iwata, B. A., Dorsey, M. F., Slifer, K. J., Bauman, K. E., & Richman, G. S. (1982). Toward a functional analysis of self-injury. *Analysis and Intervention in Developmental Disabilities, 2,* 3–20.
Jackson, G. M., Johnson, C. R., Ackron, G. S., & Crowley, R. (1975). Food satiation as a procedure to decelerate vomiting. *American Journal of Mental Deficiency, 80,* 223–227.
Johnston, J. M., & Greene, K. S. (in press). The relation between ruminating and quantity of food consumed. *Mental Retardation.*
Johnston, J. M., Greene, K. S., Rawal, A., Vazin, T., & Winston, M. (1991). Effects of caloric level on ruminating. *Journal of Applied Behavior Analysis, 24,* 597–603.
Johnston, J. M., Greene, K. S., Vazin, T., Winston, M., Rawal, A., & Chuang, S. (1990). Effects of food consistency on ruminating. *The Psychological Record, 40,* 609–618.
Kohlenberg, R. J. (1970). The punishment of persistent vomiting: A case study. *Journal of Applied Behavior Analysis, 3,* 241–245.
Koslowski, B. W. (1990). Cerebral palsy. In D. J. Gines (Ed.), *Nutrition management in rehabilitation* (pp. 7–46). Rockville, MD: Aspen.
LaGrow, S. J., & Repp, A. C. (1984). Stereotypic responding: A review of intervention research. *American Journal of Mental Deficiency, 88,* 595–609.
Lang, P. J., & Melamed, B. G. (1969). Avoidance conditioning therapy of an infant with chronic ruminative vomiting. *Journal of Abnormal Psychology, 74,* 1–8.
Leibovich, M. A. (1973). Psychogenic vomiting. *Psychotherapy and Psychosomatics, 22,* 263–268.
Libby, D. G., & Phillips, E. (1979). Eliminating rumination behavior in a profoundly retarded adolescent: An exploratory study. *Mental Retardation, 17,* 94–95.

Linscheid, T. R., & Cunningham, C. E. (1977). A controlled demonstration of the effectiveness of electric shock in the elimination of chronic infant rumination. *Journal of Applied Behavior Analysis, 10,* 500.

Lobato, D., Carlson, E. I., & Barrera, R. D. (1986). Modified satiation reducing ruminative vomiting without excessive weight gain. *Applied Research in Mental Retardation, 7,* 337–347.

Luckey, R. E., Watson, C. M., & Musick, J. K. (1968). Aversive conditioning as a means of inhibiting vomiting and rumination. *American Journal of Mental Deficiency, 73,* 139–142.

Madison, L. S., & Adubato, S. A. (1984). The elimination of ruminative vomiting in a 15-month-old child with gastroesophageal reflux. *Journal of Pediatric Psychology, 9,* 231–239.

Marholin, D., II, Luiselli, J. K., Robinson, M., & Lott, I. T. (1980). Response-contingent taste-aversion in treating chronic ruminative vomiting of institutionalized profoundly retarded children. *Journal of Mental Deficiency Research, 24,* 47–56.

Matson, J. L., & Taras, M. E. (1989). A 20-year review of punishment and alternative methods to treat problem behaviors in developmentally delayed persons. *Research in Developmental Disabilities, 10,* 85–104.

Mayes, S. D. (1988, June). *Rumination disorder: Diagnosis, treatment, and associated variables.* Paper presented at the annual meeting of the American Association on Mental Retardation, Washington, DC.

Mayes, S. D. (1992). Eating disorders of infancy and early childhood. In S. R. Hooper, G. W. Hynd, & R. E. Mattison (Eds.), *Child psychopathology: Diagnostic criteria and clinical assessment* (pp. 203–260). Hillsdale, NJ: Lawrence Erlbaum.

Mayes, S. D., Humphrey, F. J., II, Handford, H. A., & Mitchell, J. F. (1988). Rumination disorder: Differential diagnosis. *Journal of the American Academy of Child and Adolescent Psychiatry, 27,* 300–302.

McKeegan, G. F., Estill, K., & Campbell, B. (1987). Elimination of rumination by controlled eating and differential reinforcement. *Journal of Behavior Therapy and Experimental Psychiatry, 18,* 143–148.

Menking, M., Wagnitz, J. G., Burton, J. J., Coddington, R. D., & Sotos, J. F. (1969). Rumination—A near fatal psychiatric disease of infancy. *New England Journal of Medicine, 280,* 802–804.

Mestre, J. R., Resnick, R. J., & Berman, W. F. (1983). Behavior modification in the treatment of rumination. *Clinical Pediatrics, 22,* 488–491.

Minness, P. M. (1980). Treatment of compulsive hand in mouth behaviour in a profoundly retarded child using a sharp pinch as the aversive stimulus. *Australian Journal of Developmental Disabilities, 6,* 5–10.

Mulick, J. A., Schroeder, S. R., & Rojahn, J. (1980). Chronic ruminative vomiting: A comparison of four treatment procedures. *Journal of Autism and Developmental Disorders, 10,* 203–213.

Murray, M. E., Keele, D. K., & McCarver, J. W. (1976). Behavioral treatment of ruminations: A case study. *Clinical Pediatrics, 15,* 591–596.

O'Neil, P. M., White, J. L., King, C. R., Jr., & Carek, D. J. (1979). Controlling childhood rumination through differential reinforcement of other behavior. *Behavior Modification, 3,* 355–372.

Rast, J., & Johnston, J. M. (1986). Social versus dietary control of ruminating by mentally retarded persons. *American Journal of Mental Deficiency, 90,* 464–467.

Rast, J., Johnston, J. M., Drum, C., & Conrin, J. (1981). The relation of food quantity to rumination behavior. *Journal of Applied Behavior Analysis, 14,* 121–130.

Rast, J., Johnston, J. M., & Drum, C. (1984). A parametric analysis of the relationship between food quantity and rumination. *Journal of the Experimental Analysis of Behavior, 41,* 125–134.

Rast, J., Ellinger-Allen, J. A., & Johnston, J. M. (1985). Dietary management of rumination: Four case studies. *American Journal of Clinical Nutrition, 42,* 95–101.

Rast, J., Johnston, J. M., Allen, J. E., & Drum, C. (1985). Effects of nutritional and mechanical properties of food on ruminative behavior. *Journal of the Experimental Analysis of Behavior, 44,* 195–206.

Rast, J., Johnston, J. M., Lubin, D., & Ellinger-Allen, J. (1988a). Effects of premeal chewing on ruminative behavior. *American Journal on Mental Retardation, 93,* 67–74.

Rast, J., Johnston, J. M., Lubin, D., & Ellinger-Allen, J. (1988b). *Effects of esophageal stimuli on ruminative behavior.* Manuscript submitted for publication.

Richmond, J. B., Eddy, E., & Greene, M. (1958). Rumination: A psychosomatic syndrome of infancy. *Pediatrics, 22,* 49–55.

Rojahn, J. (1984). Self-injurious behavior in institutionalized, severely/profoundly retarded adults—Prevalence data and staff agreement. *Journal of Behavioral Assessment, 6,* 13–27.

Sajwaj, T., Libet, J., & Agras, S. (1974). Lemon-juice therapy: The control of life-threatening rumination in a six-month-old infant. *Journal of Applied Behavior Analysis, 7,* 557–563.

Sauvage, D., Leddet, I., Hameury, L., & Barthelemy, C. (1985). Infantile rumination: Diagnosis and follow-up study of twenty cases. *Journal of the American Academy of Child Psychiatry, 24,* 197–203.

Sheagren, T. G., Mangurten, H. H., Brea, F., & Lutostanski, S. (1980). Rumination—A new complication of neonatal intensive care. *Pediatrics, 66,* 551–555.

Sheinbein, M. (1975). Treatment for the hospitalized infantile ruminator: Programmed brief social behavior reinforcers. *Clinical Pediatrics, 14,* 719–724.

Simpson, R. L., & Sasso, G. M. (1978). The modification of rumination in a severely emotionally disturbed child through an overcorrection procedure. *American Association for the Education of the Severely-Profoundly Handicapped Review, 3,* 145–150.

Singh, N. N., Manning, P. J., & Angell, M. J. (1982). Effects of an oral hygiene punishment procedure on chronic rumination and collateral behaviors in monozygous twins. *Journal of Applied Behavior Analysis, 15,* 309–314.

Smith, D. W., & Lyon, R. (1976). Eliminating vomiting behavior in a profoundly retarded resident. *Research and the Retarded, 3,* 24–27.

Spergel, S. M. (1975). Induced vomiting treatment of acute compulsive vomiting. *Journal of Behavior Therapy and Experimental Psychiatry, 6,* 85–86.

Starin, S. P., & Fuqua, R. W. (1987). Rumination and vomiting in the developmentally disabled: A critical review of the behavioral, medical, and psychiatric treatment research. *Research in Developmental Disabilities, 8,* 575–605.

Stein, M. L., Rausen, A. R., & Blau, A. (1959). Psychotherapy of an infant with rumination. *Journal of the American Medical Association, 171,* 2309–2312.

Tierney, D., & Jackson, H. J. (1984). Psychosocial treatments of rumination disorder: A review of the literature. *Australia and New Zealand Journal of Developmental Disabilities, 10,* 81–112.

Toister, R. P., Condron, C. J., Worley, L., & Arthur, D. (1975). Faradic therapy of chronic vomiting in infancy: A case study. *Journal of Behavior Therapy and Experimental Psychiatry, 6,* 55–59.

Watkins, J. T. (1972). Treatment of chronic vomiting and extreme emaciation by an aversive stimulus: Case study. *Psychological Reports, 31,* 803–805.

White, J. C., Jr., & Taylor, D. J. (1967). Noxious conditioning as a treatment for rumination. *Mental Retardation, 5,* 30–33.

Whitehead, W. E., Drescher, V. M., Morrill-Corbin, E., & Cataldo, M. F. (1985). Rumination syndrome in children treated by increased holding. *Journal of Pediatric Gastroenterology and Nutrition, 4,* 550–556.

Winton, A. S. W., & Singh, N. N. (1983). Rumination in pediatric populations: A behavioral analysis. *Journal of the American Academy of Child Psychiatry, 22,* 269–275.
Wright, D. F., Brown, R. A., & Andrews, M. E. (1978). Remission of chronic ruminative vomiting through a reversal of social contingencies. *Behaviour Research and Therapy, 16,* 134–136.
Wright, M. M., & Menolascino, F. J. (1970). Rumination, mental retardation, and interventive therapeutic nursing. In F. J. Menolascino (Ed.), *Psychiatric approaches to mental retardation* (pp. 205–223). New York: Basic Books.
Wright, L., & Thalassinos, P. A. (1973). Success with electroshock in habitual vomiting: Report of two cases in young children. *Clinical Pediatrics, 12,* 594–597.

II DSM-IV Literature Reviews

8 Elective Mutism

A Review of the Literature

NANCY KAPLAN TANCER

1. Statement of the Issues

The purpose of this chapter is to review the literature on elective mutism to facilitate possible modifications of the diagnosis in DSM-IV.

Elective mutism (EM) was first reported by the German physician, Jussmaul, in 1877. He described physically normal children who developed mutism in certain situations and called the condition "aphasia voluntaria" or voluntary mutism (Kratochwill *et al.*, 1979). Since then, a considerable number of case reports have described these children, but there has been little systematic research. Consequently, it is difficult to utilize the current literature to assess critically the DSM-III-R category of EM and to make recommendations for its modification.

Critical diagnostic issues include the following: (1) Are the diagnostic criteria and associated features in the DSM-III-R reflective of the syndrome as it is described in the literature? and (2) What are the important unanswered questions that should guide future research efforts?

2. Significance of the Issues

This review summarizes the literature on EM from the past 15 years, compares the reports to the DSM-III-R category, and identifies areas of controversy. Recommendations for the direction of future research follow.

Attention is brought to the following issues:

1. EM has been defined very broadly so that children with diverse psychopathology are grouped together.

NANCY KAPLAN TANCER • New York State Psychiatric Institute, 722 West 168th Street, New York, New York 10032.

Advances in Clinical Child Psychology, Volume 14, edited by Benjamin B. Lahey and Alan E. Kazdin. Plenum Press, New York, 1992

2. There may be different diagnostic implications for short-lived and persistent symptoms.
3. The minimum period of symptomatology before making the diagnosis is problematic.

3. *Method*

Fifty-eight publications were examined. Most are case reports discussing symptoms, family pathology, and treatment strategies (see Table 1). Because these articles contain a large number of unverifiable and anecdotal data, only those papers that discuss more than two cases are included in the review (except in cases where the paper includes a conceptual point). Articles that do not give quantitative data are excluded as are those that do not present original data (see Table 2). Several articles (Bozigar & Hansen, 1984; Brown & Lloyd, 1975; Cunninghamm *et al.*, 1983; Goll, 1980; Lupietz & Schwartz, 1982; Nash *et al.*, 1979) could not be obtained but are included from information obtained in their abstract and in one case (Brown & Lloyd, 1975) from references made to it (Hesselman, 1983; Kolvin & Fundudis, 1982; Wilkins, 1985; Wright, 1968).

Owing to the small number of resultant usable studies, no constraints were place on diagnostic criteria. Additionally, the usual requirements of methodological rigor could not be applied.

TABLE 1
Case Reports on Elective Mutism

Senior author	Year	*N*	Age (years)	M:F	Description of study
Albert	1986	1	13	1:0	Behavioral treatment
Ambrosino	1979	1	10	0:1	Psychodynamic treatment
Atoynatan	1986	7	5–7	?	Family treatment
Austad	1980	1	7	0:1	Behavioral treatment
Bauermeister	1975	1	8	1:0	Behavioral treatment
Beck	1987	1	7	0:1	Dynamic formulation
Bozigar	1984	4	6–9	?	Behavioral treatment
Browne	1963	1	6	1:0	Psychodynamic family therapy
Carr	1989	1	6	0:1	Behavioral treatment
Chethik	1973	1	6	0:1	Psychodynamic treatment
Ciottone	1984	1	11	1:0	Holistic treatment
Croghan	1982	1	8	0:1	Behavioral treatment

(continued)

TABLE 1 (*Continued*)

Senior author	Year	*N*	Age (years)	M:F	Description of study
Cunningham	1983	41	?	?	Comparisons of behavioral treatments
Eldar	1985	1	16	0:1	10-year follow-up Diagnosed schizophrenic
Elson	1965	4	7–10	0:4	6-month–5 year follow-up of former hospital patients
Goll	1979	10	?	?	Family process
Goll	1980	10	?	?	Family process
Hill	1985	1	9	1:0	Behavioral treatment
Hoffman	1986	1	4	0:1	Behavioral treatment
Krolian	1988	2	7–8	1:1	Structured day hospital treatment
Kupietz	1982	3	4–15	3:0	Behavioral treatment
Lazarus	1983	2	6–7	0:2	Individual psychotherapy
Lesser-Katz	1986	15	3	?	Behavioral treatment
Louden	1987	1	6	1:0	Evaluation with psychometric assessments
Lowenstein	1979	21	3–8	16:5	7-year follow-up of treatment outcome
Meijer	1979	5	3–10	2:1	Psychodynamic treatment
Nash	1979	3	5–9	?	Behavioral treatment
Parker	1960	27	?	?	Behavioral treatment
Pigott	1987	1	8	1:0	Behavioral treatment
Pustrom	1964	3	8	2:1	Psychodynamic treatment
Radford	1977	1	6	1:0	Psychoanalytic treatment
Reed	1963	4	12–13	1:3	Cognitive treatment
Richards	1978	1	8	0:1	Behavioral treatment
Rosenberg	1978	1	?	?	Behavioral and family therapy
Sanok	1979	1	11	0:1	Behavioral treatment
Sluckin	1977	2	5–6	1:1	Behavioral treatment
Subak	1982	1	15	0:1	Discusses family psychopathology
Wassing	1973	1	?	1:0	Creative therapy
Wergeland	1980	11	6–11	4:7	8–18-year follow-up of treatment outcome
Williamson	1977	2	7–8	1:1	Behavioral treatment
Wright	1968	24	5–9	7:17	6-month–7-year follow-up of treatment outcome
Wright	1985	3	4–5	2:1	1-year follow-up of treatment outcome
Wulbert	1973	1	6	0:1	Behavioral treatment

TABLE 2
Review Papers (No Original Data) on EM

Senior author	Year
Cantwell	1985
Hesselman	1983
Kratochwill	1979
Labbe	1984
Lowenstein	1978
Meyers	1984
Sanok	1979

4. *Results*

4.1. *Characteristics of the Studies*

Using the inclusion criteria discussed above, 23 papers were selected for review (see Table 3).[1] In addition to case reports, several papers report on prevalence (Brown & Lloyd 1975; Reed, 1963), classification (Hayden, 1980; Reed, 1963), symptom profile (Kolvin & Fundudis, 1982; Wilkins, 1985; Wright, 1968), and follow-up (Calhoun & Koenig, 1973; Cunninghamm *et al.*, 1983; Elson *et al.*, 1965; Kolvin & Fundudis, 1982; Lowenstein, 1979; Paniagua & Saeed, 1988; Wergeland, 1980). Most lack methodological clarity and define the syndrome without precision. Together, however, they do provide a picture of EM as it is understood clinically.

Two studies (Kolvin & Fundudis, 1982; Wilkins, 1985) are influential and of special interest because they represent the only systematic attempts to specify distinguishing characteristics of EM. In the first paper (summarized in Appendix I) by Kolvin and Fundudis (1982), all 24 children with EM, aged 6–8 years, referred to a clinic for children with specific language and behavior disorders and recruited from other agencies (such as pediatrics, speech, child psychiatry, child guidance clinics), were compared to children diagnosed as speech retarded (N = 84) and to normal controls (N = 102), matched for age, sex and postal zone. In the second paper (summarized in Appendix II) by Wilkins (1985), the

[1] Of the papers cited, 15 originate from psychiatry departments, 3 originate from psychology departments, and the remaining 5 are from child-guidance and school-based clinics. Although several of the studies recruited subjects from speech and language clinics, none of the papers originate from this source.

charts of all 24 EM children aged 5.2–17.3, diagnosed at the Maudsley Hospital from 1968–1980, were compared retrospectively to children with other psychiatric symptoms matched for sex, age, year seen, IQ, and area of residence. In both papers, all children who met criteria for EM during the period of study were included. Unfortunately, the characteristics of the comparison children are only vaguely described, and the study by Wilkins, in particular, has been criticized for including a highly diverse control group (Bhide & Srinath, 1985).

4.2. *Essential Features of Elective Mutism*

Since 1877, when EM was first described, the criteria for making the diagnosis have changed very little. In the DSM-III-R the syndrome is described as (a) persistent refusal to talk in one or more major social situations (including at school) and (b) ability to comprehend spoken language and to speak.

The first, and perhaps most critical, question in Criterion A is that of defining "persistent refusal to talk." In only five of the studies reviewed (Brown & Lloyd, 1975; Hayden, 1980; Kolvin & Fundudis, 1982; Wilkins, 1985; Wright *et al.*, 1985) is the duration of speech refusal specified clearly as a defining feature (Table 3). In these studies, minimum length of speech refusal varied from 8 weeks (Brown & Lloyd, 1975; Hayden, 1980) to 1 year (Kolvin & Fundudis, 1982). This definition is of particular importance for the question of whether persistent and transient mutism represent the same disorder.

Brown and Lloyd (1975) conducted a questionnaire survey of parents of 5-year-olds, 8 weeks after school entrance, and then again 10 and 12 months later. Of 6,072 children, 42 were identified as not speaking at 8 weeks (7.2 per 1,000). Five months later, 20% of the nonspeaking children had improved, and over 90% were speaking by the 12 months follow-up. Although the child's ability to comprehend language was not established and sampling included 42% immigrant children, the study suggests that symptoms of EM presenting in young children at school entrance may be transient, possibly representing a normal separation anxiety or an adjustment syndrome that generally diminishes with familiarity and may be distinct from protracted EM. If this is true, much of the current data become especially problematic because of the possible combination of these separate groups.

Examining Criterion B, the critical diagnostic point is the establishment that no significant abnormality of language comprehension or production can account for the mutism (see Table 4). EM is defined as a motivational disorder. However, in the three studies that looked at language disorders in EM children, all found a significant proportion had

TABLE 3
Characteristics of Studies on EM

Senior author	Year	*N*	Ages (years)	M:F	Source of Ss	EM diagnostic criteria	Time with Sx EM	Assessment methods	Description of study
Atoynatan	1986	7	5–7	?	Various	Refuse to speak	?	Clinical	Family treatment
Bozigar	1984	4	6–9	?	School	Refuse to speak	?	Clinical	Behavioral treatment
Brown	1975	42	5	?	School	Refuse to speak	8 weeks	Parental report	Prevalence survey all children; Birmingham primary school (*N* = 6,072)
Calhoun	1973	8	5–8	?	School	Deficient speech	?	Clinical	Controlled study behavioral treatment EM
Cunningham	1983	41	?	?	Various	?	?	Various clinical	Comparison of behavioral treatments
Eldar	1985	1	16	0:1	?	Refuse to speak	?	Clinical	10-year case follow-up. Diagnosed schizophrenic
Elson	1965	4	7–10	0:4	Inpatient psych	Refuse to speak	?	Clinical	6-month–5 year follow-up of former hospital patients
Goll	1979	10	?	?	Inpatient speech	Refuse or no speech	?	Clinical	Family process
Goll	1980	10	?	?	Inpatient psych	Refuse or no speech	?	Clinical	Family process
Hayden	1980	68	6.0–7.11	12:5 6	Various	No speech 1 setting	8 weeks	Clinical WISC/SB	Classification of cases followed for 7 years

Kolvin	1982	24	6–8	11:13	Various	Refuse to speak and shy	1 year	Clinical	Controlled study of EM to speech-retarded (N = 84) and normal children (N = 102)
Kupietz	1982	3	4–15	3:0	School	No speech	?	Clinical	Behavioral treatment
Lesser-Katz	1986	15	3	?	Head Start	Refuse to speak	?	Clinical	Behavioral treatment
Lowenstein	1988	21	3–8	16:5	Various	Refuse to speak	?	Clinical PPVT	7-year follow-up of treatment outcome
Meijer	1979	5	3–10	2:1	?	Refuse to speak	?	Clinical	Psychodynamic treatment
Nash	1979	3	5–9	?	School	Refuse to speak	?	Clinical	Behavioral treatment
Parker	1960	27	?	?	School	Refuse to speak	?	Clinical	Behavioral treatment
Pustrom	1964	3	8	2:1	Various hospitals	Refuse to speak	?	Clinical	Psychodynamic treatment
Reed	1963	4	12–13	1:3	Various out-patients	Refuse to speak	?	Clinical	Cognitive treatment
Wergeland	1980	11	6–11	4:7	School	Refuse to speak	?	Clinical PE/EEG	8–18-year follow-up of treatment outcome
Wilkins	1985	24	5.2–17.3	7:17	All hospital cases	Refuse to speak	6 months	Clinical	Controlled study comparing EM to children with other emotional disorders (N = 24)
Wright	1968	24	5–9	7:17	School	No talk school	?	Clinical	6-month–7-year follow-up of treatment outcome
Wright	1985	3	4.25–5.6	2:1	Various	Refuse to speak	6 months	Clinical	1-year follow-up of treatment outcome

TABLE 4
Associated Features of EM

Senior author	*N*	Speech disorder	PDD or MR	EEG	Shy	Socially isolated	School refusal	Controlling	Oppositional	Other
Atoynatan	7	All delayed	No	?	?	?	?	?	?	Dependent, stubborn, delayed toileting
Bozigar	4	?	?	?	?	?	?	?	?	?
Brown	42	?	?	?	?	?	?	?	?	?
Calhoun	8	?	?	?	?	?	?	?	?	?
Cunningham	41	?	?	?	?	?	?	?	?	?
Eldar	1	?	?	?	?	?	?	?	?	?
Elson	4	?	No	Normal	Yes	Yes	Yes	?	Yes	Passive-aggressive
Goll	10	?	?	?	?	?	?	?	?	Stubborn
Goll	10	?	?	?	?	?	?	?	?	?
Hayden	68	?	No	?	Yes	Yes	Yes	Yes	Yes	Clinging, OCD and PA traits, negative, rigid, fear-ful
Kolvin	24	50%	No	25% abnor-mal	Yes	?	?	?	?	Negative, stubborn, moody, sensitive enuresis, encopresis

Kupietz	3	?	Yes	?	?	?	?	?	?	?
Lesser-Katz	15	?	?	?	Yes	?	?	?	?	Oppositional, compliant
Lowenstein	21	?	?	?	?	?	?	?	?	?
Meijer	5	?	?	?	Yes	?	?	?	?	Sensitive, dependent, vulnerable, angry
Nash	3	?	?	?	?	?	?	?	?	?
Parker	27	?	?	?	?	?	?	?	?	?
Pustrom	3	?	?	?	?	?	?	?	Yes	Stubborn, enuretic, disobedient
Reed	4	?/normal hearing	Yes	?	?	?	?	?	?	Anxious, immature, fearful
Wergeland	11	?	No	?	Yes	Yes	?	?	?	Enuretic, encopretic, stubborn, compulsive
Wilkins	24	?	Some MR	45% abnormal	Yes	?	?	Yes	Yes	Enuretic, encopretic, disruptive, negative

(*continued*)

TABLE 4 (*Continued*)

Senior author	N	Speech disorder	PDD or MR	EEG	Shy	Socially isolated	School refusal	Controlling	Oppositional	Other
Wright	24	33%	No	?	?	?	?	?	?	Depressed, anxious, manipulative
Wright	3	67%	No	?	Yes	Yes	?	?	?	Early trauma

such abnormalities. In Wright's sample (1968), 20% had an underlying language handicap, and in Kolvin and Fundudis' sample (1982), 50% had immaturities of speech and/or other speech abnormalities, although hearing was normal. Further, in Wilkins's sample (1985), 33% of the 24 EM children had language problems (6 had delayed speech and an additional 2 had articulation problems) compared to none of the 24 children with other emotional disorders ($p < 0.01$). Unfortunately, none of these studies specify whether those EM children with language disorders were able to understand and to express speech. For those EM children who are able to utilize language, the question is to what degree speech abnormalities are a part of the EM syndrome, and, if they are not, to what extent are current data contaminated by inclusion of such children in samples of EM.

4.3. *Associated Features of Elective Mutism*

A wide range of symptoms have been associated with the diagnosis of EM (see Table 4). In general, these associations can be regarded as hypothetical because the methods used to collect data were often retrospective and driven by preconceptions of etiology and psychopathology. Studies by Kolvin and Fundudis (1982) (see Appendix I) and Wilkins (1985) (see Appendix II) compared features of EM children to other children and lend support to the association of this syndrome with particular behavioral features such as negativism, shyness, controlling or oppositional behavior, and social isolation.

Several additional features were found by Kolvin and Fundudis (1982) who compared children with EM to normals and psychiatric controls: enuresis (42% vs. 15%, and 25%, respectively), encopresis (17% vs. 2%, and 7%, respectively) and EEG abnormalities. Of 19 records, two had spike and wave pattern on EEG and 3 other children had "immature EEGs." No group comparisons were made.

5. *Other Nondiagnostic Clinical Features of Elective Mutism*

5.1. *Age of Onset*

The data are generally in agreement with the DSM-III-R as to age of onset. In most cases it is specified or can be inferred as being less than 5 years (see Table 5). One exception is the report by Wilkins (1985) who found that age of onset varied widely from 3.7 to 14.0 years. This information, however, was collected from retrospective chart review and its accuracy is questionable.

There is also support for the statement that diagnosis is often made when the child is older. Kolvin and Fundudis (1982) found the average age of diagnosis was 6 years 10 months (S.D. 1 year 3 months). Although a frequency distribution of age at diagnosis was not given, it can be inferred that diagnosis was often made at school entrance because all children studied were between the ages of 6 and 8.

5.2. *Course*

As discussed previously, there seem to be two distinct groups of children diagnosed with EM. The study by Brown and Lloyd lends support to the conclusion that most cases of EM in young children are transient and resolve spontaneously, whereas others persist. Whether the same is true for EM in older groups is not known.

In the small percentage of cases that are persistent, data on course of illness are thin (see Table 5). Reports are conflicting but suggest that in some cases the condition remains chronic. In several papers, follow-up from 1 to 10 years revealed good outcomes in all cases (Calhourn & Koenig, 1973; Elson *et al.*, 1965; Wright, 1968; Wright *et al.*, 1985). Others report mixed results (Cunningham *et al.*, 1983; Kolvin & Fundudis, 1982; Lowenstein, 1979; Wergeland, 1980) with a proportion of children failing to develop normal speech and others with "emotional problems." Unfortunately, these follow-up reports are sketchy so that conclusions are not clear. Several authors (Kolvin & Fundudis, 1982; Lowenstein, 1979; Wergeland, 1980) have suggested that poor outcome may be related to family pathology.

There are virtually no data on the evolution of comorbid diagnoses other than that pertaining to developmental and elimination disorders noted above. An exception is the single case report of a 16-year-old schizophrenic girl who had received the diagnosis of EM at age 5 (Eldar *et al.*, 1985).

5.3. *Impairment*

Reports on impairment are generally in agreement with the DSM-III-R (see Table 5). Children with this condition tend to be isolated, to perform poorly in academic settings, and to have unpleasant temperaments. Of note is the lack of information about EM that develops during later childhood. There are no data on the nature of functional interference due to EM in adolescents.

5.4. *Complications*

Here again clinical data are in agreement with the DSM-III-R (see Table 5). School failure and teasing or scapegoating by peers are com-

TABLE 5

Other Clinical Correlates of EM

Senior author	*N*	Study age	Onset age	Course	Impairment	Complications	Predisposing factor	Prevalence	Sex ratio	Familial pattern
Atoynatan	7	5–7	?	All improved by 2 years	?	?	Mom depressed	?	?	?
Bozigar	4	6–9	?	All improved	?	?	?	?	?	?
Brown	42	5	≤ 5 years	90% improved 1 year	?	?	?	.66 per 1000 (1 year)	F > M	?
Calhoun	8	5–8	?	All improved 1 year	?	?	?	?	?	?
Cunningham	41	?	?	97% improved 3 weeks–11 years	?	?	?	?	?	?
Eldar	1	16	5 years	Schizophrenia	?	?	?	?	?	?
Elson	4	7–10	< 7 years	All improved 6 months–5 years	?	?	?	?	?	?

(continued)

Table 5 (*Continued*)

Senior author	*N*	Study age	Onset age	Course	Impairment	Complications	Predisposing factor	Prevalence	Sex ratio	Familial pattern
Goll	10	?	?	?	?	?	Family pathology	?	?	?
Goll	10	?	?	?	?	?	Family pathology	?	?	?
Hayden	68	6–7.11	?	?	Social school	School failure	Overprotective, trauma < 3 years	?	F > M	?
Kolvin	24	6–8	M = 6 years 10 months	46% improved	Withdrawn from peers	School failure	Speech disorders	.8 per 1000	F > M	
Kupietz	3	4–15	?	?	?	?	MR?	?	M > F	?
Lesser-Katz	15	3	?	Oppositional	?	?	?	?	?	?
Lowenstein	21	3–8	?	62% much improved	?	?	?	?	M > F	?

Meijer	5	3–10	?	?	?	?	Immigration?	?	F > M	?
Nash	3	5–9	?	?	?	?	?	?	?	?
Parker	27	?	?	?	?	?	Early trauma?	?	?	?
Pustrom	3	8	< 5 years	?	?	?	?	?	M > F	?
Reed	4	12–13	≤ 5 years	?	?	?	MR?	?	?	?
Wergeland	11	6–11	?	Some improvement 8–18 years	Isolated	?	Overprotection	?	F > M	?
Wilkins	24	5.2–17.3	3.7–14 years	?	Depressed, anxious	Depressed, anxious	Overprotective, speech disorder	?	F > M 2:1	?
Wright	24	5–9	?	All improved	Isolated, difficult	Disruptive	Overprotective, speech disorder	?	F > M	3 sets of siblings
Wright	3	4.25–5.6	< 5 years	All improved	Isolated	?	Overprotective, trauma < 3 years	?	M > F	?

mon complications of this disorder. Unfortunately, data are lacking on complications in older children where one might expect difficulties with age-appropriate independent functioning.

5.5. *Predisposing Factors*

It is not clear whether the factors listed in the DSM-III-R predispose to the syndrome of EM or whether they are simply associated with the condition. Nevertheless, the papers reviewed lend support to an association between EM and the following factors: maternal overprotection (Hayden, 1980; Wergeland, 1980; Wilkins, 1985; Wright, 1968; Wright *et al.*, 1985), language and speech disorders (Kolvin & Fundudis, 1982; Wilkins, 1985; Wright, 1968), mental retardation (Kupietz & Schwartz, 1982; Reed, 1963), and hospitalization or trauma before age 3 (Hayden, 1980; Parker, Olson, & Throdemorton, 1960; Wright *et al.*, 1985). The causative nature of these associations is altogether obscure.

5.6. *Prevalence*

EM is rare. The Newcastle epidemiological study found two children with EM in a total city cohort of 3,300 7-year-olds. This represents a rate of 0.8 per 1,000 (Kolvin & Fundudis, 1982). Using a broader definition, Brown and Lloyd (1975) reported an initial prevalence of 7.2 per 1,000, 8 weeks after school entrance, at the age of 5. This dropped by almost 90% 12 months later, to 0.66 per 1,000, to produce a rate of persistent EM consistent with that of the Newcastle epidemiological study.

5.7. *Sex Ratio*

The sex ratio for EM is unusual for a language disorder in that it occurs more often in girls than in boys. Most of the larger studies reviewed here support a higher ratio of girls to boys (Brown & Lloyd, 1975; Goll, 1979; Hayden, 1980; Kolvin & Fundudis, 1982; Meijer, 1979; Reed, 1963; Wergeland, 1980; Wilkins, 1985; Wright, 1968; Wright *et al.*, 1985). The overall ratio for the 80% of studies that specify sex also supports a higher ratio of girls to boys. Here the total number of boys studied is 81 as compared to 140 females. This gives a male to female ratio of 1 : 1.7. This ratio is skewed by Hayden's study (1980) where there were 12 males and 56 females. If this sample is removed, the remaining overall ratio becomes 1 : 1.2 (69 males and 84 females) that is in agreement with the DSM-III-R statement that EM is slightly more common in females than in males.

5.8. *Familial Pattern*

There is virtually no information on familial patterns in EM. One exception is a study by Wright (1968) in which three sets of siblings were found in a group of 24 5- to 9-year-olds referred to a diagnostic nursery because of failure to talk in school. Further, Kolvin and Fundudis (1982) found that children with EM were born significantly earlier in their sibships as compared to normal and speech-retarded children matched for age, sex, and postal zone.

6. *Differential Diagnosis*

As described previously, a significant proportion of children diagnosed with EM also meet criteria for one or more specific developmental disorders. This diagnostic feature is important because comorbid diagnoses may impact on the child's ability to comprehend spoken language and to speak.

Another important factor is whether a child can comprehend and speak the language in the setting in which the mutism occurs, at the time of diagnosis. This factor may have played a role in the high initial prevalence reported by Brown and Lloyd (1975). In this study, 42% of the children were recent immigrants speaking a new language. Unfortunately, the degree to which poor language comprehension played a role in the initial high rate of EM was not specified.

7. *Discussion*

Given the large number of cases reported over the last century, it appears certain that the syndrome of speech refusal in children capable of speaking, called EM, exists as a clinical phenomenon. Yet, having examined the literature, it is clear that the current criteria are likely to include several subgroups of children. Due to the paucity of well-controlled studies it is impossible to suggest empirically based changes to refine the nomenclature.

What is needed before more specific diagnostic criteria can be designed is systematic research aimed at carefully describing a large sample of these children and documenting differences between them. Of particular interest is the question of defining a minimum symptomatic period before assigning the diagnosis. To answer this question, one would need to look first at the descriptive differences between transient and persistent mutism. Further, the relationship between specific developmental disorders, particularly expressive language disorders, and EM requires clarification.

The problem of how to design a study to begin to answer these questions is a difficult one particularly due to the rarity of this condition. One possibility would be to set up a large epidemiological sampling of children first entering school, like that done by Brown and Lloyd (1975), with prospective follow-up of those children diagnosed as electively mute by clinicians. Careful attention should be paid to evidence of language/other developmental disorders so as to determine whether those children who exhibit mutism can comprehend and speak, as well as to assess the impact of those cognitive developmental features on the stability of the disorder.

Given the low public health interest in this disorder, there is little likelihood that studies will occur in the near future. As such, one must ask the question as to the potential usefulness of this category unchanged in the DSM-IV. Although rather vague and potentially overly inclusive in its criteria, it does remain of help to teachers, speech therapists, and mental health professionals in designing educational and therapeutic interventions.

8. *Recommendations*

Based on the literature, it seems judicious to include a minimum duration of mutism for the diagnosis of EM. Although there is no empirical basis for suggesting a specific length of time, the data presented by Brown and Lloyd (1975) suggest that some young children exhibit symptoms of mutism transiently and then go on to normal speech. This is in sharp contrast to those children whose symptoms persist. It is recommended that a minimum duration of symptoms of six months would exclude children going through a period of adjustment as well as those immigrant children learning a new language. It represents the same duration of time needed to make the diagnosis of adjustment disorder and would allow clinicians to be alerted promptly to children with serious psychopathology.

It also seems judicious that the diagnostic criteria state explicitly that children with EM must be fluent in the language spoken in the setting in which they are mute. This is of particular importance for recent immigrant children and children who come from homes or communities in which the language spoken differs from that of the school. From the literature reviewed, it appears that it would make sense to exclude children from the EM disorder for the first 6 months after immigration. During this time it would be expected that a new language was being learned, and therefore EM should not yet be considered in the differential of behavioral problems.

9. *Appendix I: Summary of Study by Kolvin and Fundudis (1982)*

Subjects

Studied 13 female and 11 male EM children (6–8 years mean age 6 years, 10 months/S.D. of 1 year, 3 months). Subjects referred from clinic for speech, language and behavior disorders, pediatrics, speech, child psychiatry, and child guidance clinics. Children were collected over 5 to 6 years.

During the same period, 84 speech-retarded children and 102 normal children were also recruited. Children were matched on three criteria: age, sex, and postal zone.

Method

Clinical comparisons were made among three groups.

Results

	Normal control group	Speech control group	EM group
Size of sample	102	84	24
Sex			
Girls	37 (36%)	30 (30%)	13 (54%)
Boys	65 (64%)	54 (64%)	11 (46%) mean
Size of sibship	3.37	4.35	3.5
Milestones (mean age in months)			
Walking alone	13.1	14.3	14.7
Speaking in phrases	21.9	NA	27.3
Bowel and bladder			
Enuresis	15 (15%)	21 (25%)	10 (42%)
Encopresis	2 (2%)	6 (7%)	4 (17%)
Mean IQ	101.17	94.94	84.95
Speech and hearing impairment	0%	100%	50%
EEG abnormalities	?	?	(6) 32%
Social withdrawal			
Greater in adults	?	?	2 (8%)
Greater in peers	?	?	14 (58%)

	Normal control group	Speech control group	EM group
Increased motor activity	?	?	7 (29%)
Parental psychopathology			
Mother	8 (8%)	?	5 (20%)
Father	3 (3%)	?	4 (16%)
5–10-year follow-up, long-term improement	?	?	11 (46%)

10. *Appendix II: Summary of Study by Wilkins (1985)*

Subjects

Studied 17 female and 7 male EM children (5.2–17.3 years/mean age 9 years, 8 months). Subjects represent all cases diagnosed at Maudsley Hospital from 1968–1980.

During the same period, 24 children with other psychiatric diagnoses (4 phobic, 7 school refusal, 4 adjustment reaction, 3 anxiety disorder, 3 depression, 2 enuresis, and 1 hysteria) were also selected. Children were matched on five criteria: sex, age, year seen, IQ, and area of residence.

Method

Case notes were reviewed and compared retrospectively.

Results

	Elective mutes	Emotional disorders
Number	24	24
F:M	17:7	17:7
Mean age first seen (years)	9.8	10.3
Number of children in family	3.2	2.9
First born	6	9
Last born	8	11
Number of twin pairs	1	1
Families		
Two-parent homes	24	12
Marital disharmony	12	12

	Elective mutes	Emotional disorders
Birth: normal/complicated	18/6	22/2
Milestones		
Normal	18	24
Delayed speech	6	0
Poor articulation	2	0
Enuresis	1	3
Physical health: normal/other	20/4	23/1
Hearing: normal/poor	23/1	24/0
Temperament (frequency in notes)		
Shy	22	18
Anxious	21	11
Depressed	19	11
Happy	3	3
Temper tantrums	9	3
Jealous	3	2
Overdependent	3	4
Manipulative	11	3
Affectionate	13	11
Mother overprotective	9	2

ACKNOWLEDGMENTS

I thank Rachel G. Klein, Ph.D., for her help in the preparation of this chapter.

11. *References*

Albert, S., & Phyllis, L. (1986). Positive reinforcement in short-term treatment of an electively mute child: A case study. *Psychological Reports, 58*(2), 571–576.

Ambrosino, S., Alessi, M. (1979). Elective mutism: Fixation and double bind. *American Journal of Psychoanalysis, 39*(3), 251–256.

Atoynatan, T. (1986). Elective mutism: Involvement of the mother in the treatment of the child. *Child Psychiatry and Human Development, 17-1,* 15–27.

Austad, C., Sininger, R., & Stricklin, A. (1980). Successful treatment of a case of elective mutism. *Behavior Therapist, 3*(1), 18–19.

Bauermeister, J., & Jemail, J. (1975). Modification of "elective mutism" in the classroom setting: A case study. *Behavior Therapy, 6*(2), 246–250.

Beck, J., & Hubbard, M. (1987). Elective mutism in a missionary family: A case study. Special Issue: No. 2 on Psychology and Missions. *Journal of Psychology and Theology, 15*(4), 291–299.

Bhide, A., & Srinath, S. (1985). Elective mutism. *British Journal of Psychiatry, 147,* 731.

Bozigar, J., & Hansen, R. (1984). Group treatment of elective mute children. *Social Work, 29*(5), 478–480.

Brown, J., & Lloyd, H. (1975). A controlled study not speaking in school. *Assoc. Workers Maladjust Child, 3*, 49–63.

Browne, E., Wilson, V., & Laybourne, P. (1963). Diagnosis and treatment of elective mutism in children. *Journal of the American Academy of Child and Adolescent Psychiatry, 2*, 605–617.

Calhoun, J., & Koenig, K. (1973). Classroom modification of elective mutism. *Behavior Therapy, 4*(5), 700–702.

Cantwell, D., & Baker, L. (1985). Speech and language: Development and disorders. In M. Rutter & L. Hersov (Eds.), *Child and adolescent psychiatry, modern approaches* (2nd ed.), pp. 531–533. London: Blackwell Scientific Publications.

Carr, A., & Afnan, S. (1989). Concurrent individual and family therapy in a case of elective mutism. *Journal of Family Therapy, 11*(1), 29–44.

Chetnick, M. (1973). Amy: The intensive treatment of an elective mute. *Journal of the American Academy of Child Psychiatry, 12*(3), 482–498.

Ciottone, R., & Madonna, J. (1984). The treatment of elective mutism: The economics of an integrated approach. *Techniques, 1*(1), 23–30.

Croghan, L., & Crtaven, R. (1982). Elective mutism: Learning from the analysis of a successful case history. *Journal of Pediatric Psychology, 7*(1), 85–93.

Cunningham, C., Cataldo, M., & Mallion, C. (1983). A review and controlled single case evaluation of behavioral approaches to the management of elective mutism. *Child and Family Behavior Therapy, 5*(4), 25–49.

Eldar, S., Bleich, A., Apter, A., & Tyano, S. (1985). Elective mutism—An atypical antecedent of schizophrenia. *Journal of Adolescence, 8*(3), 289–292.

Elson, A., Pearson, C., Jones, D., & Schumacher, E. (1965). Follow-up study of childhood elective mutism. *Archives of General Psychiatry, 13*, 182–187.

Goll, K. (1979). Role structure and subculture in the families of elective mutists. *Family Process, 18*(1), 55–68.

Goll, K. (1980). Role structure and subculture in the family of elective mutists. *Advances in Family Psychiatry, 2*, 141–161.

Hayden, T. (1980). Classification of elective mutism. *Journal of the American Academy of Child Psychiatry, 19*, 118–133.

Hesselman, S. (1983). Elective mutism in children 1877–1981. *Acta Paedopsychiatrica, 49*, 297–310.

Hill, L., & Scull, J. (1985). Elective mutism associated with selective inactivity. *Journal of Communication Disorders, 18*(3), 161–167.

Hoffman, S., & Laub, B. (1986). Paradoxical intervention using a polarization model of cotherapy in the treatment of elective mutism: A case study. *Contemporary Family therapy: An International Journal, 8*(2), 136–143.

Kolvin, I., & Fundudis, T. (1982). Elective mute children: Psychological, developmental and background factors. *Annual Progress in Child Psychiatry and Child Development*, 484–501.

Kratochwill, T., Bordy, G., & Piersel, W. (1979). Elective mutism in children. In B. Lahey & A. Kazdin (Eds.), *Advances in clinical child psychology Vol. 2* (pp. 194–240). New York: Plenum Press.

Krolian, E. (1988). "Speech is silvern, but silence is golden": Day hospital treatment of two electively mute children. *Clinical Social Work Journal, 16*(4), 355–377.

Kupietz, S., & Schwartz, I. (1982). Elective mutism: Evaluation and behavioral treatment of three cases. *NYS Journal of Medicine, 82*(7), 1073–1076.

Labbe, E., & Williamson, D. (1984). Behavioral treatment of elective mutism: A review of the literature. *Clinical Psychology Review, 4*, 273–292.

Lazarus, P., Gavil, H., & Moore, J. (1983). The treatment of elective mutism in children within the school setting: Two case studies. *School Psychology Review, 12*(4), 467–472.

Lesser-Katz, M. (1986). Stranger reaction and elective mutism in young children. *American Journal of Orthopsychiatry, 56*(3), 458–469.

Linblad-Goldberg, M. (1986). Elective mutism in families with young children. *Family Therapy Collections, 18,* 31–42.

Louden, D. (1987). Elective mutism: A case study of a disorder of childhood. *Journal of the National Medical Association, 79*(10), 1043–1048.

Lowenstein, L. (1978). A summary of the research on elective mutism. *Acta Paedopsychiatrica, 44,* 17–22.

Lowenstein, L. (1979). The result of 21 elective mute cases. *Acta Paedopsychiatrica, 45,* 17–23.

Meijer, A. (1979). Elective mutism in children. *Israel Annals of Psychiatry and Related Disciplines, 17*(2), 93–100.

Meyers, S. (1984). Elective mutism in children: A family systems approach. *American Journal of Family Therapy, 12*(4), 39–45.

Nash, R., Thorpe, H., Andrews, M., & Davis, K. (1979). A management program of elective mutism. *Psychology in the Schools, 16*(2), 246–253.

Paniagua, F., & Saeed, M. (1988). A procedural distinction between elective and progressive mutism. *Journal of Behavior Therapy and Experimental Psychiatry, 19*(3), 207–210.

Parker, E., & Olson, T., & Throdemorton, M. (1960). Social casework with elementary children who do not talk in school. *Social Work, 5,* 64–70.

Pigott, H., & Gonzales, F. (1987). Efficacy of videotape self-modeling in treating an electively mute child. *Journal of Clinical Child Psychology, 16*(2), 106–110.

Pustrom, E., & Speers, R. (1964). Elective mutism in children. *Journal of the American Academy of Child Psychiatry, 3,* 287–297.

Radford, P. (1977). A psychoanalytically-based therapy as the treatment of choice for a six-year-old elective mute. *Journal of Child Psychotherapy, 4*(3), 49–65.

Reed, G. (1963). Elective mutism in children: A reappraisal. *Journal of Child Psychology and Psychiatry, 4,* 99–107.

Richards, C., & Hansen, M. (1978). A further demonstration of the efficacy of stimulus fading treatment of elective mutism. *Journal of Behavior Therapy and Experimental Psychiatry, 9*(1), 57–60.

Rosenberg, J., & Linblad, M. (1978). Behavior therapy in a family context: Treating elective mutism. *Family Process, 17*(1), 77–82.

Sanok, R., & Ascione, F. (1979). Behavioral interventions for childhood elective mutism: An evaluative review. *Child Behavior Therapy, 1*(1), 49–68.

Sanok, R., & Striefel, S. (1979). Elective mutism: Generalization of verbal responding across people and settings. *Behavior Therapy, 10*(3), 357–371.

Sluckin, A. (1977). Children who do not talk at school. *Child-Care, Health and Development, 3*(2), 69–79.

Subak, M., West, M., & Carlin, M. (1982). Elective mutism: An expression of family psychopathology. *International Journal of Family Psychiatry, 3*(3), 335–344.

Wassing, H. (1973). A case of prolonged elective mutism in an adolescent boy: On the nature of the condition and its residential treatment. *Acta Paedopsychiatrica, 40*(2), 75–96.

Wergeland, H. (1980). Elective mutism. *Annual Progress in Child Psychiatry and Child Development,* 373–385.

Wilkins, R. (1985). A comparison of elective mutism and emotional disorders in children. *British Journal of Psychiatry, 146,* 198–203.

Williamson, D. (1977). The behavioral treatment of elective mutism: Two case studies. *Journal of Behavior Therapy and Experimental Psychiatry, 8*(2), 143–149.

Wright, H. (1968). A clinical study of children who refuse to talk. *Journal of the American Academy of Child Psychiatry, 7,* 603–617.

Wright, H., Miller, M., Cook, M., & Littman, J. (1985). Early to speak. *Journal of the American Academy of Child Psychiatry, 24,* 739–746.

Wulbert, M., Nyman, B., Snow, D., & Owen, Y. (1973). The efficacy of stimulus fading and contingency management in the treatment of elective mutism: A case study. *Journal of Applied Behavior Analysis,* 6(3), 435–441.

9 Sibling Rivalry

Diagnostic Category or Focus of Treatment?

ALICE S. CARTER AND FRED R. VOLKMAR

1. Introduction

Sibling rivalry refers to a marked change in a child's affect and/or behavior that occurs in response to the birth of a sibling. The feelings and behaviors that characterize sibling rivalry include increased negative affect with predominant feelings of jealousy, anger, and rejection, lack of positive regard for the sibling, increased oppositionality, overt or covert aggression toward the sibling, marked competition for parental affection and attention, and regression to earlier stages of development (e.g., use of babytalk, loss of bladder or bowel control). Although child clinicians report that sibling rivalry is a frequent presenting complaint, there is a dearth of empirical data about the prevalence, incidence, or stability of the phenomenon. In addition, there are no data on external validity. For example, it is not clear whether the disorder is related to other aspects of intra- or interpersonal dysfunction. Sibling rivalry disorder has been included as an official childhood emotional disorder in the World Health Organization ICD-10 diagnostic system. A similar category does not exist in DSM III-R. This chapter briefly reviews theoretical and empirical advances in the study of sibling rivalry in order to evaluate the rationale for including sibling rivalry as either a diagnostic category for children or a condition that is not attributed to a mental disorder but as a relational problem that is documented as a focus of treatment in DSM-IV.

ALICE S. CARTER • Department of Psychology, Yale University, New Haven, Connecticut 06520-7447. FRED R. VOLKMAR • Child Study Center, Yale University School of Medicine, New Haven, Connecticut 06510-8009.

Advances in Clinical Child Psychology, Volume 14, edited by Benjamin B. Lahey and Alan E. Kazdin. Plenum Press, New York, 1992.

2. *The Utility of Sibling Rivalry as a Diagnostic Category*

The central issue in assessing the utility of sibling rivalry as a diagnostic category is whether there is enough empirical evidence to conclude that sibling rivalry is a valid disorder of childhood. A second related issue is whether sibling rivalry might be better conceptualized as a condition that is not attributed to a mental disorder of childhood but that is a relational problem that is often a primary focus of child and/or family intervention. Thus in contrast to outlining explicit criteria to establish a separate diagnostic category within disorders of childhood, sibling rivalry might be better understood within the framework of psychological difficulties that arise within the family context. Adopting the current DSM III-R conventions, conceptualizing sibling rivalry in this latter framework would lead to inclusion as a V Code as opposed to an Axis I diagnosis.

Whether conceptualized in terms of a diagnostic disorder of childhood or as a condition that is often the focus of child and/or family intervention, it is essential to view sibling rivalry in the context of normal development. Further, it is critical that diagnostic criteria to define deviant behavior be sensitive to the developmental, familial, and sociocultural conditions in which sibling rivalry emerges. Sibling experiences are always shaped by three interacting, dynamic influences: the nature of the mutual relationships between parents and children, the developmental capacities and individual characteristics of the children (e.g., temperament) (Brody, Stoneman, & Burke, 1987; Solnit, 1983) and the relationships of the siblings to each other as peers (Kris & Ritvo, 1983). In addition, the sociocultural environmental context provides a background that further guides the unfolding of sibling relationships (Zukow, 1989). Although many studies of family constellations exist, it is only in recent years that researchers have begun to examine social and affective aspects of sibling relationships within the family (Furman & Buhrmester, 1985). In terms of the taxonomic validity of sibling rivalry (i.e., the utility of an independent diagnostic category), it is important to note that no information of an epidemiological nature currently exists.

3. *Patterns of Influence within the Family*

In many families, arguments between young siblings are customary and a cause for much parental concern and consternation (Abramovitch, Pepler, & Corter, 1982; Baskett & Johnson, 1982; Dunn, 1983; Newson & Newson, 1970). In addition to verbal arguments, it is clear that physical aggression between siblings is not uncommon. For example, Newson and Newson (1978), in their study of 7-year-olds, reported that 35% of boys and 34% of girls were described as physically fighting within the family. Thus if a diagnostic category is warranted, it is important to develop assessment strategies that can distinguish severe or extreme cases of sibling rivalry from those expressions of aggression and hostility that are commonly found in sibling relationships.

In addition to data that suggest that aspects of sibling rivalry occur commonly in childhood, the adaptive or growth-promoting aspects of some of the features associated with sibling rivalry must be acknowledged. Disputes with other children, including disputes with siblings, play a crucial role in the development of (1) children's acquisition of perspective taking skills, (2) increased understanding of the social consequences of interpersonal actions, (3) improved modulation of the experience and expression of aggressive affects, and (4) skills of argument and conciliation. For example, there is a positive association between preschoolers' perspective-taking skills and their ability to provide subsidiary caretaking for their infant siblings in the mother's absence (Howe & Ross, 1990; Stewart & Marvin, 1984). Given the correlational nature of these data, it is not clear whether friendly sibling relations facilitate perspective taking or vice versa (Dunn, 1988).

There is considerable evidence that both prosocial and contentious aspects of sibling relationships are influenced by patterns of interaction in other family relationships (e.g., interparental conflict) and the emotional climate in the family (Brody *et al.*, 1987; Dunn, 1988). Prosocial behaviors such as friendliness, cooperation, and affection appear to be independent from agonistic behaviors such as conflict and rivalry (cf. Dunn, 1988). In terms of general socialization experiences, parental response to aggression is of major importance in shaping children's antagonistic behavior (Dunn & Munn, 1986) as well as altruistic and empathic responses (Zahn-Waxler, Radke-Yarrow, & King, 1979). It appears that mothers who talk about newborns as persons with needs and feelings foster positive sibling relationships (Dunn & Kendrick, 1982).

Two models have been applied to understand the impact of parental intervention in sibling conflicts. First, parental intervention can be viewed as a positive reinforcer for negative conflicts as a function of the positive valence of parental attention for children. Studies that attempt to minimize sibling conflict by training parents to stay out of sibling fights suggest that such training can lead to a decrease in sibling conflict (Brody & Stoneman, 1983). Similarly, parental involvement with a new infant may minimize the opportunities for developing a sibling relationship, thus reducing the likelihood of both positive and negative interactions (Howe & Ross, 1990). Depriving children of opportunities to resolve sibling conflict may lead to maladaptive and deviant patterns of sibling interaction that are marked by empathic inadequacy, self-serving behaviors, and/or coercive manipulation. The second model views parental intervention as decreasing the likelihood of future aggressive actions. For example, Zahn-Waxler and her colleagues (1979) reported that when parents forcefully and consistently draw their child's attention to the interpersonal consequences of aggressive actions, altruistic and empathic responses to the distress of others is fostered. In fact, both models may contribute to the constellation of sibling behaviors that emerges in any given sibling pair. Howe and Ross (1990) reported that whereas maternal references to the infant's internal experience was positively associated with friendly sibling relationships, intense maternal interaction with children was negatively associated with friendly sibling relations. In addition, differential maternal behavior is clearly associated with increased negativity in sibling relationships (Brody *et al.*, 1987). Although these patterns of mutual influence within the family are complex, it is clear that sibling rivalry must be assessed and treated within the broader context of family functioning.

Siblings appear to play a role in shaping children's aggressive and coercive behaviors as well as cooperative and social fantasy play independent of the contribution of parental behavior (Dunn, 1983; Dunn & Munn, 1986; Patterson & Cobb, 1971; Patterson, 1986). Further, Patterson (1986) reported that coercive behavior by a sibling toward a target child is associated with the target child having problems with peers outside of the family. Although there is no evidence of a causal link, this association suggests that where coercion is part of a larger constellation of behaviors associated with sibling rivalry, identification and intervention should impact not only the child experiencing sibling rivalry but also the child who is the target of coercive or aggressive actions.

4. *Current Diagnostic Status*

The ICD-10 (1986) clinical description recognizes that sibling rivalry occurs in the context of normal child development and notes that a large proportion of young children show some degree of emotional disturbance following the birth of a sibling and that usually such a disturbance is mild and transient. A diagnosis of sibling rivalry is reserved only for those cases in which (1) the disturbance is persistent; (2) there is a change in a child's behavior following the birth of an immediately younger sibling; (3) rivalry with or jealousy of the younger sibling is unambiguously present; and (4) "the degree and/or persistence of the disturbance is both statistically unusual and associated with social impairment." Research criteria for the disorder in ICD-10 (1990) include:

1. Abnormally negative feelings including jealousy toward an immediately younger sibling
2. Emotional disturbance as evidenced by at least two of regression, tantrums, dysphoria, sleep disturbance, oppositional behavior or attention seeking with one or both parents
3. Onset within 6 months of the birth of the younger sibling
4. Duration of at least 4 weeks

As suggested by the criteria outlined in ICD-10, the diagnosis of a sibling rivalry disorder must reflect a pattern of extreme behaviors that interferes with the child's developmental progress. In addition, such a diagnosis must take into consideration the developmental stage of the child and recent events within the family beyond the birth of a sibling. In the absence of any epidemiological information regarding the incidence, prevalence, stability, or range of severity of children's typical responses to the birth of a sibling, it is not possible to determine statistical criteria for making a diagnosis of sibling rivalry. For example, ICD-10 criteria for sibling rivalry disorder note that the negative feelings of the child toward the younger child must be abnormally intense. However, the absence of epidemiological and other data make it unclear as to how this criterion would be operationalized in actual use. There is a similar dearth of descriptive information about children referred for mental health services who present with a primary complaint of "sibling rivalry."

5. *Toward DSM-IV*

To date, there is insufficient evidence to argue that a constellation of behaviors associated with sibling rivalry constitute a syndrome or mental disorder. These behaviors can be more conservatively viewed as evidence of a condition that is not attributed to a mental disorder but that may be the focus of individual child or family therapy. Given the evidence that many of the behaviors that comprise sibling rivalry (e.g., aggression toward sibling, feelings of competition) appear to be strongly related to patterns of family interaction and the emotional climate within the family, sibling rivalry may be best conceptualized within the larger rubric of family functioning. Conceptualized in this manner, a "V" code may be the most appropriate mechanism for identifying sibling rivalry in DSM-IV.

The absence of sufficient evidence regarding the validity, prevalence, or morbidity associated with the condition argues against according it official diagnostic (Axis I) status in DSM-IV. However, it does appear that the condition is worthy of notation as a focus of treatment and that the ability to code the condition, when it is present, would facilitate both future research and clinical service. The following description is proposed as a guideline for understanding sibling rivalry as a clinical entity.

5.1. *Proposed V Code Description*

5.1.1. *Sibling Rivalry*

This category can be used when the focus of attention or treatment is on a child's unusually marked and/or intense negative feelings to the birth of a younger sibling. Some degree of jealousy and rivalry following the birth of a younger sibling is normal. This category should be used only when the feelings are abnormal in their intensity and duration (at least 1 month), when they are accompanied by some degree of social impairment and by indications of emotional disturbance (such as regression, tantrums, dysphoria, sleep disturbance, oppositional behavior, and excessive attention seeking or clinging behaviors toward one or both parents). The category should be used only when the emotional disturbance is clearly related to and follows the birth of a younger sibling.

6. *Summary*

In summary, sibling rivalry is a frequent presenting complaint that has not been systematically studied. Empirical research documents that sibling rivalry is a commonly observed phenomena that emerges within the context of patterns of family functioning and the larger sociocultural system. Differentiating normal developmentally appropriate and adaptive sibling rivalry from that which is associated with social impairment is critical. Although the absence of sufficient evidence regarding the validity, prevalence, or morbidity associated with the condition argues against according it the status of a childhood disorder, the ability to code sibling rivalry as a clinical entity should facilitate both future research and clinical service.

7. *References*

Abramovitch, R., Pepler, D., & Corter, C. (1982). Patterns of sibling interaction among preschool-age children. In M. E. Lamb & B. Sutton-Smith (Eds.), *Sibling relationships across the lifespan: Their nature and significance* (pp. 61–86). Hillsdale, NJ: Erlbaum.

Baskett, L. M., & Johnson, S. M. (1982). The young child's interactions with parents versus siblings: A behavioral analysis. *Child Development, 53,* 643–650.

Brody, G. H., & Stoneman, Z. (1983). Children with atypical siblings. In B. B. Lahey & A. E. Kazdin (Eds.), *Advances in clinical child psychology Volume* 6 (pp. 285–326). New York: Plenum Press.

Brody, G. H., Stoneman, Z., & Burke, M. (1987). Family system and individual child correlates of sibling behavior. *American Journal of Orthopsychiatry, 57,* 561–569.

Dunn, J. (1983). Sibling relationships in early childhood. *Child Development, 54,* 787–811.

Dunn, J. (1988). Sibling influences on childhood development. *Journal of Child and Adolescent Psychiatry, 29,* 119–127.

Dunn, J., & Kendrick, C. (1982). *Siblings.* Cambridge, MA: Harvard University Press.

Dunn, J., & Munn, P. (1986). Sibling quarrels and maternal intervention: Individual differences in understanding and aggression. *Journal of Child Psychology and Psychiatry, 27,* 583–595.

Furman, W., & Buhrmester, D. (1985). Children's perception of the qualities of sibling relationships. *Child Development, 56,* 448–461.

Howe, N., & Ross, H. S. (1990). Socialization, perspective-taking, and the sibling relationship. *Developmental Psychology, 26,* 160–165.

Kris, M., & Ritvo, S. (1983). Parent and siblings: Their mutual influence. *The Psychoanalytic Study of the Child, 38,* 311–324.

Newson, J., & Newson, E. (1970). *Four years old in an urban community.* Harmondsworth: Penguin Books.

Newson, J., & Newson, E. (1978). *Seven years old in the home environment.* Harmondsworth: Penguin Books.

Patterson, G. R. (1986). The contribution of siblings to training for fighting: A microsocial analysis. In D. Olweus, J. Block, & M. Radke-Yarrow (Eds.), *Development of antisocial and prosocial behavior: Research, theories and issues* (pp. 235–261). New York: Academic Press.

Patterson, G. R., & Cobb, J. A. (1971). A dyadic analysis of "aggressive" behaviors. In J. P. Hill (Ed.), *Minnesota Symposia on Child Psychology,* Vol. 5. Minneapolis: University of Minnesota Press.

Solnit, A. J. (1983). The sibling experience. *The Psychoanalytic Study of the Child, 38,* 281–284.

Stewart, R., & Marvin, R. S. (1984). Sibling relations: The role of conceptual perspective-taking in the ontogeny of sibling caregiving. *Child Development, 55,* 1322–1332.

World Health Organization (1986). Mental and behavioral disorders, clinical descriptions and diagnostic guidelines (Draft). *International classification of diseases* (10th ed.). Geneva: WHO.

World Health Organization (1990). Mental and behavioral disorders, diagnostic criteria for research (Draft). *International classification of diseases* (10th ed.). Geneva: WHO.

Zahn-Waxler, C., Radke-Yarrow, M., & King, R. C. (1979). Child rearing and children's prosocial initiations toward victims of distress. *Child Development, 50,* 319–330.

Zukow, P. G. (Ed.). (1989). *Sibling interaction across cultures: Theoretical and methodological issues.* New York: Springer.

10 Suicidality of Childhood and Adolescence

Review of the Literature and Proposal for Establishment of a DSM-IV Category

ROBERT A. KING, CYNTHIA PFEFFER,
G. DAVIS GAMMON, AND DONALD J. COHEN

1. *Introduction*

The purpose of this review is to examine the status of suicide and suicidality in the framework of DSM-III-R and to stimulate discussion of alternative approaches for DSM-IV, including the possibility of including suicidality as a new diagnostic category in its own right. (In this review, we use the term *suicidality* to refer to the spectrum of ideation and/or behavior involving deliberate attempts to inflict death or serious physical harm to the self. To the extent that the data permit, we will try to distinguish between suicidal ideation and action and between attempted and completed suicide.)

Suicidality is a serious psychological condition that is a frequent cause of injury or death and serves as a common, compelling focus of clinical attention. However, despite its wide prevalence and serious consequences, suicidality receives scant mention in the official DSM-III-R nosology, which mentions it only as a symptom of Major Depressive Disorder or Borderline Personality Disorder.

As we shall argue on the basis of our review of the literature, the

ROBERT A. KING • Child Study Center, Yale University School of Medicine, New Haven, Connecticut 06510-8009. CYNTHIA PFEFFER • Cornell University Medical College, New York Hospital–Westchester Division, 21 Bloomingdale Road, White Plains, New York 10605. G. DAVIS GAMMON AND DONALD J. COHEN • Child Study Center, Yale University School of Medicine, New Haven, Connecticut 06510-8009.

Advances in Clinical Child Psychology, Volume 14, edited by Benjamin B. Lahey and Alan E. Kazdin. Plenum Press, New York, 1992.

current DSM-III-R treatment of suicidality (or rather its relative neglect) is problematic in several important regards. First, there is the problem of *inadequate coverage.* A significant number of clearly disturbed suicidal individuals (and even a few suicide completers) do not meet the criteria for any of the existing DSM-III-R diagnostic categories. This leads to the unsatisfactory situation of patients in clear need of clinical intervention, who nonetheless lack a diagnosable condition. Second, simply subsuming suicidality as a symptom of another diagnosis may be clinically uninformative or misleading; such a diagnosis will often fail to capture or convey the distinctive suicidal features that may be major determinants of the patient's clinical care or prognosis. (For example, *adjustment disorder,* one of the commonest diagnoses given adolescent suicide attempters, minimizes the import of the patient's suicidality and supports denial of intrinsic factors in the child by placing the focus on frequently commonplace external stressors.) Third, the current DSM-III-R neglect of suicidality hampers record keeping and clinical research about suicidal individuals by failing to provide a common rubric and generally accepted criteria for identifying them.

As work progresses on DSM-IV, it is essential that these deficiencies of DSM-III-R in the area of suicidality be addressed. DSM-IV might employ several alternative approaches to this area. The first alternative of these alternatives, which seems to us the most compelling, is to approach suicidality as a disorder in its own right. The central question to be considered is whether there are advantages to pulling together the various instances of suicidal behavior or ideation under a single rubric rather than continuing the current practice of classifying them *only* under a wide variety of other, ostensibly etiologically "primary" diagnoses. At stake is the question, as Shaffer (1982) put it, of whether "suicidal behavior can be seen as a unitary condition or 'diagnosis' arising from a limited set of antecedent circumstances with predictable consequences . . . . or is it merely an epiphenomenon of a variety of different mental states each with its own and different determinants and prognoses" (p. 414).

To qualify as a valid diagnostic category, a condition should (1) constitute a *significant mental disorder* (i.e., contribute to impaired social functioning or to personal distress); (2) be *reliably ascertainable;* (3) have *validity* in terms of distinctive predisposing or etiologic features (*antecedent* or *postdictive validity*), concomitant biological or psychological features (*concurrent validity*), and natural history or clinical course (*predictive validity*). In addition, to warrant inclusion as a new category in DSM-IV, a classification should *facilitate communication,* have *clinical utility,* and not be adequately described by existing diagnoses.

We shall review the evidence that suicidality meets these desiderata for a valid diagnostic category and propose provisional criteria for such a "suicidal disorder."

The adoption of a new diagnostic category is a process that requires much time, careful study, and the development of a consensus among both clinicians and researchers regarding its validity and utility. While this debate continues regarding the validity of suicidality as a distinct disorder, DSM-IV should at least make provisions for noting and coding the presence of suicidal ideation and behavior for clinical and research purposes. We will therefore also examine some of the additional proposals for how this might be done.

Our review focuses primarily on suicidal children, adolescents, and young adults. In emphasizing this age group, we do not imply a discontinuity with suicidality manifested in older adults. Indeed, with certain caveats noted below, we believe our conclusions and recommendations are generally applicable to older individuals as well. However, the relevance of our conclusions to adulthood remains to be studied and lies beyond the scope of this review.

2. *Limitations of DSM-III-R*

2.1. *Diagnostic Studies of Suicidal Individuals*

A review of diagnostic studies of youthful suicide attempters and completers reveals many of the difficulties of adequately classifying such individuals within the current official nosology.

The question of whether the current DSM-III-R adequately classifies suicidal individuals involves at least two distinct issues: (1) Are most suicidal patients diagnosable using DSM-III-R categories? and (2) Do these DSM-III-R diagnoses adequately capture or convey these patients' distinctive clinical features (including natural history, prognosis, treatment needs) and salient antecedents or concomitants (such as family factors, genetic influences, etc.)?

In order to answer the first of these questions we will review the literature relating suicidality to the existing DSM-III-R Axis I and II disorders, beginning with what is known about completed suicides and then turning to individuals who attempt suicide or have suicidal ideation.

2.1.1. *Diagnostic Studies of Completed Suicides*

Most youthful suicide completers are clearly disturbed. However, these individuals' disturbances fall into a variety of DSM-III-R categories. Furthermore, a certain small proportion of suicide completers clearly manifest psychopathological symptoms but do not meet *any* of the formal diagnostic categories at all.

Estimates of the prevalence of psychiatric disorder among suicide completers are strongly influenced by methodological considerations (Clark & Horton, 1991). Postmortem psychiatric diagnosis of completed suicides is obviously fraught with ascertainment difficulties including retrospective reporting biases and the absence of the most important informant (Brent, 1989; Brent *et al.*, 1988). Psychological "postmortems" of completed young adult suicides find about 90% warranted DSM-III diagnoses (e.g., Rich *et al.*, 1986); similar studies of completed child and adolescent suicides estimate rates of psychiatric disorder ranging from 98% to 12% (Clark & Horton, 1991; Kovacs & Puig-Antich, 1989; Marttunen *et al.*, 1991), with the lowest rates often deriving from studies involving less intensive and more problematic means of diagnostic ascertainment.

Although depression is often considered the most important contributing factor in both completed and attempted suicides, the reported prevalence of depression in completed suicide cases varies widely with the sample and method of assessment. Furthermore, it is important to note that a significant number of suicidal individuals either do not appear depressed or do not meet the full DSM-III-R criteria for a depressive disorder. *Aggression* and *impulsivity* appear to play a role in suicide both in combination with and independent of depression. Thus conduct disorder and substance abuse are common diagnoses in completed suicides and may occur in the absence of a diagnosable affective disorder (Fowler *et al.*, 1986; Shaffer *et al.*, 1988). After adolescence, individuals with schizophrenia constitute a significant fraction of completed suicides, with perhaps as many as 10% of all schizophrenics ultimately committing suicide; although a substantial proportion of these individuals may also have a diagnosable depressive disorder (Drake *et al.*, 1985; Roy, 1986), in many cases schizophrenic suicidality is preceded by a period of psychotic turmoil rather than depression (Planansky & Johnston, 1973).

Several psychological postmortem studies illustrate the diagnostic heterogeneity of young suicide completers. For example, Shaffer's (1974) postmortem study of 30 young British adolescent suicides found 57% had mixed antisocial and affective symptoms, 13% had only affective symptoms, 17% had only antisocial symptoms, and 13% had neither type of symptomatology. In preliminary data from their more recent and extensive New York adolescent suicide postmortem study, Shaffer *et al.* (1988) reported prevalence rates among male suicides for major depression of only 21%, substance abuse 37%, and antisocial behavior of 67%; the corresponding rates for completed female suicides were major depression 50%, substance abuse 5%, and antisocial behavior 30%, suggesting distinctive gender-related diagnostic patterns. Hoberman and Garfinkel (1988) rated 50% of decedents as having a diagnosable psychiatric disorder; 28% were rated as having a depressive disorder, 10% alcohol abuse, 12% drug abuse, 7% conduct disorder, 2% schizophrenia, and 2% bipolar.

Turning to personality disorder, most studies of completed suicides have examined maladaptive personality traits, rather than categorical Axis II Personality Disorder diagnoses. These studies suggest that several personality patterns may be associated with completed suicide. Shaffer (1974) discerned four types of personality in young adolescent suicides: paranoid, impulsive, uncommunicative, and perfectionistic–self-critical types. In their more recent study, Shaffer and colleagues (1988) found about one-third were impulsive, one-third compulsive–perfectionistic, and one-third fit no specific pattern. The finding of Shaffi *et al.* (1985) that 65% of adolescent suicides had inhibited personalities, whereas 70% had antisocial behavior, is a reminder that the two patterns of behavior are not mutually exclusive.

Among the categorical Axis II diagnoses, Borderline Personality Disorder (BPD) and Antisocial Personality Disorder (APD) are the two DSM-III-R personality disorders most clearly associated with completed and attempted suicides in both adolescents and adults (Frances & Blumenthal, 1989; Marttunen *et al.*, 1991). Long-term follow-up studies suggest a suicide rate for BPD of 4% to 7.5% (Akiskal *et al.*, 1985; Stone *et al.*, 1987). Frances and Blumenthal (1989) estimate that 5% of individuals with APD eventually commit suicide. Borderline personality disorder is also a risk factor for frequent, serious suicide attempts. The association of suicidality with BPD is not a tautological one, as the association persists even when suicidality is not used as one of the criteria for making the BPD diagnosis. BPD very often coexists with substance abuse (Crumley, 1982) and has a good deal of diagnostic overlap with affective disorders (Widiger, 1989).

2.1.2. Diagnostic Studies of Suicide Attempters and Ideators

We turn next to review the relationship of categorical DSM-III-R diagnoses to attempted suicide and suicidal ideation.

Diagnostically, suicide attempters and ideators appear to be even more heterogeneous than suicide completers. As with suicide completers, depression is an important risk factor, but the presence of a depressive disorder is by no means a necessary or sufficient condition for the occurrence of suicidal ideation or behavior.

Thus in both inpatient and outpatient settings (Pfeffer *et al.*, 1985; Robbins & Alessi, 1985), Major Depressive Disorder is common in adolescents and preadolescents with suicidal ideation or suicide attempts. For example, among child and adolescent psychiatric patients, Carlson and Cantwell (1982) found severe suicidal ideation correlated with increasingly severe depression, with Major Depressive Disorder diagnosed in 83% of the child and adolescent inpatients with the severest suicidal ideation. In studies of nonclinical adult populations, the prevalence of suicidal ideation also increases with the severity of depression scores (Vandivort & Locke, 1979).

However, although depressive symptoms and/or a diagnosis of depressive disorder are common in suicidal children and adults, depression is not a necessary concomitant of either suicidal ideation or attempts, especially in community samples. For example in the community study cited, 41% of the adult subjects who reported suicidal ideation did not report depression (Vandivort & Locke, 1979). Similarly, in a nonclinical college sample, about half of the students who admitted having made a suicide attempt did not meet diagnostic criteria for major depression at any time in their lives (Levy & Deykin, 1989). Among adolescents reporting suicide attempts in a community-based study using the DISC, Velez and Cohen (1988) found an increased frequency of depressive symptoms but only a 19% current prevalence of DSM-III Major Depressive Disorder. Reviewing a variety of reports, Goldney and Pilowsky (1981) concluded that only 50% to 75% of suicide attempters were depressed. Similarly, in an inpatient setting, Cohen-Sandler *et al.* (1982) found that 35% of the suicidal child and adolescent patients did not appear to be depressed.

As with completed suicide, attempted suicide and suicidal ideation are also associated with diagnoses other than affective disorders, in particular conduct disorder, drug and alcohol abuse, and Borderline Personality Disorder (Alessi *et al.*, 1984; Friedman *et al.*, 1983; Pfeffer, 1988). Especially in clinical samples where selection bias may play a role, the frequent association between conduct disorder, substance abuse, borderline personality disorder, and affective disorder make it difficult to tease out their relative contributions to suicidality; indeed, suicidality appears to increase with comorbidity (Friedman *et al.*, 1983). However, the link between these disorders and suicidality is at least partially independent of any coexisting depression. For example, among the suicidal child and adolescent patients studied by Carlson and Cantwell (1982), about 18% had suicidal ideation accompanied by *low* depression scores; most of these had "behavior disorder diagnoses," whereas only a few had a DSM-III depressive disorder . Similarly, Apter *et al.* (1988) found that those adolescent psychiatric inpatients with a diagnosis of Conduct Disorder had higher suicidality scores on the K-SADS than did patients with a diagnosis of Major Depressive Disorder, even though the former were less depressed than the latter. In their study of a nonclinical college population, Levy and Deykin (1989) concluded that "[m]ajor depression and substance abuse were independent and interactive risk factors for suicidal ideation and for suicide attempts" (p. 1462). Finally, in both inpatient psychiatric and community-based studies, panic disorder has recently been shown to be associated with a markedly increased prevalence of suicidal ideation and suicide attempts; the mechanism of this increased risk is not clear but appears to be independent of the coexistence of major depressive disorder (Weissman *et al.*, 1989).

One common but problematic diagnostic category often assigned to adolescent suicide attempters is *adjustment disorder,* which may be given as the principal or only diagnosis for as many as 37% of adolescent attempters in some samples (e.g., Khan, 1987). In practice, this label often means nothing more than that the suicide attempt has occurred in some apparent relation to an upsetting event, most often the breakup of a romantic relationship, a parental separation, or a fight with a caretaker. Adjustment reaction is a particularly common primary diagnosis given to suicidal adolescents seen in the emergency ward (King *et al.*, 1989). On the one hand, this may represent the limitations of emergency room diagnostic practices; it is possible that more extensive diagnostic evaluation might have revealed the presence of other DSM-III-R disorders. On the other hand, it is also possible that suicidal adolescents seen in emergency room may represent a more heterogeneous group than those who are ultimately hospitalized and may include more patients who, although disturbed, do not meet the full criteria for any DSM-III-R diagnosis. (Trautman *et al.* (1991) found no categorical diagnosis in 13% of carefully studied female adolescent suicide attempters seen in the pediatric emergency ward. In a community sample, Kashani *et al.* [1989] noted that 14% of the children reporting suicidal ideation did not meet the criteria for any Axis I disorder.)

Beyond these empirical questions, there are conceptual difficulties with the use of "adjustment disorder" as a diagnostic label for suicidal youth; these theoretical difficulties are considered further in the discussion of "adjustment disorder with suicidal features."

2.2. *Consequences of the Limitations of the DSM-III-R*

2.2.1. *Failure to Identify an Important Clinical Focus of Attention*

Implicit in the DSM-III-R's neglect of suicidality is the notion that suicidality is "epiphenomenal." This reductionistic view is best epitomized by Miles's (1977) contention that suicide is simply "a sequella or complication of various other conditions, and that the majority of suicides are secondary to such conditions. The obvious corollary is that the basic and specific treatment is of the underlying condition rather than of the suicidal inclination per se" (p. 231).

However, by failing to identify suicidality as an important focus of clinical attention in its own right, this reductionistic approach poses several clinical and practical problems. First, there is no way to deal diagnostically with suicidal patients who do not meet the criteria for any of the categorical diagnoses. Second, the current nosology ignores clinically important features of suicidal patients that may not only distinguish them from nonsuicidal patients but may also be major determinants of their clinical course.

The first limitation of the DSM-III-R approach to suicidality is apparent with respect to suicidal individuals who, although they manifest psychiatric symptoms, do not meet the criteria for any of the existing DSM-III-R diagnostic categories. This leads to the unsatisfactory situation of patients in clear need of clinical intervention (i.e., at the very least, careful assessment), but who nonetheless lack a diagnosable condition. The overuse of "Adjustment Disorder" as a diagnostic catch-all for many such suicidal adolescents, even when they fail to meet the criteria for that condition, is a symptom of this shortcoming.

Completely subsuming instances of suicidality under existing DSM-III-R diagnoses entails other conceptual and practical difficulties as well. Although some DSM-III-R diagnoses are clearly risk factors for suicidality, the presence of a categorical diagnosis is a very nonspecific marker for suicidality. Thus using pre-DSM-III categories, Miles (1977) estimated that roughly 15% of patients with depression ultimately die of suicide; 10% of those with schizophrenia; 5% of those with psychopathic personality; and 10% of those with opiate addiction. Conversely, then, 85% to 95% of patients with these serious disorders do *not* kill themselves. Similarly, even among samples of depressed child and adult psychiatric inpatients, only about a third have a history of suicide attempts; as many as two-thirds of depressed child and adolescent psychiatric patients may report suicidal ideation (Mitchell *et al.*, 1988; van Praag & Plutchik, 1988).

The limitations of categorical diagnosis are further highlighted by the study of Trautman *et al.* (1991), who found no significant diagnostic differences between a group of adolescent female suicide attempters and a contrast group of nonattempting psychiatric outpatients.

Thus even when a DSM-III-R diagnosis is applicable to a suicidal patient, that diagnosis may fail to capture or convey sufficiently the suicidal aspects of the patient's condition. Rather than being a mere "epiphenomenon" of another diagnosis, the patient's suicidality (and the factors related to it) may in many cases be the major determinants of clinical care or prognosis. As we shall review below, there is evidence that suicidality may have distinctive antecedents, concomitants, and consequences that are at least partially independent of categorical diagnosis. These antecedents and concomitants seem to include impulsivity, aggressivity, alterations in self-concept, deficits in social problem-solving skills, various experiential factors, and altered neurotransmitter regulation. Beyond their possible etiological importance as potential mediating variables in the causal chain leading to suicidality, these factors may also have important clinical implications that are not fully reflected in the current categorical diagnoses assigned to suicidal patients.

2.2.2. *Obstacles to Record Keeping and Research*

A related problem concerns clinical research and record keeping about suicidal patients and their care. Currently, such activities are hampered because suicidal patients cannot readily be identified from records of admitting or discharge diagnoses. Instead, in any compilation of diagnoses seen in a given setting, suicidal patients are scattered across and "submerged" under a variety of other diagnostic categories, even though their suicidality may have been the most compelling focus of clinical attention. DSM-III-R lacks a rubric under which cases involving suicidality can be collected and studied and fails to provide a set of generally sanctioned criteria for defining such cases.

2.3. *Summary*

To summarize, suicidal status appears only partially linked to current diagnostic categories. Although most young suicidal individuals have psychopathologic symptoms, they may meet the criteria for a wide variety of DSM-III-R diagnoses or none at all. Conversely, categorical diagnosis is a very nonspecific discriminator and descriptor of suicidal patients. For every individual with depression, conduct disorder, or substance abuse who is suicidal, there exist many with the same diagnosis who are not suicidal.

In the section that follows we shall explore the hypothesis that the crucial aspects of suicidality may lie less in the area of categorical diagnosis than in several realms that cut across current diagnostic categories. Described from a psychological perspective, these appear to include deficits in the regulation of impulsivity and aggression, crucial areas of self-concept and perceived self-competency, quality of attachment and family experience, social adaptive skills, and sensitivity to certain cultural and experiential factors (including exposure to suicidal behavior). In turn, these psychological dimensions may reflect underlying biological, genetic, or familial factors that are also partially independent of current diagnostic categories.

3. *Suicidality as a Diagnostic Category*

In this section we shall review the arguments for regarding suicidality as a diagnostic category. To qualify as a valid diagnostic category, a condition should meet several criteria (Rutter & Gould, 1985). It should (1) constitute a *significant source of morbidity,* producing dysfunction or distress; (2) be the product of *mental disorder;* (3) be *reliably ascertainable;* and (4) have *content validity* in terms of possessing distinctive antecedents, concomitants, and consequences that distinguish it from other conditions. We will examine suicidality from each of these perspectives in turn.

3.1. *Is Suicidality a Significant Source of Morbidity or Mortality?*

The significant loss of young life due to suicide is well known and has been extensively reviewed (Centers for Disease Control, 1986; Shaffer *et al.*, 1988). Although the actual medical lethality of suicide attempts varies, such attempts seem prima facie to entail significant psychological distress. Fleeting suicidal thoughts of low intensity appear to be common but little-studied phenomena; it is possible that in many cases such thoughts may not be associated with significant distress or psychopathology. However, even in nonclinical samples, persistent and/or strong suicidal ideation in children and adolescents are significantly associated with increased psychopathology (Pfeffer *et al.*, 1984, 1988; Velez & Cohen, 1988).

3.2. *Is Suicidality in Children and Adolescents a Product of "Mental Disorder"?*

A vast literature from antiquity to the present debates the question of under what circumstances suicide might be regarded as a rational, philosophically justifiable, or socially sanctioned act rather than the product of mental disorder (Alvarez, 1974). A full consideration of this question is beyond the scope of this review. Certainly, in some societies and epochs "altruistic" suicide (as Durkheim defined it) may be a culturally sanctioned or encouraged response to specific circumstances. It may also be argued that for some older individuals in our society who are faced with a painful fatal or irreversibly debilitating illness, suicidal thoughts or action may represent a rational, rather than psychopathological response to an intolerable situation. (Even in such cases, however, the clinician still has the responsibility to assess the suicidal individual to rule out treatable depression.)

DSM-III-R is of only limited help with how to make this distinction. Indeed, the authors of DSM-III-R acknowledge the difficulties of delineating precise boundaries for the concept of "Mental Disorder," which they define as

> a clinically significant behavioral or psychological syndrome or pattern . . . associated with present distress . . . or disability . . . or with a significantly increased risk of suffering death, pain, disability, or an important loss of freedom. . . . [T]his syndrome or pattern must not be merely an expectable response to a particular event. . . . Whatever its original cause, it must currently be considered a manifestation of a behavioral, psychological, or biological dysfunction in the person. Neither deviant behavior, e.g. political, religious, or sexual, nor conflicts that are primarily between the individual and society are mental disorders unless the deviance or conflict is a symptom of a dysfunction the person as described above. (p. xxii)

As a practical matter, however, these ambiguities rarely arise in our society with suicidal children and adolescents. In this age group, suicidal ideation and behavior is highly correlated with various forms of psychopathology, even when these may not meet the criteria for a specific DSM-III-R disorder (Pfeffer *et al.*, 1984, 1988; Shaffer *et al.*, 1988). For contemporary Western youth, there are few, if any, circumstances mandating "altruistic" suicide. In contrast to older suicides, completed youthful suicides are rarely precipitated by severe physical illness (Hoberman & Garfinkel, 1988; Rich *et al.*, 1986; Shaffer, 1974).

3.3. Is Suicidality Reliably Ascertainable?

As with depression, several approaches to the assessment of suicidality exist. The clinical interview, often considered the gold standard or criterion against which other measures are judged, seeks to ascertain by unstructured or informal means the presence and severity of suicidal ideation and the occurrence, frequency, purposiveness, and severity of self-injurious behaviors that may express suicidal intent; in addition, the clinical interview attempts to evaluate the complex psychosocial and psychopathological context in which suicidal phenomena occur. In recent years, clinical interviews have been complemented by other approaches. Diagnostic interviews such as the Schedule for Affective Disorders and Schizophrenia for school-age children; Present Episode Version (K-SADS-P) (Chambers *et al.*, 1985) have applied structured methods to characterize more accurately psychiatric phenomenology and behavior. Other instruments such as the Suicide Intent Scales of Beck and associates (1979) and the Child Suicidal Potential Scales (Pfeffer *et al.*, 1984) have been used to characterize in greater detail and with greater precision various aspects of suicidality.

We know of no rigorous studies that attempt to determine the accuracy (reliability and precision) of the clinical interview in assessing suicidal phenomena. Nonetheless, most clinicians would argue that comprehensive clinical interviewing, particularly of multiple informants, provides an accurate evaluation of suicidality.

The psychometric properties of structured diagnostic interviews and other formal assessment instruments have been studied extensively. The results of such studies generally support the clinical intuition that suicidal phenomena can be accurately characterized. (See Lewinsohn *et al.* [n.d.] for a review of instruments suitable for research purposes.)

In most structured diagnostic interview formats, items assessing suicidality have been confined to the depression sections. Therefore, the information concerning the accuracy of such items is limited to that subgroup of subjects who enter the depression section. Moreover, most reliability studies have examined the reliability with which interviewers make categorical diagnostic judgments, whereas item-by-item reliability studies or those assessing the reliability with which suicidal phenomena are characterized are rarer. Although these limitations are unfortunate, they probably reflect the experience of investigators that suicidal phenomena are fairly readily well-characterized. Those studies that address the issue support this conclusion (Andreasen *et al.*, 1981; Chambers *et al.*, 1985; Mazure *et al.*, 1986). For example, Chambers *et al.* (1985) report excellent test–retest coefficients for the Suicidal Ideation and Behavior Scale of the K-SADS-P (r = .81) and for the semicontinuous variables comprising the scale (ideation, r = .69; number of attempts, r = .78; seriousness, r = .39, and medical threat, r = .62). The internal validity of the scale is also substantial (Cronbach alpha = .74).

The degree to which child and parent informants agree in reporting suicidal phenomena varies across studies. For example, Angloid *et al.* (1987) found strong agreement between parents and children on K-SADS items assessing suicidality; in contrast, in a community study using the DISC, Velez and Cohen (1988) found that mothers were generally unaware of suicide attempts reported by their children. The origins of these discrepancies is an important area for further study.

Scales that specifically assess various suicidal phenomena also generally have acceptable performance characteristics (Lewinsohn *et al.*, n.d.). Intraclass correlations for items of the Beck Suicidal Intent Scale, for example, generally range from .80–1.00 (Brent *et al.*, 1988).

3.4. *Does Suicidality Have Distinctive Antecedents, Concomitants, or Consequences?*

Construct and external validity is the central issue in deciding whether suicidality is best regarded as an epiphenomenal symptom of various other conditions or a categorical disorder in its own right (Shaffer, 1982). Do children and adolescents who are suicidal differ from other children and adolescents (and resemble each other) in important ways other than their suicidality? This is a key distinction between a symptom and a disorder. The fact that suicidality would comprise a definitionally monosymptomatic disorder is not in itself a disqualification; other monosymptomatic disorders such as Motor Tic Disorder, Trichotillomania, Functional Encopresis, and Functional Enuresis occupy venerable places in the DSM-III-R. The question at stake is whether making such a diagnosis tells one anything beyond the fact that the symptom is present. If so, assigning the diagnosis also conveys potential information about predisposing or etiologic factors, associated psychological or biological features, and/or clinical course or prognosis. If not, the diagnosis is a tautological exercise in reification (i.e., simply a fancy way of asserting the presence of the symptom).

3.4.1. *Concomitant Validators*

3.4.1.1. Psychological Concomitants. Suicidal children and adolescents are characterized by a variety of personality and cognitive features that cut across diagnostic categories. Thus, various clinical studies have suggested an association between suicidality and aggressiveness, irritability, low frustration tolerance, resentfulness, and/or impulsivity (Frances & Blumenthal, 1989; Plutchik & van Praag, 1986). For example, in the Cohen-Sandler *et al.* (1982) study of child and adolescent psychiatric inpatients, aggressivity was the major symptomatic discriminator between the suicidal patients (many of whom were not depressed) and the depressed, nonsuicidal patients, with 50% of the former but only 9.5% of the latter having a history of threatening others. Dichotomizing suicidal children and adolescents by the presence or absence of assaultiveness, Pfeffer *et al.* (1983, 1989) found that assaultive suicidal children were characterized by intense aggression, accidents, and violence at home, including parental suicidal and assaultive behavior; in contrast, suicidal, but nonassaultive patients were characterized by depression, environmental stresses, and drug abuse.

Other investigators have examined the association between suicidality and cognitive features that might serve as intervening variables, for example, hopelessness (Kazdin *et al.*, 1983), failure to generate active cognitive coping strategies (Asarnow *et al.*, 1987), lack of perceived competence in critical realms (Harter & Marold, 1989), external locus of control, and a defective sense of self-continuity. Thus in some (but not all) samples, hopelessness is strongly related to suicidality, even when depression is statistically controlled (Kazdin *et al.*, 1983; Rotheram-Borus & Trautman, 1988). Subdividing a clinical sample of child and adolescent suicide attempters by their degree of hopelessness, Brent (1987) discerned two groups: (1) "a group of non-hopeless adjustment and conduct disorders who make unplanned attempts of variable intent" and (2) "a group of hopeless, affectively disturbed patients who made planned attempts of high suicidal intent" (p. 90).

3.4.1.2. Biological Correlates. A possible link between abnormalities in serotonergic regulation and suicidality has been suggested by a variety of postmortem and *in vivo* csf and receptor studies, as well as fenfluramine challenge tests (Coccaro *et al.*, 1989). The most consistent finding has been that of lowered concentrations of the serotonin metabolite 5-HIAA in the csf of suicide attempters and completers (see reviews by Asberg, 1989). However, there are contradictory findings as to whether this relationship is limited to active, violent suicide attempts or confined to certain diagnostic categories of patients. However, studies of criminals and patients with personality disorder suggest low csf 5-HIAA is also correlated with impulsivity and aggression (Brown *et al.*, 1982; Coccaro *et al.*, 1989; Linnoila *et al.*, 1983; Virkkunen *et al.*, 1989). Because these personality traits are in turn associated with suicidality, it is unclear to what extent abnormal serotonin regulation is related to suicidality *per se* or to a broader cluster of personality traits, such as aggressivity and/or impulsivity, which in turn may predispose some individuals to suicidality.

In addition to being potentially significant concomitants of suicidal behavior, altered patterns of CSF monoamine neurotransmitter metabolites may also be potential predictors of suicidal behavior as well. For example, the Karolinska Hospital group found that suicide attempters with very low levels of CSF 5-HIAA at the time of their index admission were far more likely to die of suicide within the subsequent year than were those attempters with relatively higher levels (Asberg, 1989). Among depressed patients, Roy *et al.* (1986, 1989) found a relationship between low CSF homovanillic acid (HVA) and subsequent completed and attempted suicide.

Additional evidence for a relationship between serotonergic regulation and suicidality is provided by the observation that fluoxetine, a serotonin reuptake blocker widely used as an antidepressant, can induce intense, persistent, and violent suicidal ideation *de novo* in certain depressed patients; in some of these patients the appearance of suicidality appeared unrelated to other changes in depressive symptomatology (King *et al.*, 1991; Teicher *et al.*, 1990).

In summary, neurobiological studies of suicidal individuals support the notion that suicidality may be the outcome of multiple factors that are at least partially independent of or interactive with depression and other major psychiatric disorders. These studies are consistent with the data from personality and genetic studies in suggesting that the confluence of impulsivity and aggression may be an important determinant of suicidality.

3.4.2. Antecedent or Postdictive Validity

Research suggests several types of antecedents may predispose individuals to suicidal behavior or ideation. These include family factors, genetic factors, and exposure to a friend or acquaintance who has made a suicide attempt.

3.4.2.1. Family Factors. Compared to clinical controls, suicidal youngsters have been reported to have more disturbed families on a variety of measures including lack of family warmth; child abuse or neglect; parental absence; parental conflict; and parental psychopathology (as indicated by parental depression, parental psychiatric hospitalization, and parental suicidal ideation and behavior) (Pfeffer, 1989). Although fraught with all the methodological problems of life events research, several studies have also concluded that compared to a depressed comparison group, young suicidal patients have higher levels of recent and cumulative stressful life events, especially those that involve potential object loss or loss of social supports (Cohen-Sandler *et al.*, 1982; Pfeffer, 1989).

At present, the mechanisms underlying these familial associations are unclear. For example, these familial associations may represent the deleterious impact of nongenetic processes such as modeling or the experiential induction of such personality traits as aggression, impulsivity, self-reproach, or anxiously ambivalent attachment. Alternatively, as we shall discuss below, such familial associations might reflect the effects of intergenerationally shared genetic factors.

3.4.2.2. Exposure to Suicidal Individuals. A variety of studies have concluded that exposure to a friend or relative who has made a suicide attempt is significantly more common among young suicide attempters and completers than among nonsuicidal controls (Shafii *et al.*, 1985). The effects of such exposure may also be responsible for the clusters of attempted and completed suicides that have been reported in response to a suicide in the community (Brent *et al.*, 1989) or to fictional and nonfictional accounts of suicide in the mass media (Davidson & Gould, 1989). Indeed, as many as 2% to 3% of completed adolescent suicides may occur as part of such clusters, which appear to represent a true excess in the overall rate of suicides rather than an acceleration of suicidal behavior in individuals likely to have otherwise made an attempt at a later date (Gould *et al.*, 1990). Although many adolescents who make a suicide attempt in response to the suicidal behavior of a peer may have a history of prior depression and/or suicidality, some friends of a suicide completer may become suicidal even in the absence of these risk factors (Brent *et al.*, 1989).

3.4.2.3. Genetic Factors. Several clinical studies suggest that at all stages of the life cycle suicidal behavior is associated with a family history of attempted or completed suicide (see review by Roy, 1989). As noted earlier, this family clustering may reflect nongenetic processes as well as shared genetic risk factors. Nonetheless, several lines of evidence suggest the possibility that the vulnerability to suicide may be genetically transmitted and that such transmission is at least partially independent of the vulnerability to depression or other major psychiatric disorders. These studies are thus especially relevant to the question of whether suicidality has distinctive antecedents.

In reviewing the studies that follow we will be concerned with two questions. First, is there evidence that there are heritable predisposing factors for suicidality? Second, are these factors distinctive for suicide, or do they merely reflect a genetic predisposition to other major psychiatric disorders commonly associated with suicidal behavior, that is, affective disorder, schizophrenia, alcoholism, antisocial behavior, and/or drug abuse? Attempts to demonstrate a distinctive genetic factor in suicide are often confounded by the likelihood that the vulnerability to these disorders may also be genetically transmitted. Among the major weakness of some of the studies to be reviewed are their relatively crude or (unspecified) criteria for excluding the presence of these psychiatric diagnoses in suicidal probands or their relatives.

Pedigree studies. The relationship between suicide and family loading for affective disorders among the Amish was studied by Egeland and Sussex (1985), who found 26 suicides in their study population over the past century. A strong relationship between suicide and affective disorder was evident in the finding that 24 of the suicides met RDC criteria for a major affective disorder; most of these had a heavy family loading for affective disorder. (In contrast, the 1 suicide diagnosed as having a minor depression came from a family without any history of psychiatric disorder.) Although the Amish study identified many pedigrees with heavy loading for major affective disorder, suicides were not evenly distributed across these pedigrees. Rather, four pedigrees accounted for

73% of the suicides, with the remaining suicides more distantly related to these same family lines. Thus among the Amish community studied, complete suicide occurred almost exclusively in conjunction with major affective disorder; however, the data suggest that suicide may be influenced by additional familial factors that operate over and above the presence of vertically transmitted affective disorder. The epidemiology of suicide among the Amish may differ from that of other populations. Specific cultural features of the Amish community may account for the rarity of suicide in this group and its virtual limitation to older individuals with major affective diagnoses. The high stability of community and family structure, strong religious sanctions against suicide, and the absence of alcoholism and drug abuse may serve to minimize the incidence of youthful suicides that reflect those risk factors that are relatively independent of major affective disorder.

Twin studies. Twin studies suggest genetic transmission of a vulnerability to suicide but also reveal the difficulty of identifying *what* is inherited. For example, pooling twin studies from different countries, Haberlant (1967, cited in Roy, 1989) identified 149 twin pairs of which one twin was known to have committed suicide. All of the 10 pairs in which both twins suicided were monozygotic; no dyzygotic pairs were concordant for suicide. In half of the pairs concordant for suicide, the vulnerability to suicide may have reflected a shared vulnerability to a major psychiatric disorder. Thus 4 of the 10 pairs of twins were also concordant for affective disorder, whereas another pair was concordant for schizophrenia. It is not clear how strong the evidence was that the other 5 twin pairs concordant for suicide either lacked or were discordant for major psychiatric disorders.

Adoption studies. An adoption study carried out in Denmark by Shulsinger *et al.* (1979) reviewed the records of the 5,483 adoptees in the Copenhagen adoption register and identified 57 completed suicides and a comparison group of 57 nonsuicided adoptees, matched for age, sex, social class, time of adoption, and census tract. No suicides were found among the adoptive relatives of either group. However, the suicided adoptees had significantly more biological relatives who had committed suicide than did the control group of adoptees (12 vs. 2). Moreover, although half of these suicided biological relatives had a history of psychiatric hospitalization or police record of alcoholism, the other half did not. The authors concede that absence of hospitalization does not exclude the presence of a major psychiatric disorder. Nonetheless, they concluded that the study demonstrated that "genetic factors play a role in the transmission of suicidal behavior and that this role to some extent might be independent of the common mental disorders most frequently associated with suicide" (p. 286).

Finally, Wender *et al.* (1986) studied the frequency of psychiatric disorders in the biological and adoptive families of adopted individuals with affective disorders compared to those of a matched control group of adoptees without a record of a psychiatric illness or suicide. Both attempted and completed suicides were significantly more common in the biological relatives of the affectively disordered adoptees than in the biological relatives of the control adoptees. One interesting finding emerged from the examination of different diagnostic subgroups of probands. One group carried the diagnosis of *affect reaction,* a term used for histrionic behavior or impulsive, reactive suicide attempts. In comparison with the biological relatives of adoptees with chronic and severe depressive illness, the biological relatives of adoptees with "affect reaction" had a significantly higher suicide rate. As this diagnosis seems more indicative of impulsivity than depression, this finding underlines the important, perhaps genetically influenced role of impulse control in suicide.

In summary, then, twin, adoption, and high-risk family studies support the notion that (1) there are heritable factors predisposing individuals to suicidal behavior and (2) these factors may be to some extent independent of the major psychiatric disorders frequently associated with suicide. In addition, at least one study tentatively suggests that impulsivity and emotional lability may be potentially heritable risk factors for suicidality equal in importance to the predisposition to depression.

3.4.3. *Predictive Validity*

Studies of both completed suicides and individuals with either suicidal attempts or ideation suggest that suicidality is often a persistent form of maladaptation. As many as 45% to 55% of youngsters who commit suicide are known to have made a previous suicide attempt or threat (Fabernow, 1989; Shaffi *et al.*, 1985; Shaffer, 1974). Over the short term, 10% to 50% of adolescent suicide attempters repeat a suicide attempt (Goldacre & Hawton, 1985; Stanley & Barter, 1970). For example, in a follow-up of suicidal children and adolescents, Stanley and Barter (1970) found that approximately half of the suicidal children went on to repeat their suicidal behavior during the follow up period, whereas none of a control group of children seen for nonsuicidal psychiatric emergencies showed suicidal behavior during that time. Various long-term (5–10 years) follow-up studies of suicide attempters report completed suicide rates ranging from less than 1% for emergency room patients up to 9% for psychiatric inpatient attempters (Pfeffer, 1988; Shaffer *et al.*, 1988). Pfeffer *et al.* (1988) studied the persistence of suicidal ideation in a nonclinical school-age population; they found 50% of the children who had reported suicidal ideation 2 years earlier continued to do so at time of follow-up. Persistent suicidality was associated with depressive symptoms, preoccupations with death, and general psychopathology, but not with any specific DSM-III diagnosis.

3.5. Discussion

The data reviewed support the notion that suicidality meets the requirements of valid diagnostic category. Suicidality in children and adolescents is a *significant source of morbidity and/or mortality* and is in most cases *the product of mental disorder,* albeit not always of a type meeting the criteria for a specific DSM-III-R diagnosis. In addition, given access to the same data, there appears to be *satisfactory agreement* as to whether a child or adolescent has suicidal ideation or behavior.

The data also suggest that the construct of suicidality has *antecedent, concurrent, and predictive validities.* Currently, we cannot specify precisely the experiential, psychological, or neurobiological factors that (either alone or in conjunction with a major psychiatric disorder) are necessary and sufficient to produce suicidal ideation or behavior. The growing body of research reviewed suggest that many suicidal children and adolescents have similar familial and experiential risk factors, share common psychological personality traits and deficits, and remain vulnerable over time to continued or recurrent suicidality. In addition, research with suicidal adults raises the possibility that suicidality is associated with specific neurobiological abnormalities, which may also be predictive of future suicidal behavior.

Although these various factors may also be associated with an increased risk for certain DSM-III-R disorders, their relationship to suicidality is at least partially independent of the presence of any specific DSM-III-R disorder. At any rate, this is an empirical question to be studied and whose conclusion should not be prejudged by nosologically reducing all instances of suicidality to other, presumably more "primary" disorders.

The crucial issue for the time being is whether a particular provisional grouping will facilitate the work of treating and studying various patients and clinical phenomena. The inclusion of a formal category of suicidality in the DSM-IV would serve to highlight the existence of an important clinical condition with important preventive, therapeutic, and prognostic implications beyond those implicit in any other coexisting diagnoses.

Finally, including suicidality as a diagnostic category in its own right would have *clinical utility* and *facilitate communication* by providing a nosological locus for consolidating instances of suicidality and agreed-upon criteria for doing so.

3.6. *Proposed Criteria for Suicidal Disorder in DSM-IV*

In this spirit, we propose the following provisional criteria for a Suicidal Disorder of Childhood and Adolescence to serve as a starting point for further discussion and refinement of criteria.

Our proposal is limited to childhood and adolescence because this is the age group on which our literature review has focused. However, a strong case exists for *not* confining the disorder by age. A review of the adult suicide literature would most likely support many of the same conclusions and recommendations for classifying suicidal adults. Nonetheless, the degree to which the phenomenology, antecedents, concommitants, and consequences of suicidality show continuity versus discontinuity across developmental epochs deserves further study. (One possible discontinuity may concern the role of debilitating physical illness. Among older individuals there might well exist occasional instances of "rational" suicidality [i.e., in the face of a painful fatal illness] that are not appropriately attributable to mental disorder; if so, it would be necessary to frame suitable criteria to exclude these exceptional cases.)

Proposed Suicidal Disorder of Childhood and Adolescence

Subtypes: (1) Suicidal ideation
(2) Suicidal behavior

Suicidal Disorder, Ideational Type (without Suicidal Behavior)

A. Serious concern with, rumination about, or planning toward deliberate actions that the individual believes would probably or certainly result in death, as indicated by at least one of the following:

1. Recurrent thoughts or images of killing oneself
2. Rumination about or planning for methods for killing oneself
3. Leaving notes or other messages about the possibility that the child or adolescent has considered or might kill himself or herself
4. Threats that the child makes to others that he/she will kill himself or herself under particular circumstances or in general
5. Making preparations for actually killing oneself, such as obtaining a weapon, poison, rope, or the like.

Suicidal Disorder with Suicidal Behavior

A. Deliberate action that the individual believes would probably result in his or her death, as indicated by the following:

1. The child or adolescent has engaged in an action which he or she believed could be seriously harmful to his or her physical health.
2. The primary intention of the action was to cause serious physical harm or death.

Where criteria are also met for other specific Axis I or II disorders, such as Major Depressive Disorder, Substance Abuse, or Borderline Personality Disorder, these codiagnoses should also be listed on the appropriate axis.

These proposed criteria exclude persistent or troubling thoughts about dying or about how others will feel after one is dead; behavior that carries risks (such as smoking, unprotected sex, driving fast, daredevil play, autoerotic strangulation) but for which the primary intent is not self-destruction but other motivations (such as group participation, the thrill of the experience, exuberance, etc.); self-injurious behavior that is *exclusively* related to intoxication, other organic states, or ignorance, without the primary intention to cause oneself harm (e.g., walking into traffic when drunk, taking an overdose of a prescribed medication because of lack of knowledge about proper dosage, etc.).

The descriptive text for the proposed disorder should also include the caveat that the clinical considerations involved in making the diagnosis of suicidal disorder may not be the same as those involved in legal or official judgments, such as involuntary commitments or coroner's findings. Furthermore, although the diagnosis is an indication for careful clinical evaluation, its presence does not necessarily imply the need for hospitalization or any other specific therapeutic intervention.

4. *Alternative Nosological Options for Suicidality in DSM-IV*

In light of the limitations of DSM-III-R's treatment of suicidality, it is essential that DSM-IV include some means for noting and coding the presence of suicidality. Although we have argued that there are cogent reasons to recognize suicidality as a distinct disorder, the resolution of this complex question will require much careful study and debate. In the absence of suicidality as a disorder in its own right, several other options have been proposed for DSM-IV or employed in the ICD framework. These include supplementary codes of various types or the creation of a new subcategory, "adjustment disorder with suicidal features."

4.1. *Suicidality in ICD*

The ICD-9-CM treats suicidality in a fragmentary way, albeit in a different manner than DSM-III-R. No explicit mention of suicidality is made in the chapter on mental disorders; however, the index lists "suicidal risk" and "suicidal tendencies" under "Unspecified neurotic disorders (300.9)." Actual suicide attempts are assigned an E Code (External Causes of Injury and Poisoning) from a list of various modes of self-injury or poisoning, entitled "Suicide and self-inflicted injury (E950-E959)—Includes: injuries in suicide and attempted suicide; self-inflicted injuries specified as intentional."

In the provisional ICD-10 (September, 1988, draft), suicide is mentioned in the chapter on mental, behavioral, and developmental disorders under the rubric "Emotionally unstable personality disorder, borderline type (F60.31)" which is said to entail a liability for unstable relationships that "may be associated with a series of suicidal threats or acts of self-harm (although these may also occur without obvious precipitants)" (p. 145). Under Depressive episode (F31), the text notes "Acts of self-harm, most commonly self-poisoning by prescribed medication, that are associated with mood (affective) disorders, should be recorded by means of an additional code from Chapter XX External Causes of Morbidity and Mortality, Section X. These codes do not involve judgments about differentiation between attempted suicide and 'parasuicide,' both being included in the general category of self-harm" (p. 81).

4.2. *Supplementary Codes*

One proposed means of noting the presence of suicidality in the DSM-IV is to assign it a supplementary code, conceptually distinct from the Axis I or II categorical disorders. This proposal appears to have several difficulties, some related to the specific system of supplementary codes developed for DSM-III and ICD and some related the use of supplementary codes in general.

Although the E codes used in ICD-9-CM for noting the presence and specific form of intentional self-injury provide useful information, the format does not capture suicidal ideation or gestures that do not involve actual physical injury or poisoning.

The V codes, as conceptualized in DSM-III-R and ICD-9-CM, pose a more fundamental problem. V codes are used for "conditions not attributable to a mental disorder that are a focus of attention or treatment" (DSM-III-R) or "factors influencing health status and contact with health services" involving a patient who is not currently sick or a condition which "is not in itself a current illness or injury" (ICD-9-CM). As we have argued, suicidal behavior and ideation in children and adolescents is virtually always associated with psychopathology, even when the pattern of associated symptoms or dysfunction does not meet the criteria for one of the existing specific DSM-III-R diagnostic categories. Hence, the use of a V code for suicidal children or adolescents appears conceptually inappropriate, even when suicidality occurs in the absence of a currently diagnosable categorical diagnosis.

Some of these problems may be sidestepped in a new system of supplementary codes proposed for DSM-IV. These Z codes would be used to record specified "clinically significant conditions" (e.g., Drug-Induced Movement Disorders), but, unlike the current V codes, they would not carry the disclaimer that the condition was "not attributable to a mental disorder." Hence, the Z codes could either be used alone or in combination with an Axis I disorder. Although the conceptual relationship of the Z codes to the categorical disorders of Axis I remains to be clarified, the inclusion of Z codes for suicidal ideation and suicidal attempts might provide a useful mechanism recording and coding the presence of suicidality. However, even the Z code system is likely to encounter a practical problem common to supplementary codes in general: Data regarding conditions or circumstances not included on Axis I or II are often omitted and hence lost. Although in an ideal world the entire multiaxial system and attendant supplementary codes would be used and recorded, in actual clinical practice and record keeping, this is frequently not the case.

4.3. *Adjustment Disorder with Suicidal Behavior*

Yet another option proposed for DSM-IV is to include a new type of adjustment disorder, namely Adjustment Disorder with Suicidal Behavior (or ideation).

This appears to us to be an unsatisfactory solution for several reasons. First, the DSM-IV would still lack a common rubric and set of criteria under which instances of suicidal behavior or ideation could be consolidated. Second, the proposal highlights the problems and limitations inherent in the category of Adjustment Disorder as currently defined and applied to suicidal children.

Adjustment Disorder in DSM-III-R has several key features: (1) it entails a reaction to an identifiable psychosocial stressor (or stressors) occurring within 3 months of the onset of the stressor(s); (2) the disturbance does not meet the criteria for any specific disorder; (3) the disturbance is "not merely one instance of a pattern of overreaction to stress"; and (4) the maladaptive reaction has persisted for no longer than 6 months. Seen from the perspective of the stressor, the disorder emphasizes the adaptive demands of a significant challenge that cannot be adequately met. In actual practice, the diagnosis of adjustment reaction is often used to convey or emphasize either the "subthreshold" nature of the psychopathology and/or the reactive nature of the problem.

In many cases of attempted and completed adolescent suicide, it is possible to identify a "precipitant" in the sense of a proximate event that apparently triggers the suicidal behavior (Hoberman & Garfinkel, 1988; Shaffer, 1974). Often, however, these events are commonplace and seemingly unremarkable. For many suicidal youngsters, it is misleading and clinically counterproductive to emphasize the external "precipitant" rather than intrinsic factors, such as their underlying and often persistent propensity to respond maladaptively. Indeed, for many suicidal children or adolescents, the suicidal upset *is* "one instance of a pattern of overreaction to stress."

Furthermore, as noted above, suicidality is frequently recurrent or chronic, even in suicidal children who fail to meet criteria for a DSM-III-R disorder (Pfeffer *et al.*, 1988). Although these recurrent exacerbations of suicidality may appear temporally related to identifiable stressful vicissitudes, the notion of a *recurrent* adjustment disorder with suicidal features seems incompatible with both the core concept of adjustment disorder and its explicit 6-month duration limit.

5. *Summary*

DSM-III-R's neglect of suicidal phenomena poses important practical and theoretical problems. As a practical matter, DSM-III-R's lack of any provisions for noting or tabulating instances of suicidality severely hampers clinical record keeping, data collection, and research in this area. More serious, its implicit view of suicidality as merely a symptom of other disorders leaves no means to take note of disturbed suicidal individuals who fail to meet the criteria for a DSM-III-R diagnosis. Thus in the current nosology, an emotionally disturbed youngster can require emergency psychiatric intervention and inflict serious self-injury or even death, yet still not warrant a psychiatric diagnosis! However, should an adolescent regularly wet the bed or pull his or her hair out, these difficulties will be duly noted in the record as officially recognized Axis I psychiatric disorders. Thus, paradoxically, in DSM-III-R many young people with potentially the most dangerous or life-threatening emotional difficulties are "absent, though present."

Finally, DSM-III-R's reductionistic view of suicidality as simply an epiphenomenon of other, presumably etiologically primary, disorders is open to question. What from one perspective seems epiphenomenal may, from another perspective, be an important area to study. It can be argued that a hundred years hence, with a deeper understanding of pathogenic processes, "suicidality" will appear to future nosologists much as "fever" does to us now. However, the same may be said of many, if not almost all of the current DSM-III-R categories. At any rate, it is important not to prejudge the important empirical question of whether suicidal individuals have significant commonalities that cut across current diagnostic categories. The data reviewed suggest that suicidal individuals may indeed share distinctive antecedent, concomitant, and predictive features. If so, it may be both valid and useful to consider suicidality as a diagnostic category in its own right, a category with potentially important preventive, therapeutic, and prognostic implications beyond those implicit in any comorbid diagnoses. Whether the inclusion of such a diagnostic category in DSM-IV would facilitate the study and treatment of suicidal patients and suicidal phenomena deserves careful study and discussion. However this important question is resolved, it is essential that DSM-IV include a mechanism for noting and coding the presence of suicidal ideation and behavior.

ACKNOWLEDGMENT

The assistance of Dr. David Shaffer is gratefully acknowledged.

6. *References*

Akiskal, H. S., Chen, S. E., Davis, G. C., *et al.* (1985). Borderline: An adjective in search of a noun. *J. Clin. Psych., 45,* 42–48.

Alessi, N. E., McManus, M., Brickman, A., *et al.* (1984). Suicidal behavior among serious juvenile offenders. *Am. J. Psychiatry, 141,* 286–287.

Alvarez, A. (1974). *The savage god: A study of suicide.* Harmondsworth, U.K.: Penguin Books.

Andreasen, N. C., Grove, W. M., Shapiro, R. W., Keller, M. B., Hirschfeld, R. M., & McDonald-Scott, P. (1981). Reliability of life-time diagnosis: A multicenter collaborative project. *Arch. Gen. Psychiatry, 38,* 400–405.

Angold, A., Weissman, M. M., John, K., Merikangas, K. R., *et al.* (1987). Parent and child reports of depressive symptoms in children at high and low risks of depression. *J. Child Psychol. Psychiat., 28,* 901–915.

Asarnow, J., Carlson, G., & Guthrie, D. (1987). Coping strategies, self-perceptions, hopelessness, and perceived family environments in depressed and suicidal children. *J. Consult Clin. Psychol., 55,* 361-365.

Apter, A., Bleich, A., Plutchik, R., Mendelsohn, S., & Tyano, S. (1988). Suicidal behavior, depression, and conduct disorder in hospitalized adolescents. *J. Am. Acad. Child Adolesc. Psychiatry, 27,* 696–699.

Asberg, M. (1989). Neurotransmitter monoamine metabolites in the cerebrospinal fluid as risk factors for suicidal behavior. In *Report of the Secretary's Task Force on Youth Suicide, Volume 2: Risk Factors on Youth Suicide,* Alcohol, Drug Abuse and Mental Health Administration, DHHS Pub. No. (ADM) 89-1622. Washington, DC: U.S. Government Printing Office, pp. 193–212.

Beck, A. T., Kovacs, M., & Weissman, A. (1979). Assessment of suicidal intention: The scale for suicide ideation. *J. Cons. Clin. Psychol., 47,* 343–352.

Brent, D. A. (1987). Correlates of the medical lethality of suicide attempts in children and adolescents. *J. Am. Acad. Child Adolesc. Psychiatry, 26,* 87–91.

Brent, D. A. (1989). The psychological autopsy: Methodological considerations for the study of adolescent suicide. *Suicide & Life-Threatening Behavior, 19,* 43–57.

Brent, D. A., Perper, J. A., Kolko, D. J., & Zelenak, J. P. (1988). The psychological autopsy: Methodological considerations for the study of adolescent suicide. *J. Am. Acad. Child Adolesc. Psychiatry, 27,* 362–366.

Brent, D. A., Kerr, M. M., Goldstein, C., Bozigar, J., Wartella, M., & Allen, M. J. (1989). An outbreak of suicide and suicidal behavior in a high school. *J. Am. Acad. Child Adolesc. Psychiatry, 28*(6), 918–924.

Brown, G. L., Ebert, M. E., Goyer, P. F., Jimerson, D. C., Klein, W. J., Bunney, W. E., Goodwin, F. K. (1982). Aggression, suicide, and serotonin: Relationship to CSF amine metabolites. *Am. J. Psychiatry, 139,* 741–746.

Carlson, G. A., & Cantwell, D. P. (1982). Suicidal behavior and depression in children and adolescents. *J. Am. Acad. Child Adolesc. Psychiatry, 21,* 361–368.

Centers for Disease Control. (1968). *Youth Suicide Surveillance Summary: 1970–1980.*

Chambers, W. J., Puig-Antich, J., Hirsch, M., Paez, P., Ambrosini, P. J., Tabrizi, M. A., & Davies, M. (1985). The assessment of affective disorders in children and adolescents by semistructured interviews: Test-retest reliability of the Schedule for Affective Disorders and Schizophrenia for School-Aged Children, Present Episode Version. *Arch. Gen. Psychiatry, 42,* 696–702.

Clark, D. C., & Horton, S. L. (1991). Assessment *in absentia:* The value of the psychological autopsy method for studying antecedents of suicide and predicting future suicides. In R. Maris, A. Berman, J. Maltsberger, & R. Yufit (Eds.), *Assessment and prediction of suicide.* New York: Guilford Press.

Coccaro, E. F., Siever, L. J., Klar, H. M., Mauer, G., Cochrane, K., Cooper, T. B., Mohs, R. C., & David, K. L. (1989). Serotonergic studies in patients with affective and personality disorders. *Arch. Gen. Psychiatry, 46,* 587–599.

Cohen-Sandler, R., Berman, A. L., & King, R. A. (1982). Life stress and symptomatology: Determinants of suicidal behavior in children. *J. Am. Acad. Child Psychiatry, 21,* 565–574.

Crumley, F. E. (1982). The adolescent suicide attempt: A cardinal symptom of a serious psychiatric disorder. *American Journal of Psychotherapy, 36,* 158–165.

Davidson, L., & Gould, M. (1989). Contagion as a risk factor for youth suicide. In *Report of the Secretary's Task Force on Youth Suicide. Volume 2: Risk Factors for Youth Suicide,* Alcohol, Drug Abuse, and Mental Health Administration, DHHS Pub. No. (ADM) 89-1622. Washington, DC: U.S. Government Printing Office, pp. 88–106.

Drake, R. E., Gates, C., Whitaker, A., & Cotton, P. G. (1985). Suicide among schizophrenics: A review. *Compr. Psychiatry, 26,* 90–100.

Egeland, J., & Sussex, J. (1985). Suicide and family loading for affective disorders. *JAMA, 254,* 915–918.

Farberow, N. L. (1989). Preparatory and prior suicidal behavior factors. In *Report of the Secretary's Task Force on Youth Suicide. Volume 2: Risk Factors for Youth Suicide,* Alcohol, Drug Abuse, and Mental Health Administration, DHHS Pub. No. (ADM) 89-1622. Washington, DC: U.S. Government Printing Office, pp. 34–55.

Fowler, F. C., Rich, C. L., & Young, D. (1986). San Diego suicide study: II. Substance abuse in young cases. *Arch. Gen. Psychiatry, 43,* 962–965.

Frances, A., & Blumenthal, S. J. (1989). Personality as a predictor of youthful suicide. In *Report of the Secretary's Task Force on Youth Suicide, Volume 2: Risk Factors for Youth Suicide,* Alcohol, Drug Abuse and Mental Health Administration, DHHS Pub. No. (ADM) 89-1622. Washington, DC: U.S. Government Printing Office, pp. 160–171.

Friedman, R. C., Aronoff, M. S., Clarkin, J. F. *et al.* (1983). History of suicidal behavior in depressed borderline inpatients. *Am. J. Psych., 140,* 1023–1026.

Goldacre, M., & Hawton, K. (1985). Repetition of self-poisoning and subsequent death in adolescents who take overdoses. *Br. J. Psychiatry, 146,* 395–398.

Goldney, R. D., & Pilowsky, I. (1981). Depression in young women who have attempted suicide. *Aust. N.Z. J. Psychiat., 14,* 203–211.

Gould, M. S., Wallenstein, S., & Kleinman, M. (1990). Time-space clustering of teenage suicide. *Am. J. Epidemiol., 131,* 71–78.

Harter, S., & Marold, D. (1989). *A model of risk factors leading to adolescent suicidal ideation.* Paper presented at Society for Research in Child Development, 1989.

Hoberman, H. M., & Garfinkel, B. D. (1988). Completed suicide in children and adolescents. *J. Am. Acad. Child Adolesc. Psychiatry, 27,* 689–695.

Kashani, J. H., Goddard, P., & Reid, J. C. (1989). Correlates of suicidal ideation in a community sample of children and adolescents. *J. Am. Acad. Child Adolesc. Psychiatry, 28*(6), 912–917.

Kazdin, A. E., French, N. H., Unis, A. S., *et al.* (1983). Hopelessness, depression, and suicidal intent among psychiatrically disturbed inpatient children. *J. Consult. Clin. Psychol., 51,* 504–510.

Khan, A. U. (1987). Heterogeneity of suicidal adolescents. *J. Am. Acad. Child Adolesc. Psychiatry, 26,* 92–96.

King, R., Ort, S., & Cheng, K. (1989). *Young adolescent suicide attempters in the emergency ward: Phenomenology, patterns of clinical care, and outcome.* Paper presented at Mental Health Services for Children and Adolescents in Primary Care Settings: Research Conference sponsored by NIMH, New Haven, June, 1989.

King, R. A., Riddle, M. A., Chappell, P. B., Hardin, M. T., Anderson, G. M., Lombroso, P., & Scahill, L. (1991). Emergence of self-destructive phenomena in children and adolescents during fluoxetine treatment. *J. Am. Acad. Child Adolesc. Psychiatry, 30,* 179–186.

Kovacs, M., & Puig-Antich, J. (1989). Major psychiatric disorders as risk factors in youth suicide. In *Report of the Secretary's Task Force on Youth Suicide, Volume 2: Risk Factors for Youth Suicide,* Alcohol, Drug Abuse and Mental Health Administration, DHHS Pub. No. (ADM) 89-1622. Washington, DC: U.S. Government Printing Office, pp. 143–159.

Levy, J. C., & Deykin, E. Y. (1989). Suicidality, depression, and substance abuse in adolescence. *Am. J. Psychiatry, 146,* 1462–1467.

Lewinsohn, P., Garrison, C. Z., Langhinrichsen, J., & Marsteller, F. (n.d.). *The assessment of suicidal behavior in adolescents: A review of scales suitable for epidemiologic and clinical research.* Child and Adolescent Disorders Research Branch, NIMH contract numbers 316774 and 316776.

Linnoila, M., Virkkunen, M., Scheinin, M., Nuutila, A., Rimon, R., & Goodwin, F. K. (1983). Low cerebrospinal fluid 5-hydroxyindoleacetic acid concentration differentiates impulsive from nonimpulsive violent behavior. *Life Sciences, 33,* 2609–2614.

Marttunen, M. J., Aro, H. M., Henriksson, M. M., & Lonnqvist, J. K. (1991). Mental disorders in adolescent suicide. *Arch. Gen. Psychiatry, 48,* 834–839.

Mazure, C., Nelson, J. C., & Price, L. (1986). Reliability and validity of the symptoms of major depressive illness. *Arch. Gen. Psychiatry, 43,* 451–456.

Miles, C. P. (1977). Conditions predisposing to suicide: A review. *J. Nerv. Ment. Dis., 164,* 231–246.

Mitchell, M. D., McCauley, E., Burke, P. M., & Moss, S. J. (1988). Phenomenology of depression in children and adolescents. *J. Am. Acad. Child Adolesc. Psychiatry, 27*(1), 12–20.

Pfeffer, C. R. (1988). Suicidal behavior among children and adolescents: Risk identification and intervention. In A. J. Frances & R. E. Hales (Eds.), *Review of Psychiatry,* Vol. 7, Washington, DC: American Psychiatric Press, Inc.

Pfeffer, C. R. (1989). Family characteristics and support systems as risk factors for youth suicide. In *Report of the Secretary's Task Force on Youth Suicide, Volume 2: Risk Factors for Youth Suicide,* Alcohol, Drug Abuse and Mental Health Administration, DHHS Pub. No. (ADM) 89-1622. Washington, DC: U.S. Government Printing Office, pp. 71–87.

Pfeffer, C. R., Plutchik, R., Mizruchi, M.S. (1983), Suicidal and assaultive behavior in children: Classification, measurement, and interrelations. *Am. J. Psychiatry, 140,* 154–157.

Pfeffer, C. R., Zuckerman, S., Plutchik, R., & Mizruchi, M. S. (1984). Suicidal behavior in normal school children: A comparison with child psychiatric inpatients. *J. Am. Acad. Child Adolesc. Psychiatry, 23,* 416–423.

Pfeffer, C. R., Plutchik, R., Mizruchi, M. S., *et al.* (1986). Suicidal behavior in child psychiatric inpatients and outpatients and in nonpatients. *Am. J. Psychiatry, 143,* 733–738.

Pfeffer, C. R., Lipkins, R., Plutchik, R., & Mizruchi, M. (1988). Normal children at risk for suicidal behavior: A two-year follow-up study. *J. Am. Acad. Child Adolesc. Psychiatry, 27,* 34–41.

Pfeffer, C. R., Newcorn, J., Kaplan, G., Mizruchi, M. S., & Plutchik, R. (1989). Subtypes of suicidal and assaultive behaviors in adolescent psychiatric inpatients: A research note. *J. Child Psychol. Psychiat., 30,* 151–163.

Planansky, K., & Johnston, R. (1973). Clinical setting and motivation in suicidal attempts of schizophrenics. *Acta Psychiatr. Scand., 49,* 680–690.

Plutchik, R., & van Praag, H. M. (1986). The measurement of suicidality, aggressivity, and impulsivity. *Clinical Neuropharmacology, 9,* 380.

Rich, C. L., Young, D., & Fowler, R. C. (1986). San Diego suicide study: I. Young vs. old subjects. *Arch. Gen. Psychiatry, 43,* 577–582.

Robbins, D. R., & Alessi, N. E. (1985). Depressive symptoms and suicidal behavior in adolescents. *Am. J. Psychiatry, 142,* 588–592.

Rotheram-Borus, M. J., & Trautman, P. D. (1988). Hopelessness, depression, and suicidal intent among adolescent suicide attempters. *J. Am. Acad. Child Adolesc. Psychiatry, 27,* 700–704.

Roy, A. (1986). Depression, attempted suicide, and suicide in patients with chronic schizophrenia. *Psych. Clinics of NA, 9,* 193–206.

Roy, A. (1989). Genetics and suicidal behavior. In *Report of the Secretary's Task Force on Youth Suicide, Volume 2: Risk Factors on Youth Suicide,* Alcohol, Drug Abuse and Mental Health Administration, DHHS Pub. No. (ADM) 89-1622. Washington, DC: U.S. Government Printing Office, pp. 247–262.

Roy, A., Agren, H., Pickar, D., Linnoila, M., Doran, A. R., Cutler, N. R., & Paul, S. M. (1986). Reduced CSF concentrations of homovanillic acid and homovanillic acid to 5-hydroxyindoleacetic acid ratios in depressed patients: Relationship to suicidal behavior and dexamethasone nonsuppression. *Am. J. Psychiatry, 143,* 1539–1545.

Roy, A., DeJong, J., & Linnoila, M. (1989). Cerebrospinal fluid monoamine metabolies and suicidal behavior in depressed patients. *Arch. Gen. Psychiatry, 46,* 609–612.

Rutter, M., & Gould, M. (1985). Classification. In *Child and adolescent psychiatry* (2nd ed.), ed. M. Rutter and L. Hersov. Oxford: Blackwell Scientific Publications, pp. 304–321.

Schulsinger, R., Kety, S., Rosenthal, D., & Wender, P. (1979). A family study of suicide. In

M. Schou & E. Stromgren (Eds.), *Origins, prevention and treatment of affective disorders,* (pp. 277–287). New York: Academic Press.

Shaffer, D. (1974). Suicide in childhood and early adolescence. *Journal of Child Psychology and Psychiatry, 15,* 275–291.

Shaffer, D. (1982). Diagnostic considerations in suicidal behavior in children and adolescents. *J. Am. Acad. Child Adolesc. Psychiatry, 21,* 414–415.

Shaffer, D., Garland, A., Gould, M., Fisher, P., & Trautman, P. (1988). Preventing teenage suicide: A critical review. *J. Am. Acad. Child Adolesc. Psychiatry, 27,* 675–687.

Shafii, M., Carrigan, S., Whittinghill, J. R., & Derrick, A. (1985). Psychological autopsy of completed suicide in children and adolescents. *Am. J. Psychiatry, 142,* 1061–1064.

Stanley, E. J., & Barter, J. T. (1970). Adolescent suicidal behavior. *Am. J. Orthopsychiatry, 40,* 87–96.

Stone, M. H., Hurt, S. W., & Stone, D. K. (1987). The PI500: Long-term follow-up of borderline inpatients meeting DSM-III criteria. I. Global outcome. *Journal of Personality Disorders, 1,* 291–298.

Teicher, M. H., Glod, C., & Cole, J. O. (1990). Emergence of intense suicidal preoccupation during fluoxetine treatment. *Am. J. Psychiatry, 147,* 207–210.

Trautman, P. D., Rotheram-Borus, M. J., Dopkins, S., & Lewin, N. (1991). Psychiatric diagnoses in minority female adolescent suicide attempters. *J. Am. Acad. Child Adolesc. Psychiatry, 30,* 617–622.

Vandivort, D. S., & Locke, B. Z. (1979). Suicide ideation; Its relation to depression, suicide and suicide attempt. *Suicide & Life-Threatening Behavior, 9,* 205–218.

van Praag, H. M., & Plutchik, R. (1988). Increased suicidality in depression: Group or subgroup characteristic? *Psych. Res., 26,* 273–278.

Velez, C., & Cohen, P. (1988). Suicidal behavior and ideation in a community sample of children. *J. Am. Acad. Child Adolesc. Psychiatry, 27,* 349–356.

Virkkunen, M., DeJong, J., Bartko, J., Goodwin, F. K., & Linnoila, M. (1989). Relationship of psychobiological variables to recidivism in violent offenders and impulsive fire setters. *Arch. Gen. Psychiatry, 46,* 600–603.

Weissman, M. M., Klerman, G. L., Markowitz, J. S., & Ouellette, R. (1989). Suicidal ideation and suicide attempts in panic disorder and attacks. *N. Eng. J. Med., 321,* 1209–1214.

Wender, P. H., Kety, S. S., Rosenthal, D., Schulsinger, F., Ortmann, J., & Lunde, I. (1986). Psychiatric disorders in the biological and adoptive families of adopted individuals with affective disorders. *Arch. Gen. Psychiatry, 43,* 923–929.

Widiger, T. A. (1989). The categorical distinction between personality and affective disorders. *Journal of Personality Disorders, 3,* 77–91.

Index